CABI: a century of scientific endeavour

CABI is a trading name of CAB International

CABI Head Office
Nosworthy Way
Wallingford
Oxfordshire OX10 8DE
UK

T: +44 (0)1491 832111
F: +44 (0)1491 833508
E: cabi@cabi.org
www.cabi.org

CABI North American Office
875 Massachusetts Avenue
7th Floor
Cambridge, MA 02139
USA

T: +1 617 395 4056
F: +1 617 354 6875
E: cabi-nao@cabi.org

Library of Congress Cataloging-in-Publication Data

Blight, Denis.

CABI : a century of scientific endeavour / Denis Blight.

p. cm.

Includes index.

ISBN 978-1-84593-873-4 (alk. paper)

1. C.A.B. International--History. 2. Agriculture--Research--History.
3. Agriculture--Research--International cooperation--History. I. C.A.B. International. II. Title.

S540.8.C33B65 2011

630.6'01--dc22

2010053217

ISBN: 978 1 84593 873 4

Commissioning editor **Carol McNamara**

Project manager **Diana Jones**

Contributors **Peter Baker, Dennis Greenland, Keith Harris, David Hawksworth, Bill Hominick, Norman Jones, Tecwyn Jones, Caroline Scotter-Mainprize, Jeff Waage, Rob Williams**

Researchers **Michael Amphlett, Christine Davies, Tim Ison, Tony Pittaway, Lesley Ragab, Barbara Ritchie, Eleanor Stretch**

Production editor **Tracy Head**

Designed and typeset by **Sarah Hilliar**

Printed and bound by **Gutenberg Press, Malta**

CABI: a century of scientific endeavour

Denis Blight AO, FRSA

Executive Director
The Crawford Fund
Deakin ACT, Australia

Co-author **Ruth Ibbotson**
Edited by **David Hemming**

www.cabi.org

CONTENTS

Imperial Mycological Institute, Ferry Lane, Kew. ©CABI

FOREWORD

Having joined CABI in 2005, I am still considered something of a new hire! However, in the five years that I have been here I have been privileged to lead a very special organization. During those five years there have been many changes in the way CABI works and is structured, but these have been part of the constant process of adaptation to a world that is changing at an increasingly rapid pace. As we began to dig into CABI's history for this book, we gained a much better understanding of the basis upon which its progenitor Institutes and Bureaux were constituted and recognized that this round of change was but the latest in a long series that began almost as soon as the life of CABI began.

As evolution is about survival of the fittest, then it is certain that this continuing process has helped CABI to remain fit for purpose during its first century, and enabled it to continue to meet the needs of its members and customers by solving problems in agriculture and the environment. I hope this book will help a much wider audience to understand the many, varied and valuable contributions that CABI has made to improving agriculture and conserving biodiversity during this time, as well as providing a valuable reference to those who follow in guiding it through the next 100 years.

The people who worked for the early incarnations of CABI had no idea that they were setting out on what would become such a long and eventful journey, but they had a clear vision of the need to combat pests and diseases so as to protect the health of humans, animals and plants and thereby improve livelihoods and the quality of life, particularly in the developing tropical regions of the world. Starting life as a small research committee, the organization developed into a loosely linked federation of Institutes and Bureaux before reintegrating as the Commonwealth Agricultural Bureaux and finally becoming the unified intergovernmental organization we know today, operating in ten centres around the world.

Each stage of its history has not only shaped the organization but has also left its mark in the values, culture and ways of working that still exist today, and which can at first seem puzzling to the newcomer. This book will help everyone associated with the organization to appreciate and understand how we got here – I wish I had been able to read it when I first joined!

CABI's strength has always been its objective, science-based approach with a unique combination of hands-on research and high-quality publishing expertise. In recent decades that has been augmented by greater involvement in making a real difference worldwide by putting research into use through development projects, implementing sustainable agricultural practices and raising the incomes of poor rural farmers. But the key to the survival and growth of this organization has been the commitment, talent, energy and sheer hard work of its staff, both past and present. I'm delighted that this history gives due prominence to some of the exceptional individuals who have played a part in shaping CABI today. The willingness of many ex-staff to contribute has been enormously helpful and shows the strength of allegiance that the organization creates.

Denis Blight, his editors and co-authors have done a wonderful job of unpicking the many tangled threads of CABI's development over the past 100 years and re-weaving them into a lucid and fascinating story. Through it, we can see how CABI and its people have been influential in a variety of areas, from promoting the importance of peer review of scientific papers to initiating the introduction of the UK's School Milk Act in 1946, and conducting pioneering work in the area of biopesticides and biological control.

Of course no history can ever be regarded as complete or definitive and the subject matter that we had to draw upon was rich and varied, so let me offer apologies to anyone who feels their contribution has not been adequately reflected. But I hope you will enjoy reading this book as a portrait of a unique and innovative organization and of the many dedicated, and sometimes colourful, people who have contributed to it over the years. I feel both humbled and honoured to be following in their footsteps as we take CABI into its second century, which I am sure will see as much change, impact and excitement as the first!

Trevor Nicholls

Entomology building, Queensgate, London. ©CABI

ABOUT THIS **HISTORY**

The history of CAB International does not follow a simple chronological path. The Institute of Entomology and the Mycological Institute were founded within years of each other and evolved in parallel, but separate, lines; eight information Bureaux were established in 1929 but similarly had separate paths more aligned to their independent host institutions, and to the ambitions, interests and in some cases foibles of their leaders, than to each other. A small number of Bureaux were added over the years to make the story more complex. The Institute of Parasitology, founded as a Bureau in 1929, evolved in a distinctive way more or less independently of the two Institutes that preceded it; and it had a delicate relationship with the British Museum (Natural History), driven by a personal dispute between key figures in their leaderships that is said to have lasted 50 years. The Institute of Biological Control emerged from the Institute of Entomology but forged its own path – made so by the colourful characters that led and staffed it, the changing fortunes of the science and by Research Stations dispersed around the world with stories of their own, but all adding strength to a unique international network.

The Bureaux were centralized and co-located in 1987 so that eight history lines merged into one; and then the four Institutes in 1998 were conjoined, merging their stories too. The two resultant lines, as if reinforced by their merging experiences, remained separate from each other. The Research Stations, named CAB International Centres, gained a measure of independence early in the 21st century and thus their own semi-separate stories. Only at the end of CABI's first one hundred years have all of the story lines been brought closer together.

This history has been written largely from accounts by and of the people who made it. I am particularly indebted to Keith Harris and Tecwyn Jones, former Directors of the Institute of Entomology, to David Hawksworth, a former Director of the Mycological Institute, and to Bill Hominick, a former Director of the Institute of Parasitology. I am also grateful to Jeff Waage, a former Director of the Institute of Biological Control and Chief Executive of CABI Bioscience, and to Matthew Cock and many other former and current staff of CABI who told me their stories, commented on my drafts, carried out picture research and provided photographs and other information. One former Executive Director, Norman Jones, lent me his memories, as did two former Deputy Directors-General, Dennis Greenland and Rob Williams. In addition, I am grateful to Dave Hemming for providing valuable input and helping to edit sections of the book, to Peter Baker and Caroline Scotter-Mainprize for their work on the final chapter, and to the staff in CABI's commercial and book departments for handling the layout, editing and production of the book.

Ruth Ibbotson has been a valuable source of support and institutional memory to the point where she deserves the description of co-author. I have, as far as is possible, attributed the stories to the sources of all those mentioned.

As a former Director-General of CABI I am, of course, an unreliable witness, particularly when it comes to episodes in which I was a principal. However, as was the case when I was their chief executive, the staff, as well as other witnesses, have tried to keep me honest.

Finally, I am grateful to my successor, Trevor Nicholls, who invited me to write this history but bravely placed no limits or constraints on what I might include in it.

DG Blight AO, FRSA

CABI'S PLACE IN 100 YEARS OF HISTORY

One hundred years ago, insects were causing enormous damage to human health and agriculture.

CABI came into existence as a new form of intergovernmental body to help the UK and its dominions and colonies tackle that problem by providing science and information, with the aim of boosting economic development in the British Empire. Over time it became a commonwealth, and then a truly international organization. Its membership structure and funding by subscription and fees for services remains unique amongst intergovernmental organizations, as do its governance arrangements. However, many were unaware of its crucial role, its virtues hidden, something that has continued to cause problems throughout its history.

The number of 'scientific and technical journals published has doubled every ten to fifteen years since 1900. A scientist who in the late 19th century could keep up with new research by reading for about 30 minutes a day would, by 1980, have to read for thirteen hours a day.'[1] In dealing with that explosion in information, CABI has been at the leading edge from its first abstract journal. CABI was an early adopter of the new information and communication technologies but, like many other publishers, it faced serious challenges as incomes from printed journals declined and revenues from new media, whose technologies carried a high entry cost, climbed but only slowly.

CABI also pioneered the delivery of plant health services, from classical biological control (CBC) to integrated pest management (IPM), incorporating more measured biological control techniques and farmer field schools (FFS) in the 1980s. More recently, Plantwise, with its global plant health clinics, which provide support through regional, national and community structures to hundreds of millions of farmers, potentially the basis for a global pest and disease surveillance system, has reaffirmed its founders' vision.

Delivering this unique combination of information, research and support has always been a financial challenge. CABI's member countries supported it financially from its foundation, but have made clear over the years that it should 'maximize its income and reduce its reliance on membership contributions'.[2] They decided in 1990 to reduce contributions and, by 2000, these represented less than 5% of total income, making it difficult for CABI to deliver public goods without charge to member countries and to invest in growth. The Partnership Facility (CABI-PF, later called the CABI Development Fund) and a decision in 2009 to modestly increase member country contributions helped, but the two sources now meet only a fraction of CABI's costs. International financial crises remind CABI to build uncertainty into its business models.

The last 100 years have seen dramatic developments in biological sciences, developments that CABI has both recorded and contributed to. The Institute of Entomology was founded when new ideas were emerging on the role of insects in all areas of human activity, and especially in the conveying of diseases to humans, domesticated animals and crops. Developments in the 1960s in biological control were often led by CABI's Institute of Biological Control, and reviewed in the Institute's publications. The Institute had to respond to concerns over the cross-border movement of biological control agents (BCAs) and led work on a sophisticated code of conduct for their use.

A scientist takes notes. ©CABI

Kumar Rajesh, collaborator for Himalayan balsam biocontrol project, Nepal. ©CABI

CAB Abstracts records has published research in the applied life sciences from the beginning of the 20th century. The following gives just a flavour of the discoveries, including some, in italics, by CABI scientists, collaborators or advisers:

- *the discovery – by RT Leiper, the sometime Director of CABI's Institute of Parasitology – in 1915 of the snail host of the parasite causing* schistosomiasis, *an important tropical disease today still affecting 200 million people worldwide*;

- an outbreak of the Colorado potato beetle in France in 1923, an important early example of a harmful invasive species transported by man;

- early records of an 'unknown disease of elms', which became known as Dutch elm disease;

- the isolation in 1926 of anti-beriberi vitamin (vitamin B_1);

- Fleming's discovery of an antibacterial substance in the fungus *Penicillium notatum* (of which one of the original specimens is housed in CABI's genetic resource collection) in 1929;

- Richard Doll's discovery in 1950 of the link between smoking and lung cancer;

- the development of the poliomyelitis vaccine in 1953 – the Salk vaccine and a second live vaccine developed by Sabin have been used to all but eradicate polio from the world today;

- the link hypothesized by Lord Boyd Orr – the first Consultant Director to CAB's Bureau of Nutrition – *between ill health and undernourishment*;

- the reporting by Crick and Watson in 1953 of a structure for deoxyribose nucleic acid (DNA), 'built up of a pair of helical chains, each coiled around a common axis';

- *a review of the book* Silent Spring, *which described the immediate and long-term effects of pesticides on wildlife and humans and argued that the development of pesticides had paid too little attention to their negative effects on wildlife – over the next decade taxonomists from CABI's Institutes of Entomology and of Biological Control, both specializing in the identification of beneficial insects, supported global efforts to encourage IPM that combined minimal use of pesticides with biological control and beneficial cultural practices*;

- *the discovery by scientists from the Commonwealth Institute of Biological Control (CIBC) of* Elaeidobus kamerunicus, *which pollinates oil palms, reported in 1983*;

- the first description in 1987 of a new disease of cattle in the UK (bovine spongiform encephalopathy), and the variant BSE epidemic spread to humans;

- the identification of the SARS (severe acute respiratory syndrome) agent as a novel coronavirus; and

- *in a subject studied at the Institute of Parasitology, the resistance of the malaria parasite to drugs, including that to artesunate drugs, the most recent weapon in the drugs arsenal, on the Thai/Cambodia border in 2007.*

Opposite, clockwise from top left: mating schistosome flukes, Eye of Science; coloured TEM of brain fibrils in BSE, EM Unit VLA; coloured SEM of a bark beetle, Manfred Kage; coloured TEM of a cluster of corona viruses, Dr Gopal Murti. ©SPL

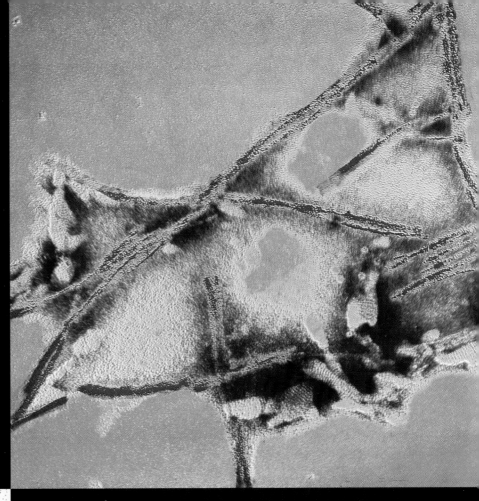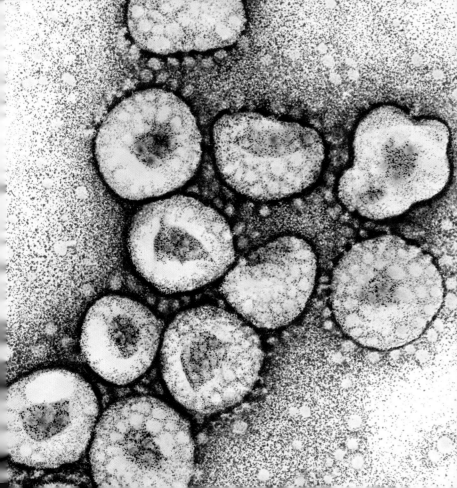

CABI books, often authored by CABI scientists, also reviewed key developments in science, and have now grown from titles focused on the Institutes' expertise to a major publishing programme that covers a much wider scope.

World events have affected CABI too. In the debate in 1910 that led to CABI's founding, a Member of Parliament compared funding for research on entomology and a war against the so-called 'Mad Mullah' of British Somaliland, arguing that the ratio between funding provided for the former compared with the latter of one to two hundred should have been reversed. The low priority given to science funding has been a recurrent issue for CABI. Two world wars impacted on CABI's development, including the need to relocate the Imperial Parasite Service (which became the Institute of Biological Control) from the UK to Canada during the Second World War. Decolonization and independence after the War changed CABI's membership structure from Imperial to Commonwealth. CABI Review Conferences in the 1960s suspended collaboration with the Government of South Africa over apartheid (reversed in the late 1990s).

Recession and its effect on funding hit CABI as some governments, in the 1980s and 1990s, reduced public spending and gave lower priority to agriculture and agricultural research. More recently financial, political and security crises and their effects on currency exchange rates have affected CABI's revenues, as have the increased costs of defined-benefits pension schemes.

CABI has helped countries build stronger national agricultural research systems (NARS), but had to adjust to their changing needs as a result. In the early 20th century scientists from the nascent CABI advised on research systems around the world; insect collections were established, with Institute of Entomology help, in Nigeria in the 1950s using the Institute's identification services to build up a national reference collection of pest species and beneficial insects that could limit pest populations, a 'process repeated in Africa and Asia but also in Canada, Australia, New Zealand and parts of Central and South America; and the CIBC established an Indian Station in 1957', which marked 'the beginning of organized and systematic biological control research in India'.[3] In the early 21st century, when NARS in developed member countries and the more advanced developing countries had strengthened, the nature of demands on CABI's services changed.

CABI made dramatic changes to its structure to render itself more effective. Initially, the Institute of Entomology and the Mycological Institute (and later Parasitology and Biological Control) provided, within each Institute, both identification and abstracting services. New Bureaux, across eight or more scientific disciplines, were located within further separate UK research institutions. Thus abstractors stayed in touch with their scientific fields, but differing abstracting methods evolved within each Bureau. Computerization (in 1973) and then co-location of the abstracting units (in 1987), and an associated rationalization of the coverage and procedures, addressed this concern. With the income-generating information services separated off, the Identification Services of the Institutes came under pressure to cover their costs, leading to identification charges.

CABI had by now become CABI Publishing, formed from the information Bureaux, and CABI Bioscience, formed from the four Institutes. The separation between CABI Bioscience and CABI Publishing, whilst strengthening the cohesion within each, inevitably sharpened the distinction between the two, reinforced around the turn of the millennium as each division acquired its own administration and marketing structures. A subsequent emphasis on 'One CABI, with integration, streamlining and new product development' that drew on a mix of CAB Abstracts and Bioscience resources, has sought to address this divergence.

CABI in 2010 finds itself in an era where agriculture and biology – and the management of pests and diseases and concerns on the environment and biodiversity (including microbial biodiversity) – are again at the centre of international development. According to the CABI Science Review of 2009[4], (there is)

" *increasing demand for food and agricultural commodities and worries about food security (and) greater movement of pests and diseases and invasive species through trade; new or increased incidence of pests, diseases and invasive species through climate change; demand for environmentally friendly production, storage and processing systems; lack of international monitoring and awareness of distribution and impacts of pests, diseases and invasive species; (and) decline in global capacity in entomology, pathology and other aspects of plant health.* "

Just as in 1910, there have been many advances in knowledge and scientific methods, including those in 'molecular sciences, bio-informatics and information and communication technologies that are highly relevant to CABI's scientific activities'.

CABI's bold, but always difficult, decisions to centralize, merge, outsource, devolve, streamline and refocus on core business may well have lessons for the reform process of the Consultative Group on International Agricultural Research and, for that matter, for other international agencies. They have allowed it to remain a major contributor to agricultural and applied science and information for 100 years, and to prepare for the future.

FOUNDATIONS IN EMPIRE AND COMMONWEALTH

A small grant to fight 'one of the enemies of mankind' in a vote on a war in the British Empire was the start of CABI's story.[5] In the early 20th century the British Colonial Office recognized that its imperial responsibilities extended beyond maintaining order and collecting taxes, and recognized the devastating impact of pests and diseases on man, animals and crops in the tropics. This coincided with a new, more professional, approach to biology – according to Baker and Bayliss,[6] 'a different kind of biologist was emerging in Britain, in many ways unlike the amateur naturalist'.

It was a time of continuing unrest in parts of the British Empire. A weariness with this was reflected in the debate in the House of Commons in 1910 in which £1000 of funding to the Entomology Research Committee was first approved (later to be supplemented by a further £1000 from colonial governments in Africa), marking the beginning of CABI. The approval was part of a Supplementary Vote for additional funds for the civil service, including a sum not exceeding £57,000 for military action against the so-called 'Mad Mullah' in British Somaliland, a campaign costing £4 million over 10 years. The Empire was said by one Member to be involved in a 'series of futile military expeditions' and in which 'a great many valuable lives and a good deal of money were wasted'. However, there was support from both sides for the 'Vote for pathological research (that was) intended to fight one of the enemies of mankind' and the proposal that there was no need 'to defend the grant of this sum of £1000' to be 'devoted to scientific research as to the matter of certain tropical diseases'. One Member contrasted the devotion of just £1000 to tropical research and £200,000 to policing Somaliland. He respectfully urged 'that if we had spent another £199,000 in research on tropical diseases, we should have done very much more to consolidate and expand the British Empire'.

Winston Churchill summed up the mood when he said that

❝ *all the members of this House, wherever they sit, who take an interest in the scientific treatment of tropical diseases will appreciate that in developing more highly the power of research, which is now possessed by the Colonial Office, and by calling this new (Entomological Research) Committee into being we take an important step forward far more than the comparatively small sum of money which is involved would indicate – an important step forward which may conceivably be of priceless advantage not only to our own fellow countrymen who are serving beyond the seas, but to the great mass of the aboriginal population committed to their charge.* **❞**

Winston Leonard Spencer Churchill (right), 1910. ©Getty Images

This was also a period of economic and political uncertainty and one that witnessed a changing relationship between the UK and its Dominions in particular (including Australia, New Zealand and Canada) and, to a lesser extent, with the colonies – a changing relationship that interplayed with the idea of collaboration in scientific research within the Empire.

The exact birth-date of CABI is difficult to pinpoint. The Entomological Research Committee was formed in 1909 but did not gain funding from Parliament until 1910. Publication of the *Bulletin of Entomological Research* started in 1910. The Imperial Bureau of Entomology was not established until 1913.

Sir Charles Howell Thomas, chairman of the Executive Council of the Imperial Agricultural Bureaux, emphasized in 1934 that the underlying principle was 'that of cooperative services for the common good. Since each part of the Empire joined in providing the necessary finance, the institute could render services to each part at a much smaller cost than if each tried to do the same work for itself. The spirit which animated the officers of these institutes and bureaux ensured that their activities would be carried out from the common point of view of all the contributing countries.'[7] A *Times* report of 1937 noted 'no such comprehensive service is elsewhere available. Scientific workers in the United States and in Continental Europe rely more and more on Imperial Bureaux Publications.'[8]

The Imperial Institutes and Bureaux were renamed as Commonwealth entities in 1948. The matter was raised in the UK Parliament, when Member of Parliament Sir Arthur Harvey asked George Brown, the Minister of Agriculture, 'if he is aware that the Imperial Bureau of Dairy Science, Reading, has changed its name to the Commonwealth Bureau of Dairy Science, and that it is using notepaper and envelopes on which the word "Imperial" has been struck out and the word "Commonwealth" written above; and what is the reason for this change?' Brown replied that the Executive Council had decided that 'Commonwealth' rather than 'Imperial' was more in keeping with modern trends. Harvey then asked, 'Is the Hon. Gentleman ashamed of the word "Imperial"?'[9]

In what Schedvin in his history of CSIR described as 'the Indian summer of neo-mercantilism', scientific experts linked to CABI's Imperial progenitor visited Australia in the late 1920s. They advised on its emerging programmes in terms that 'bore the imprint of scientific imperialism.'

The following four chapters describe the origins and history of CABI's Institutes: Entomology (1913), Mycology (1920), Parasitology (1929) and Biological Control (1927) until their merger in 1998, and then the Information Bureau from 1929 up until centralization in 1987.

Sir Guy Marshall (1871–1959)
Founder of CABI[10]

Sir Guy Anstruther Knox Marshall who, from 1913 to 1942, was the Director of the Imperial Institute of Entomology, the seed from which CABI grew, can be seen in many ways as the founder of CABI. He was born in India in 1871 and educated at Charterhouse. Having been unsuccessful in the Indian Civil Service, he joined a firm of mining engineers in Salisbury, Southern Rhodesia, as it was then known, in 1895. Despite a lack of formal scientific training, he had an intense interest in natural history and with Sir Edward Poulton he published a paper in the *Proceedings of the Royal Entomological Society of London* in 1902. In 1906 he returned to the UK determined to devote his life to entomology. In 1907 he was about to set sail to became Curator of the Sarawak Museum when he was struck down with illness. This meant that in 1909 the Secretary of State for the Colonies was able to appoint Marshall as Scientific Secretary to the Imperial Entomological Research Committee (IERC) (Tropical Africa). Almost immediately, he started the publication of the *Bulletin of Entomological Research* and, through his energy and enthusiasm, in 1913 the Imperial Bureau of Entomology was established.

As adviser to the Colonial Office, he played a very important role between the two world wars in guiding the development of entomological work in the colonies. He had a particular interest in tsetse fly research, the vector of trypanosomiasis or sleeping sickness, stemming from his early experience of this pest in southern Africa. He stimulated, inspired and helped entomologists from the Commonwealth in their work of controlling insect pests. He was a firm believer in commercial companies and insecticide manufacturers employing their own entomologists, and his influence did much to raise the standard of insecticidal products and the service rendered to the public.

Apart from his other activities, Marshall was a leading specialist on the Curculionidae (weevils) for more than half a century. He published 200 works on the systematics of weevils, including his descriptions of 2269 new species. He, personally, rapidly identified the large quantities of weevil material received at the Institute even after his retirement in 1942, working constantly at the British Museum until a few weeks before his death.

Green and black locust. ©iStockphoto

ENTOMOLOGY: INSECT DELIGHT

Entomology – the study of insects – is a critical component of studies of human and animal health, crop health and pest management, pollination, soil ecology, biodiversity, ecology, evolution and indeed the majority of areas of human interest involving living organisms. Based on current knowledge, the 1.3 million known insects account for about two-thirds of all known species. Many of the most damaging agricultural pests are insects, as are the majority of their natural enemies. Identification is usually difficult for a non-specialist and may require microscopic examination or dissection and careful comparison of key features with preserved reference specimens. Hence, it is no coincidence that in the first years of CABI, a partnership was established with the world's largest and most important insect collection, British Museum (Natural History) (BMNH), in order to provide an identification service for insect pests and their natural enemies.

The Imperial Bureau of Entomology: the First Institute of CABI

Entomological adventurers, bed bugs and a bulletin

Around the turn of the 20th century, insects (and other arthropods) were causing devastating problems through disease and damage to crops in Africa. In 1909 the British Colonial Office proposed an Entomological Research Committee (ERC) to tackle the serious impacts of insects in the Empire. In 1909 the Treasury gave this Committee, a forerunner of CABI, an annual budget of £2000 (equivalent to £200,000 in 2010) to provide identification and information services. The first Secretary of the Committee was GAK (later Sir Guy) Marshall (See box 'Sir Guy Marshall: founder of CABI', Chapter 2), and he dispatched two entomologists, Sheffield Airey Neave and James J Simpson, to Nyasaland and Nigeria, respectively, to collect insects and other arthropods relevant to applied entomology (See 'Two Naturalists in Africa', this Chapter).

Finding and describing insects was crucial to controlling them. In 1909 the Committee published its first 'Instructions to Collectors', detailing apparatus and techniques and offering support to economic entomologists working in Africa. It covered collecting and preserving fleas, bed bugs, ticks and lice as well as mosquitoes and other flies, particularly for medical and veterinary entomology. Then in 1910 the Committee began publishing the *Bulletin of Entomological Research*,

effectively CABI's first journal, which mainly focused on pest and disease-carrying insects of Africa.

To tackle insect problems, the ERC recognized that it was vital to collect together all current research. In 1911, the Governors of the British Colonies, Protectorates and Dominions were invited by the Secretary of State for the Colonies to discuss with the ERC proposals to investigate injurious insects throughout the British Empire. After a further conference in 1912, an Imperial Bureau of Entomology was proposed:

- to collect and coordinate all information bearing upon injurious or useful insects (and other arthropods);

- to organize a system for securing authoritative identification, with reasonable promptitude, of all insects of economic importance submitted by Departments of Agriculture and Public Health officials;

- to compile gradually a comprehensive card index of the whole literature of the subject; and

- to publish a monthly journal giving an up-to-date review of current literature.

In 1913 the Bureau was established, at the BMNH with Marshall as Director, and the *Review of Applied Entomology* (*Series A, Agricultural* and *Series B, Medical and Veterinary*) first published: CABI's first abstract journal. The Bureau identified 1700 relevant primary journals and emphasized the need for cooperation, since no single institution in the world would have all of these journals. The editor also noted that 'some centralized system for the publication of a compact yet comprehensive survey of the subject is in the highest degree desirable', and that 'to entomologists in general it should be a matter of congratulation that their favourite study … should be made the subject of so valuable and instructive an experiment in … cooperation'.

The British Colonial Office establishes an Entomological Research Committee. — 1909

The Treasury grants the Committee an annual budget of £1000 (equivalent to £200,000 in 2010), to be matched by the colonies, to provide identification and information services. The first Secretary of the Committee is GAK (later Sir Guy) Marshall, who sends Sheffield Airey Neave and James J Simpson to collect insects in Africa. — 1909

The Imperial Bureau of Entomology is established in the British Museum (Natural History), and 27 Elvaston Place, South Kensington, London. — 1913

The *Review of Applied Entomology* (*Series A, Agricultural* and *Series B, Medical and Veterinary*), CABI's first abstract journal, begins publication. — 1913

The institute moves to 89 Queen's Gate, South Kensington, London. — 1916

James Waterston joins the team to work on Chalcidoidea – parasitic Hymenoptera (natural enemies of many insect pests) – the first of a team of specialist entomologists. — 1917

The first Imperial Entomological Conference is held in London, to review the Bureau's work. — 1920

BP (later Sir Boris) Uvarov – a refugee from the Soviet Union – joins as a specialist in Hymenoptera, Hemiptera and Orthoptera (which includes locusts). He later becomes the founding director of the Anti-Locust Research Centre. — 1920

The Bureau establishes a parasite laboratory at Farnham Royal, which supports the biological control of pests, and is later developed into the Commonwealth Institute of Biological Control (CIBC). — 1927

The Committee on Locust Control of the Economic Advisory Council (of the Colonial Office) gives the Institute responsibility for Africa and western Asia and, from 1931, the Institute became recognized as the international centre for anti-locust research. — 1929

The Bureau is renamed the Imperial Institute of Entomology (IIE). — 1930

To make a difference, the Bureau needed to do its own research, and from 1919, it recruited scientific assistants with specialized taxonomic expertise. By 1940 it had about a dozen taxonomists to cover key groups of harmful and beneficial insects for world agriculture, forestry and the storage of food and other produce. As they could not cover all relevant groups, wherever possible, an international network of collaborating taxonomists filled in the gaps.[11]

Two Naturalists in Africa[12,13]

Sheffield Airey Neave (1879–1961) and James Jenkins Simpson (1881–1937) were part of the new breed of biologists that emerged in the UK towards the end of the 19th century, when the role of arthropods in the transmission of disease was confirmed and so career opportunities were growing. These very different individuals played a key role in establishing CABI's expertise in entomology.

Neave, the grandson of a governor of the Bank of England, attended Eton and Magdalen College, Oxford. Before he joined the ERC, Neave had collected and published work on African vertebrates and invertebrates (especially butterflies and ticks) from expeditions he had made to Rhodesia and the Congo Free State between 1904 and 1908. He wrote how preserving arthropods in the tropics differed from similar work in temperate climates. Neave's collections of insects, molluscs, fish, amphibians, reptiles, birds and mammals were identified by him or other specialists. Several were new to science and bear his name.

Neave was sent by the ERC to East Africa to collect arthropods, blood-sucking Diptera (including mosquitoes, tsetse flies and tabanids), bed bugs, fleas and lice, as well as ticks. He was instructed to find people who would collect and record, and to supply them with apparatus. He travelled using native porters and found them invaluable as collectors, especially boys aged between 12 and 15. He operated a payment-by-results method and believed that success came from sound preparations, careful organization of equipment and with the help of native assistants.

In 1913 Neave was appointed Assistant Director of the Bureau (later Institute) of Entomology. He was not only a successful field naturalist but also an able administrator.

Airey Neave MP[14] was the son of SA Neave, and the first British prisoner of war to make a home run from Colditz. He was assassinated at Westminster, London, in 1978.

Sheffield Airey Neave. ©CABI

Simpson's life and career was less even and less privileged. He was the son of an Elgin gardener, who graduated from Aberdeen University in 1904. Simpson's career began in 1906 with the Indian Government, investigating pearl oyster fisheries of Mergui Archipelago of Southern Burma and the Moskos Islands. ERC sent him to Nigeria with similar instructions to those given to Neave. He spent two tours in West Africa, despite friends warning him that the region was the 'white man's grave' with an evil 'reputation synonymous with the last resort of the impecunious, the stranded and hopelessly depraved'. Simpson nevertheless helped build up of 'an excellent reference collection' at Moor Plantation, Ibadan, along with successive entomologists from CIE.

Simpson believed it was important to educate 'the natives' in the connection between insects and disease and that if the number of insects could be reduced there would be a consequent benefit to themselves and to their herds. He was invalided home in 1915 to recuperate from poor health, but during the First World War he joined the West African Frontier Force to work on tropical diseases and their carriers. His final post was Turkey where he went to organize the Department of Oceanography and Marine Biological Research, to improve the local fishing industry. In 1937, at 55, whilst travelling from Greece, he was reported as missing from the ship *Kyrenia*, presumed drowned.

Preparing the insect specimens correctly was essential for identifying pests. The Bureau took on a preparator of specimens, Leonard B Wyatt (appointed in 1910 to support the Committee), a scientific assistant, DH Gotch (1913), and two assistant preparators, EA Bateman and HE Box (1914 and 1915, respectively). All worked in the BMNH. However, Gotch and Bateman were killed in World War I, and Box never returned to the Bureau. In 1918, as a 14-year-old, Percy J Newby was appointed assistant preparator and stayed until his retirement in 1969. J Waterston joined in 1917 as a scientific assistant to work on Chalcidoidea (parasitic Hymenoptera that are natural enemies of many insect pests), and he was the first of a team of specialist entomologists.

Percy Newby (1904–1997)

Percy Newby became an insect preparator in the BMNH for the Imperial Bureau of Entomology, just 5 years following its establishment. Soon after his appointment, on 11 November 1918 (Armistice Day), he left work and went off to join the celebrations, thinking he would lose his job as a result. However, he continued to work in the Museum for another 50 years until he retired in 1969 from what had become the Commonwealth Institute of Entomology (CIE). In 1952 he was promoted and took charge of the preparatory section of the Institute and, in 1969, received the British Empire Medal for his long service to entomology. He was, in his quiet way, a most knowledgeable first-stage identifier of insects, and his initial sorting of specimens determined which specialist received them for detailed examination.

Keith Harris's lasting recollection of him is the speed with which he travelled through the Department of Entomology, up and down stairs, bearing boxes of specimens and piles of documents. His legs always seemed to travel faster than the rest of him and he moved with what appeared to be unseemly haste for one who had spent most of his life working in a museum. According to Harris, it was a strange coincidence that the Institute, of which Newby was one of the last links with its early days, ceased to exist just 2 years after his death.

A Russian émigré tackles the Moroccan locust

It was political unrest in Georgia that brought a world expert in locust swarms to CABI. BP (later Sir Boris) Uvarov was born in Uralsk in what is now Kazakhstan, which meant that in 1920, Georgian nationalism threatened his job at the State Museum of Georgia. A British soldier deployed in Georgia, who happened to be an entomologist, suggested that he came to work for the Bureau. Joining as a scientific assistant, he was to become the founding director of the Anti-Locust Research Centre. His work covered several species of locusts and grasshoppers affecting agriculture, the Moroccan locust being one of the worst pests in North Africa, Asia Minor, the Caucasus and Central Asia.

His crucial theory of the periodicity and migrations of locusts revolutionized thinking about how to combat these pests[15], further detailed in his handbook for the study and control of locusts and grasshoppers[16] (published by the Bureau). Uvarov paid for his niece, Olga, to leave the Soviet Union in the early 1930s. She became the first woman President of the Royal College of Veterinary Surgeons in 1976–77.

Marshall established a laboratory at Farnham Royal, England, in 1927, run by Neave (1927–28) and then by William Robin Thompson (1928–58). This laboratory was funded by the Empire Marketing Board to support biological control of pests, especially in Australia, Canada and New Zealand, and later developed into the Commonwealth Institute of Biological Control (CIBC) (described further in Chapter 6).

In 1929, the Committee on Locust Control of the Economic Advisory Council gave the Institute responsibility for organizing research on locust problems in Africa and western Asia and, from 1931, the Institute became the international centre for anti-locust research. Uvarov supervised the centre with just one technical assistant and a typist. The centre received reports of locust breeding and movements, which were mapped and analysed, a process that led to effective control of incipient swarms in their outbreak areas. In addition, a locust-breeding laboratory was established at the BMNH, under AG Hamilton, to experiment on factors influencing the development of the three main species (desert locust, red locust and African migratory locust) and, with funding from ICI, to study the effects of insecticides.

1992 Tecwyn Jones is appointed Director following Harris's retirement, and is closely involved in the development of BioNET International.

1993 The Institute's charge-free identification service ends. During the year, the Institute provides 450 reports and details the identities, biology and distributions of 14,797 specimens submitted from 54 countries around the world.

1994 Val Brown is appointed as Director and makes substantial changes to the organization and operation of the Institute, in particular enhancing its environmental work.

1998 The Institute is merged with the other three Institutes into CABI Bioscience.

The impact of locusts: countless hoppers in obscene waves

Uvarov's remarkable personal effort is recorded in Elspeth Huxley's history of the Kenya Farmer's Association, *No Easy Way*, published in 1957.[17] Extracts illustrate the impact:

'All Africa, the Middle East and most of India are subject to (locust) plagues that struck in biblical days and have been striking ever since, at intervals no one could foretell and no one had discovered. (In 1927) East Africa had (now) been free for twenty years and the fear of locusts had faded.

The desert locust was the first to come. It reached Kenya from North Africa and India early in 1928. No organization then existed even to record these warnings, much less to act upon them.

A second threat was gathering meanwhile from another species, the migratory locust. This was assembling its forces in West Africa, about 300 miles south of Timbuktu. In 1929, the whole of West Africa was overrun and in 1930 voracious swarms headed eastwards. They crossed French Equatorial Africa, entered Sudan and the Belgian Congo and appeared in Kenya and Uganda. These unfortunate territories then became the granary of untold millions of locusts of the two species, advancing from two directions and settling down to breed and multiply.

Sky-blackening swarms fell greedily on growing crops, leaving a few shreds of stalks behind. Pasture and veldt appeared to seethe with countless hoppers advancing in obscene waves and leaving a scorched earth behind them. Branches of trees broke under their weight. Against this there was at first nothing that could be done but the beating of tin cans, the shouting of despairing people and the lighting of fires in the forlorn hope of driving the swarms on to one's next-door neighbour. The worst year was 1931, when 40% of the European maize crop was destroyed, and 20% of the African, and milk yields dropped by 60% because of the destruction of the pastures.

To crown it all, a third kind of locust appeared in 1930, this time from the south: the red locust, which bred in north-eastern Rhodesia, chose this moment to overrun practically the whole of Africa south of the Sahara.'

Elspeth Huxley introduces Uvarov and CAB International into her history as follows:

'Some fifteen years before, a young scientist wandering in the eastern reaches of the vast Russian territories where Asia and Europe meet, had been fascinated by the mysteries of these invasions and had decided to devote his life to their unravelling. It was in this early stage of his career that Dr BP Uvarov made his first major discovery – one which Dr Faure in distant South Africa, was making almost simultaneously. This was that the locust has two distinct phases in its life, the solitary and the gregarious. In its solitary phase it is a harmless grasshopper, and so it may continue for its whole lifetime. But sometimes, for reasons hidden then from everyone, it will change not merely its habits but its shape and colour, and enter the gregarious phase. Then it will gather in vast swarms and fly to far-off countries – eating, destroying and breeding as it goes.

(The scientists), among whom the name of Dr BP Uvarov will always be pre-eminent, resolved to fight and conquer (the locusts).'

Huxley also provides an account of the role of the Imperial Institute of Entomology in the war against locusts:

'It started, as so many things do, with a committee: the Locust Sub-Committee of Civil Research set up in April 1929 under the chairmanship of Sir Henry Miers and with Mr Francis Hemming as secretary. Two years later it changed its name to the Committee on Locust Control of the Economic Advisory Council, but it remained the same body and continued until 1939. By this time it had laid the foundations of a system that was to checkmate two subsequent invasions and save untold millions of pounds worth of food.'

Huxley also described how the 'research and information-gathering role' called for by the Locust Sub-Committee was given to

'The Imperial Bureau of Entomology, whose high-sounding name masked a couple of rooms and a clerk at the BMNH under the part-time directorship of a distinguished entomologist, Sir Guy Marshall. For the princely sum of less than £800 a year the services of two trained scientists were secured: Dr BP Uvarov and Miss Z Waloff. Two people comprised the whole anti-locust headquarters staff of the Commonwealth for ten years. They built up a system that has enabled locust plagues to be overcome in two continents. And Dr Uvarov's driving single-mindedness, his deep knowledge of the enemy and his determination that nations should collaborate, created the international teamwork without which the battle would have been lost. The total expenditure on all this, for ten years, was £7,906. 18s. 4d.

The job of the headquarters staff in London was primarily to map the movements of locust swarms in order to discover where they were likely to go. Requests for regular information were sent to every British and foreign government in Africa and western Asia, as well as to many individuals; and in 1931 the first International Locust Conference was held in Rome (which) recognized the Imperial Institute of Entomology as the international centre for collecting, coordinating and studying all the information about locusts (and) Dr Uvarov became a beneficent spider in the centre of a world-wide web.'

The Bureau becomes an Institute

In 1930 the Bureau was renamed the Imperial Institute of Entomology (IIE) and, in 1933, became part of the CAB organization. *The Globe* was pleased to note in 1930 that the Bureau had appointed a woman research assistant, and commented: 'We should like to see biology, which affords such wide opportunities for men, affording equal scope for women.'[18] In 1933–34 the Institute processed and identified more than 100,000 specimens sent in by 181 correspondents, mostly working overseas in UK territories, and issued 386 identification reports relating to more than 8000 species. Some 50,300 of the specimens received were presented to the British Museum (Natural HIstory) and included 470 types of species new to science. This level of activity continued for 60 years. The well-stocked Institute Library was becoming the major UK library for economic entomology.

In 1939 four volumes of the *Index Zoologicus*, edited by Neave as Secretary of the Zoological Society of London, were published, providing bibliographical details of about 190,000 generic and subgeneric names published in zoology between Linnaeus's 1758 edition of *Systema Naturae* (then the standard work on species names) and 1935. This compilation continues today.

Fiction highlights fact

An unusual indicator of the Institute's growing impact is found in the detective novel *The Spider Strikes*, by Michael Innes (1939),[19] featuring Inspector Appleby. Rather than a deadly arachnid, 'The Spider' of the title is a notorious criminal and prankster. A character called Mr Shoon remarks:

" Have you ever reflected on the extent to which the complicated mechanism of our civilisation depends upon a few such nerve-centres – is controlled, moreover, by a mere handful of experts? Consider the Imperial Institute of Entomology … There we have a scattering of men engaged in the abstruse study of crop and forest pests, of disease-bearing insects. A mere scattering, I say, of unprotected scientists under a single roof! Nothing would be simpler than to eliminate them … There could be nothing simpler in the world. And what would be the consequence? In India, six thousand miles away, the death-roll would increase by at least half a million within a year, while the damage to property would be reckoned in hundreds of millions of pounds. "

Parasitic Hymenoptera for biological control

From the 1920s onwards, the Bureau studied the taxonomy of Hymenoptera that were parasites of eggs, larvae or pupae of pest species – to identify species that might be used to control pests. The superfamily Chalcidoidea (chalcid wasps), a large and diverse group, was a major target. Waterston's work was continued by GEJ Kerrich, RD Eady and BR Subba Rao and, from 1970, by Z Bouček, a Czech entomologist, whose study of Australasian Chalcidoidea (Bouček, 1988) had worldwide impact. Another focus was the superfamily Ichneumonoidea of parasitic wasps, especially the family Braconidae, most of which are specialized larval parasitoids of beetles, caterpillars and fly larvae; and DS Wilkinson, GEJ Nixon and ID Gauld published important studies and identification guides to assist biological control efforts.

World War II, and post-War austerity, hinders the Institute

The War meant that some of the Museum's reference collections and the Museum and Institute libraries had to be moved from London.

Tobacco hornworm (*Manduca sexta*) with parasitic braconid wasps (*Cotesia congregata*) hatching from attached cocoons, Kenneth H Thomas. ©SPL

Neave had become Director of the Institute in 1942 on the retirement of Marshall. For those remaining in London the threats were very real.

John W Evans,[20] a scientific assistant at the Institute, described the impact of the 'bombardment of southern England by self-propelled bombs (V-1s and V-2s) [which] lasted for 80 days [when] over 8000 of them were launched and the 2300 which reached London killed nearly 5000 people'. Evans' room was in the New Spirit Building and, whenever the sirens sounded an alert, which happened very frequently, he would take shelter in one of the windowless spirit stores where the shelves were lined with preserved animals. When a flying bomb fell in Cromwell Road just outside the entrance gates of the Museum, there was no time to go to the spirit room. So, after he had heard its engine stop he took shelter under his laboratory bench.

He was fascinated by a Camberwell beauty observed 'fluttering against one of the staircase windows. This was one of the most handsome as well as almost the rarest of all butterflies recorded in England', and was the only time Evans saw one alive, and it remains a relatively rare migrant from Europe to the UK. He said, 'the mystery of how it came to be in the Museum was never solved'.

Evans' compilation, *The Injurious Insects of the British Commonwealth*, was a very useful handbook for budding colonial entomologists. Harris says: 'It was my *vade mecum* as a student and novice researcher and it highlighted the value of the *Review of Applied Entomology*'.

By 1944 the information services of the Institute had moved to 41 Queen's Gate, headquarters of the Royal Entomological Society of London, but still relied substantially on the libraries of the BMNH and on the expertise of its staff. The Director's office remained in the Museum.

Beetles (including weevils)

The beetles (Coleoptera) are important as pests of crops or of stored products, but also as natural enemies of weeds. Marshall studied the taxonomy of weevils, but the first full-time coleopterist was Gilbert E Bryant, appointed in 1924. He worked for 45 years, becoming a world authority on chrysomeloid beetles (leaf beetles), describing 850 new species. ML Cox, appointed in 1979, published on the classification, phylogeny and biology of Chrysomelidae.[21,22] EAJ Duffy, appointed in 1952, was a specialist on timber-boring beetles.[23,24,25] Other CIE coleopterists included RD Pope and, later, RG Booth, both specializing in coccinellids (ladybirds), and RB Madge, specializing in carabid beetles (ground beetles).

1950s are a time of growth

Research and survey work was still vital and, in 1952, a 'Colonial Pool of Entomologists' was established, based at the Institute. Financed by Colonial Development and Welfare Research funds, the Pool continued until 1972. By 1955 such was the growth of the Institute that 56 Queen's Gate was purchased to accommodate administrative staff, the CIE Library, the Publications Office and information staff. The taxonomists remained in the adjacent BMNH.

Camberwell beauty (*Nymphalis antiopa*). ©Shutterstock

Seven-spot ladybird (*Coccinella septempunctata*). ©iStockphoto

Identification had dramatic results

The painstaking identifications were crucially important. For example, the detection, in a routine identification, of the presence of the New World screwworm in Libya (*Cochliomyia hominivorax*) (introduced through a shipment of infected sheep) led to the 'bombing' of infected regions in the country with sterile males, successfully eradicating the potentially devastating pest and avoiding disaster in Mediterranean livestock and wildlife.

Hemiptera: scale insects, leafhoppers and planthoppers

Within the order Hemiptera, which contains many serious pests, the Institute focused on scale insects, initially by Wilfrid J Hall and then by DJ Williams who, in a career spanning 50 years, worked on the scale insects of the tropical South Pacific Region[26,27,28] and on the mealybugs of Central and South America.[29] His work is especially relevant to plant quarantine; the recognition of invasive species; and to biological control of the cassava mealybug in tropical Africa (see section on Institute of Biological Control in Chapter 6). RG Fennah, MSK Ghauri and MR Wilson worked mainly on leafhoppers and planthoppers.[30] Other hemipterists worked on predaceous bugs, especially NCE Miller and, later, GM Stonedahl on mirids, anthocorids and reduviids.

The Institute's first dipterist (fly specialist) was Fritz van Emden, a refugee from Nazi Germany, appointed in 1938. In 1940 the Director of the Institute (SA Neave) had to certify van Emden's loyalty to Great Britain to prevent his internment. His research focused on blood-sucking species, including tsetse flies, and on parasitic tachinid flies, but he was also an eminent coleopterist. He was succeeded in 1959 by RW Crosskey, who published extensively on tachinids and simuliids.[31,32] KM Harris succeeded him and published mainly on harmful and beneficial Cecidomyiidae (gall midges), but also on lepidopterous stem borers and other pests of tropical cereal crops. IM White joined in 1982, working on tephritid flies, pest species and potential biocontrol agents of invasive weeds.[33]

Keith Harris' fieldwork in Nigeria and subsequent taxonomic research in the BMNH typifies the Institute's work. Identifying the complex of species associated with the sorghum midge[34,35] established that, despite reports to the contrary, it was a single cosmopolitan species and very widely distributed. This allowed the international development of resistant varieties of sorghum for use in North and South America, Africa, Asia and Australia, with annual cost benefits of many millions of dollars. Harris and his colleagues specialized in particular in the identification of species of phytophagous families, such as the Cecidomyiidae, Agromyzidae and Tephritidae, and also the parasitic Tachinidae.

Institute scientists were integrated into two sections at the BMNH and, according to Harris, outsiders often found it difficult to recognize the boundaries between the two. This had been the way since the beginning, with an agreement for long-term collaboration, but with one major proviso: that the Institute would curate and add to the Museum's reference collections and would not maintain its own separate collections. The Museum provided accommodation (partly funded by the Empire Marketing Board) and support and, in return, received specimens and information through the worldwide activities of the Institute.

Carabid beetle. ©iStockphoto

Planthopper on teasel weed. ©Raymond Rieser

Training the world's taxonomists

In 1979, NC Pant initiated a series of International Courses on Applied Taxonomy of Insects and Mites of Agricultural Importance. The basement at 56 Queen's Gate was converted into a teaching laboratory, and the 6-week courses were devised and taught by Institute and BMNH taxonomists. According to Harris,[36] these courses 'enhanced personal interactions between taxonomists and attracted funding, but they required substantial inputs of staff time, both in preparation and execution, and appreciable inputs from the BMNH'. By 1990, more than 200 trainees from 54 different countries had participated. Courses were conducted in India, Malaysia and Kenya. The Commonwealth Fund for Technical Cooperation was a major source of funding for participants from Commonwealth countries.

Lepidoptera and the Moths of Borneo

Although Lepidoptera (which include moths and butterflies) are key to agriculture, forestry and food storage, it was not until 1964 that JD Bradley was recruited to work full-time on their taxonomy. He focused on the Microlepidoptera and, in 1978, a second lepidopterist, JD Holloway, joined to work on the Macrolepidoptera, writing on the *Moths of Borneo*, work especially relevant to the study of biodiversity and the effects of deforestation in the Indo-Australian tropics.[37]

The 1980s was a decade of change and reorganization

The importance of accurate taxonomic research was shown by the Institute's work on the African rice midge, thought to be the same species as the Asian rice midge. The study showed that it was a distinct species, which led to its control by new rice varieties using genes for resistance discovered in indigenous African rice. The Institute was becoming increasingly involved in providing information for crop protection and plant quarantine about the distribution of pests, initially as hard copy but later in electronic formats. This led, in time, to the development of the CABI Crop Protection Compendium (CPC).

During the 1980s the Institute collaborated on major crop pests with the Food and Agriculture Organization (FAO) and with the Consultative Group on International Agricultural Research (CGIAR) Centres (especially the International Institute of Tropical Agriculture (IITA), the International Crops Research Institute for the Semi-Arid Tropics (ICRISAT) and the International Rice Research Institute (IRRI)) and with the Africa Rice Centre (formerly WARDA), the International Centre of Insect Physiology and Ecology (ICIPE) and the European and Mediterranean Plant Protection Organization (EPPO). The Institute, for example, collaborated with ICRISAT on pests of sorghum and pearl millet, with WARDA on rice gall midge and with ICIPE on stem borer research. The collaboration with ICRISAT resulted in a joint ICRISAT/CABI publication of handbooks on the African maize stalk borer, *Busseola fusca*, by Harris and Nwanze in 1992;[38] and on the millet stem borer, *Coniesta ignefusalis*, by Youm, Harris and Nwanze.[39]

By the 1980s, 35 staff were divided almost equally between the BMNH and 56 Queen's Gate. In 1987 the Information Services staff moved to Wallingford, Oxfordshire, as part of the CABI centralization process and the CIE Library moved to Silwood Park to form part of the joint CIE/Imperial College 'Michael Way Library'. Part of 56 Queen's Gate was then used as the London office of CABI. In 1991 the name of the Institute was changed to the International Institute of Entomology (IIE), with the sub-description 'an Institute of CAB International'.

Identifying pests: who pays?

In 1992 the Institute's Identification Services processed more than 22,000 specimens submitted from 79 different countries and issued 615 identification reports. In 1993, however, the Institute introduced charges for identifications as member countries encouraged CABI to earn more revenue. By 1996, identifications carried out by the three Institutes over the previous 3 years had dropped to 17,613, with the decline greatest in material received from developing member countries. If fewer of the identifications crucial to controlling pests were being done at CABI, what was the alternative?

1992: The development of BioNET International

Tecwyn Jones became Director in 1992 after Harris retired, and was closely involved in the development of BioNET International, a revolutionary approach to identifying important organisms. This was conceived as a world-wide technical cooperation network composed of a series of national and regional 'Locally Organized Operational Partnerships' (LOOPs), supported by a consortium of biosystematic networks. By 1993 the Caribbean LOOP for arthropods, nematodes and fungi and plant bacteria had made good progress, with LOOPs in India, South-east Asia and southern and eastern Africa in hand. The 1996 Conference 'emphasized the enormous potential' of the programme in empowering member and other countries to manage their biotic resources. Such capacity building meant lower reliance on CABI identification and related services as its relationships with developing member countries, in particular, matured and changed. The programme continues with relative independence from CABI.

Woodland skipper. ©pieceoflace photography

The withdrawal of free taxonomic services and the establishment of BioNET

by Tecwyn Jones

Several months before I was appointed Director of IIE in November 1992, I attended a lunchtime meeting, chaired by (CABI Deputy Director-General) Dennis Greenland, and the Directors of CABI's Institutes for Mycology, Parasitology, Entomology and Biological Control. At this meeting it was explained to me that Mrs Thatcher's policy, which required public institutes such as museums to become self-financed, had been implemented not only in the UK but much more widely (e.g. in the USA and Europe, etc., to differing degrees). This had led to the withdrawal of free taxonomic services, which had traditionally been provided to developing countries since the beginning of colonization. Charges were now being raised by public institutes for all taxonomic services, which were totally beyond the available financial resources of developing countries.

The response of the taxonomic Institutes to this situation was to seek funds from their national aid agencies such as ODA in the UK and from USAID in the USA, to enable the Institutes to provide free taxonomic services to developing-country clients. When this proved to be unsuccessful, developing countries themselves approached their traditional donors (both bilateral and multinational) for funds to enable them to buy taxonomic services, but this also proved to be totally unsuccessful.

In my view the very concept of poor developing countries buying costly taxonomic services from rich, developed-country institutes was absurd in itself and outdated. I said that we should be enabling developing countries to become taxonomically self-sufficient. This, whilst unachievable then at the national level, was a realistic objective at the sub-regional level if developing countries within these sub-regions agreed to share/pool their taxonomic expertise and resources. I cited the East Asian sub-region as an example.

At Greenland's request, I wrote a proposal for a worldwide network – BioNET International with the sub-regional LOOPs, supported by consortia of developed-country taxonomic institutes designated collectively as BIOCON. I presented it at a meeting of Caribbean countries at Trinidad. The governments concerned promptly agreed to establish BioNET International's first LOOP – CARINET. Later that year when I was appointed Director IIE, I was encouraged to give priority to developing the BioNET International concept, finding international and national funds and otherwise assisting the developing sub-regions to create and operate their LOOPs. By the time I left, using largely Swiss aid and UNDP funding, CARINET, PACINET, ANDIONET and perhaps others had been established and BIOCON was active in Europe, USA, South Africa, India and Oceania.

1994 Going green as climate change hots up

The massive potential impact of climate change on the world's ability to feed itself became increasingly apparent in the 1990s. Val Brown, who became Director in 1994, focused the Institute on these concerns.

For example, in 1997 CABI scientists artificially manipulated local climatic conditions to show the potential impact of warmer winters and drier or wetter summers on grassland ecosystems. They found that the make-up of local plant communities was dramatically affected, and investigated the direct and indirect effects of climate change on a wide range of insects.

CABI researchers also examined schemes encouraging farmers to protect biodiversity in agricultural landscapes: cereal fields using less fertilizer and pesticide inputs to provide the habitat for rare plant, insect and bird species; the ecological impact of the 'extensification' of grassland management; and the conversion of arable land to grassland on chalk soils.

CABI's conservation ecology programme continued in the Overseas Territories; a Darwin Initiative to build capacity for insect biodiversity studies in Guyana; a commitment to the UK's biodiversity action plan; and investigations of climate change and multitrophic interactions (involving multiple levels in the food chain). The last-named programme examined the direct and indirect mechanisms operating in tritrophic (i.e. plant–herbivore–parasitoid) systems, and the ways in which they are modified by fungal endophytes (fungi that live inside plants).[40]

By 1999 BioNET had achieved: (i) the training of five postgraduate/postdoctoral fellows; (ii) the training of 38 technicians from southern Africa (in the fields of entomology, nematology, mycology and virology; and (iii) the provision of a CD-ROM of Identification Keys (a global database of taxonomic expertise), a CD-ROM of Pests of Gramineae of Southern Africa, and the Crop Protection Compendium to various LOOP institutions.

In 1998 the Institute merged with the three other Institutes

Once merged into CABI Bioscience, the Institute gradually lost most of its dedicated staffing, housed at the renamed Natural History Museum (NHM). In 2001 the remaining three staff members were transferred to the Museum under arrangements that, theoretically at least, enabled the identification services once offered by the Institute to be provided by the Museum, albeit under different terms and conditions.

Entomology continues to play a major role in CABI's bioscience and publishing activities, as illustrated by the Plantwise initiative and products such as the Crop Protection Compendium (see Chapter 11).

Opposite: entomologist, French Guiana, Patrick Landmann. ©SPL

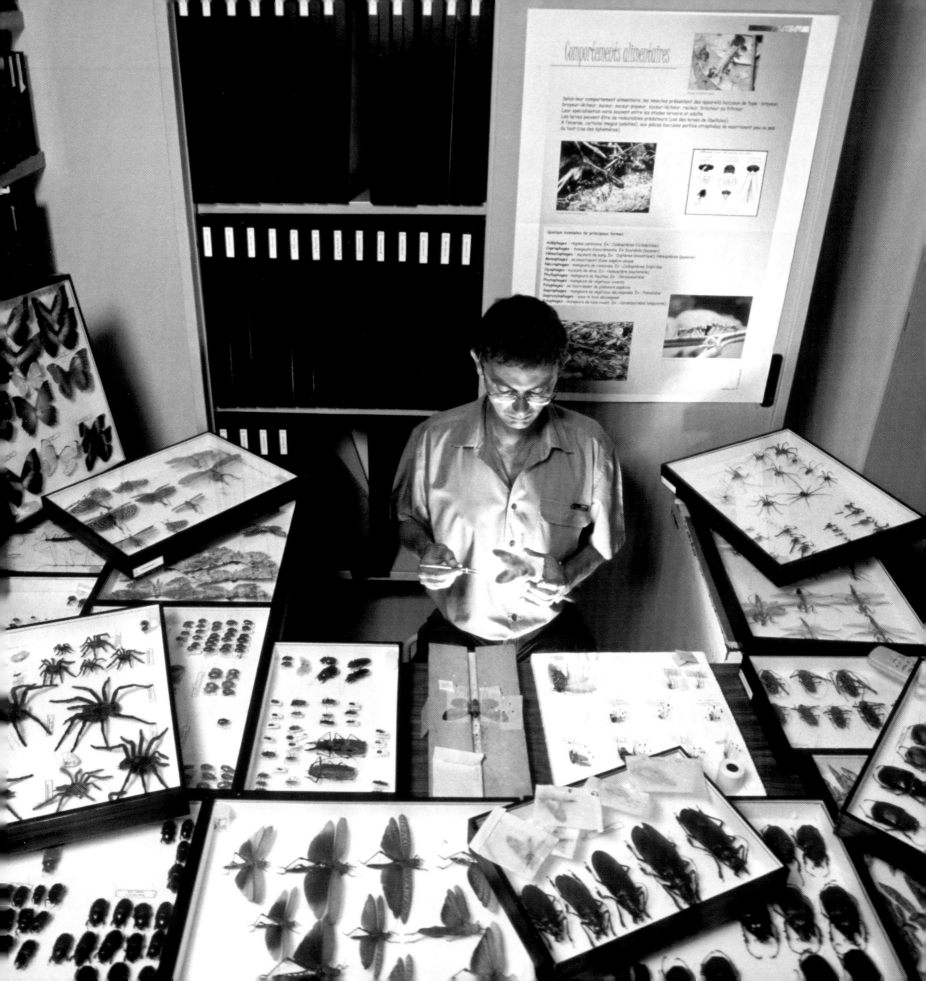

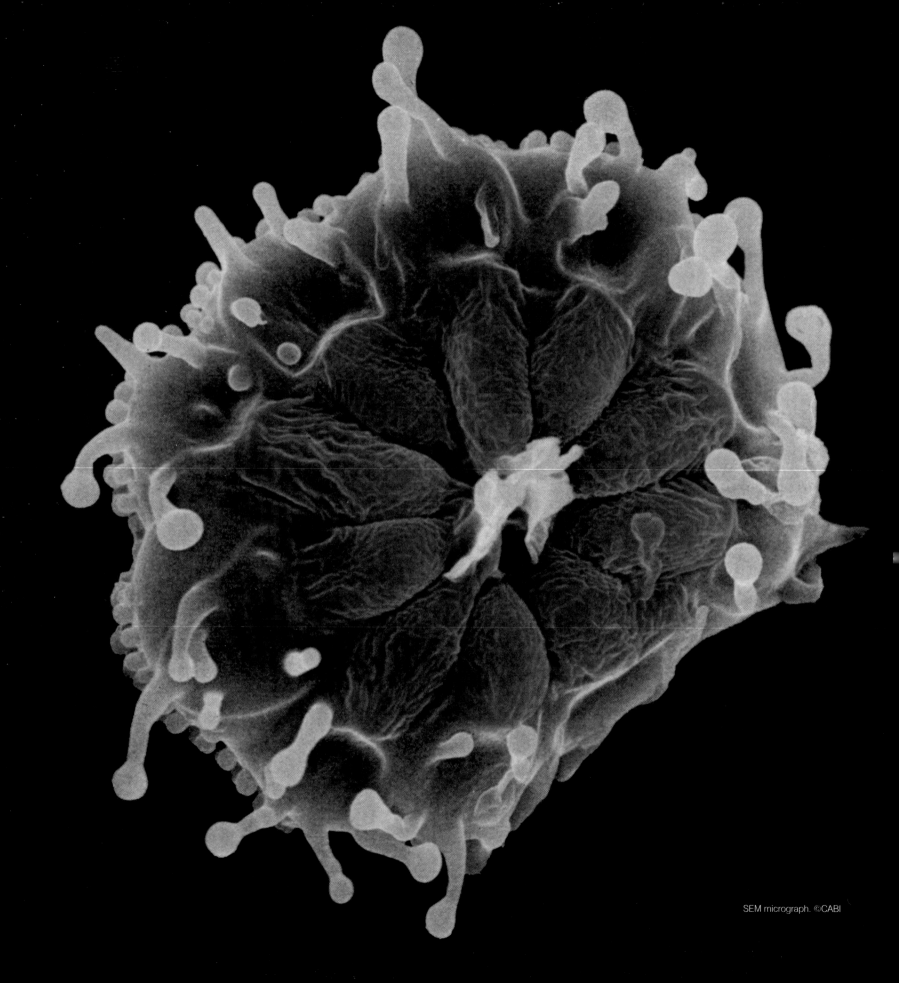

SEM micrograph. ©CABI

MYCOLOGY: THE KINGDOM OF FUNGI

Mycology is the scientific study of fungi. The Kingdom Fungi is quite separate from the plant and animal kingdoms, and its members should not be considered as 'lower plants'. Current best estimates suggest that the fungi comprise around 1.5 million species, making it the most diverse major group of organisms apart from the insects. Fungi play a crucial role in life on earth, as decomposers of plant tissues so releasing the nutrients for uptake by other organisms, in mycorrhizal partnerships with plant roots that promote uptake of water and nutrients, as lichen symbionts with algae and cyanobacteria, and in both beneficial and deleterious relationships with higher plants and animals. Many species are chemical factories producing a wide range of bioactive compounds, including toxins and pharmaceuticals. Fungi provide food for a very wide range of animals, including man.

The genetic resource, or living collection of fungi, remains as a core resource for CABI. According to the CABI Science Review 2009, in this collection 'CABI possesses one of the most prestigious living fungal collections internationally, including capacity for cryopreservation'. The collection was derived from the Mycological Institute, but has successfully made the transition 'from an old to a new identity and practice'. It includes one of the original specimens deposited by Fleming, who discovered an antibacterial substance in the fungus *Penicillium notatum* (now *Penicillium chrysogenum*) in 1929. CABI's industrial and environmental laboratory, also inherited from the Mycological Institute, is a key asset involved, for example, in the development of test kits for the detection of fungi in aircraft and boating fuels.

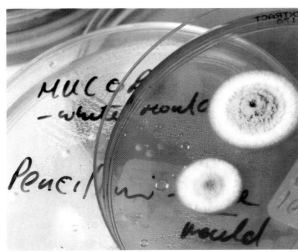

Penicillium mould. ©iStockphoto

David L Hawksworth[41] sets out the case for biodiversity

Biodiversity is of immense importance and incalculable value to planet Earth, and through it to humankind. It is not only about stunning orchids and endangered charismatic animals such as tigers, but also about the multifarious socio-economic consequences of biological interactions amongst organisms. The issue is the maintenance of the life-support systems of Earth, on which all of us depend.

The rewards from as yet scarcely explored biodiversity can be enormous. Five drugs derived directly from or based on chemicals from fungi achieved sales of US$3.8 billion in 1991. Cyclosporin, from another fungal species, improves the survival rate of patients receiving transplant organs. Importing a single species of oil palm-pollinating weevil from West Africa to Malaysia in the early 1980s through CABI's IIBC (International Institute for Biological Control) was worth some US$115 million (a year) to the industry.

Hawksworth also underlines the importance to plant pathologists, agronomists, plant regulatory officials and others who encounter diseases caused by previously unknown or understudied fungi, that many species of fungi are yet to be described. He cites a hypothesis that there are 1.5 million fungal species on earth, which implies that more than 1.4 million remain to be described.

CABI's history in mycology is characterized by an evolution from identification simply by morphology to identification by both morphology and molecular biology. The combination is important in ensuring accuracy, and can, on occasion, be a matter of life and death.[42]

1918 The Imperial War Conference approves the establishment of a mycology bureau, modelled on the entomology bureau, to deal with 'the fungoid diseases of plants'.

1920 The Imperial Bureau of Mycology is established at Kew Green, London with an annual budget of £2000, and seven countries[43] committed to paying this for 3 years. Edwin J Butler (later Sir Edwin) is appointed founding Director of the Bureau, and employs SJ Wiltshire as publication assistant and Edward W Mason as a mycologist.

1921 The first diseased material (of *Hevea brasiliensis* (rubber)) is submitted for diagnosis on 1 October by the Assistant Government Entomologist in Fiji.

1922 About 180 specimens are received at the Institute (and about 2000 in the period 1922 to 1945), a significant workload for a single mycologist.

1922 The first issue of the abstract journal, the *Review of Applied Mycology*, is published.

1925 The Bureau begins to publish occasional works on specific topics. In 1925, Mason first lists the fungi received for identification. Subsequently, Mason's *Annotated Accounts of Fungi Received at the Imperial Mycological Institute* appears on almost a 4-year cycle.

1929 The Second Imperial Mycological Conference underlines the need for information on the worldwide geographical distribution of crop diseases.

1930 The Bureau is renamed the Imperial Mycological Institute and moves to purpose-built premises on Ferry Lane, Kew with a library, a herbarium and a museum showing the major diseases of tropical crops.

1936 A second mycologist is appointed to join Mason, when Guy R Bisby returns from Canada.

1941 Early in World War II the number of specimens received for identification falls to 230.

1942 Six maps on the geographical distribution of plant diseases are published on the basis of material provided by the Institute's abstractors.

1943 Occasional works published by the Bureau since 1925 on specific topics are formalized as Mycological Papers.

1943 *An Introduction to the Taxonomy of Fungi* is published: a practical textbook on the nomenclature and taxonomy of fungi, a core expertise of CABI since the establishment of the Institute and of CABI to this day.

1944 *The Review of Medical and Veterinary Mycology* is launched.

1945 The title Herb. IMI No. 1 is given to a specimen – in this case, a species now known as *Trimmastostroma scutellare* that was found on a Japanese larch tree.

1948 The Institute is renamed the Commonwealth Mycological Institute.

1955 The 'new building' is opened by the Duke of Edinburgh in July, big enough to house the Institute's expanding library, the herbarium and office and laboratory space.

1959 A service for tropical plant-pathogenic bacteria follows the appointment of A Christopher Hayward.

1971 The UK Overseas Development Administration (ODA, later the Department for International Development, or DFID) appoints a number of Liaison Officers attached to CABI Institutes, including the Mycological Institute. This reinforces CABI's focus on plant health in development.

1978 A scanning electron microscope[44] is installed at the Institute. From the early 1980s, Institute staff can also use a tunnelling electron microscope and chemical facilities at the adjacent Royal Botanic Gardens, which 'enabled the Institute to develop novel approaches to the systematics of micro-fungi'.

1980 By the mid-1980s,[45] some 9000 identifications were being undertaken each year for a wide range of countries (120 in 1975–80), mainly from the Commonwealth.

1982 Phyllis M Stockdale receives an award for service to Medical Mycology for work on the taxonomy of dermatophytes (fungi that cause skin infections).

Whilst the name of the Institute has changed several times since its establishment (from Imperial to Commonwealth to International), it is referred to in this section as the Institute unless the context requires otherwise.

World War I highlighted the danger to foodstuffs

The growing impact of food shortages caused by World War I focused attention on the need to conserve foodstuffs and protect supplies from natural damage. This was behind the Imperial War Conference of 1918 decision to establish the Imperial Bureau of Mycology, recognizing the success of the Imperial Bureau of Entomology. Walter Long, Secretary of State for the Colonies, introduced the issue at the Conference, saying, 'The next subject is a very small question put up by the Colonial Office. It is a suggestion as to an Imperial Bureau of Mycology. I do not think it need take any time at all … I am informed it has to do with fungus'.[46]

WB Brierley, at the British Board of Agriculture, had in 1916 proposed a new Bureau of Mycology to sit alongside the Bureau of Entomology within an overall bureau for phytopathology (plant diseases). He proposed that it would parallel Entomology's functions: publishing a bulletin of mycological research and a complete, up-to-date review of applied mycology; encourage the collection and identification of specimens; compile card indices on the literature, diseases, parasites, census, etc. of mycology; investigate problems of special importance; function as a pure culture supply laboratory; form a reference, loan and exchange collection of specimens illustrating plant pathology; and work in collaboration with universities and teaching institutions and be a centre of postgraduate studies.

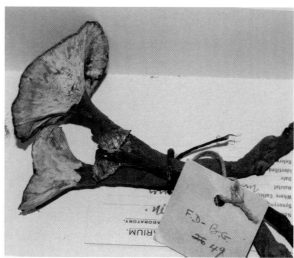

Dried fungi specimen from the CABI collection now housed at Kew. ©CABI

Operations begin in 1920 with nine staff and crowded facilities

Edwin J Butler, who had seen the devastating effects of fungal plant diseases during nearly 20 years as Imperial Mycologist in India, was appointed founding Director of the Bureau. It started in 1920 with an annual budget of £2000, with seven countries[47] committed to sharing an annual budget at this level for 3 years. A *Times* editorial noted the damage caused by fungal diseases, saying that 'armed with knowledge, human effort can subdue them. There could be no better instrument for acquiring and propagating such knowledge than the new Imperial Bureau of Mycology.'[48] The Bureau was first housed at 17–19 Kew Green, London. Butler[49] saw the Bureau as a centre for information and identification of injurious fungi, hoping that staff and visiting international scientists would undertake 'original research into plant diseases'. He recognized the value of studying fungal diseases of animals and man and fungi of importance in technical manufactures and trades.

The Bureau started with a staff of nine and modest facilities. In 1930, it moved into purpose-built premises on Ferry Lane, Kew with a grant from the Empire Marketing Board of £8000 and some £8000 from its own reserves. The 'Old Building', as it became known, was built in a corner of the Royal Botanic Gardens but was leased from the Ministry of Agriculture for 99 years. The new premises included a library, a herbarium and a museum showing the major diseases of tropical crops.

The Bureau becomes an Institute

In 1930 the Entomology and Mycological Bureaux were renamed as Institutes to distinguish them from the newly formed Imperial Agricultural Bureaux that only compiled information. SJ Wiltshire and Edward W Mason covered the information and identification aspects, respectively. However, the Bureau/Institute was initially weighted towards the information service, and it was not until 1936 that a second mycologist was appointed.

The Information Service

The first issue of the abstract journal, the *Review of Applied Mycology*,[50] was published in 1922. In Butler's view, however, it was not enough. He wanted the Bureau to be able to provide 'complete references' to any problem that individuals in the field might encounter. Alongside a 'subject catalogue', he planned a host-plant index listing fungi recorded on plants of economic importance. Butler's aim was achieved, after his resignation, when the *Index of Fungi* first appeared as a supplement to the *Review* in 1940. The *Index* listed currently published names of new genera, species and varieties of fungi. In 1947, the *Bibliography of Systematic Mycology* was started, covering 1943–46; it gave readers a list of currently published papers and books on all aspects of fungi.

Sir Edwin John Butler FRS (1874–1943)[51]

Butler went to Queen's College, Cork, and then studied in Paris, Antibes, Freiburg and Kew. At the recommendation of Kew, in 1900, he was appointed as the first Cryptogamic Botanist to the Government of India at Calcutta.

In 1902, Butler was transferred to Dehra Dun, Uttar Pradesh, India under the Imperial Agricultural Department. During a visit to Coorg he studied spike disease of sandalwood. In 1905 he became Imperial Mycologist at the Imperial Agricultural Research Institute at Pusa, working on a monograph of the Indian wheat rusts in 1906. Between 1910 and 1912 he additionally held the office of Director and Principal at the Agricultural College in Pusa.

Although he was the founding Director of the Imperial Bureau of Mycology, he still made use of a little room on the top floor of the 'Old Building' at Kew so that he could continue his mycology as a side-interest. In 1921 he was made a Companion of the Indian Empire, and in 1931 he published the *Fungi of India* along with GR Bisby. He was knighted in 1939. Several species of fungal pathogens were named by him and many named after him.

Knowing where diseases are has always been critical for their control. The Second Imperial Mycological Conference in 1929 had noted the need for worldwide geographical distribution information on crop diseases, and in 1942 the Institute published six *Distribution Maps of Plant Diseases*, gaining 180 subscribers within a year. The Maps were the foundation for subsequent activities by CABI, including the landmark *Crop Protection Compendium* and Plantwise.

In 1925 the Bureau began to publish occasional works on specific topics. Mason's *Annotated Accounts of Fungi Received at the Imperial Mycological Institute* appeared almost on a 4-year cycle. On the initiative of Geoffrey C Ainsworth (Assistant Mycologist 1939–45, Assistant Editor 1957–60, Assistant Director 1961–64 and Director 1964–68), from 1943, these became known as *Mycological Papers* and a key channel for the Institute's research output. By the end of 1945, 12 *Annotated Accounts* had been published.

The Bureau also wrote directly to people who corresponded with mycological problems. Letters came from every corner of the globe, usually in handwritten form. Almost invariably they received a typed, polite and comprehensive reply, usually prepared by staff of the Institute but signed by Butler himself. The exchanges often ranged across political issues: one letter, written in the 1930s from an Australian who had recently visited Germany, noted that 'we [citizens of the British Empire] are not much liked here'.

The Identification Service

'Hardly a day passes without the arrival at Kew of a carefully packaged test-tube containing a fungus which has baffled mycologists in its native land, accompanied by an urgent appeal for help,' is how a *Times* article entitled 'A campaign on Kew Green: microscopic foes of the Empire,' introduced the Institute's identification work.[52] Mason developed the identification service almost single-handedly. Although, unlike Butler, he had no first-hand experience of tropical fungi, and published very little, he had 'an intensely creative and philosophical mind, an eye for the inter-relatedness of things and a capacity to absorb himself in his science'. He was quite a reserved man, who had been injured on military service in World War I and walked with a slight limp.

The Bureau built up expertise gradually, using investigations as a way of identifying more obscure genera and species. There were large groups of fungi that were frequently encountered and economically important, but inadequately understood. Around 180 specimens were received at the Institute in 1922 and about 2000 between 1920 and 1945.

By the mid-1930s the demand for identifications was fast outgrowing the Institute's capacity. Lack of funds delayed the appointment of an additional mycologist until 1936, when Bisby joined the staff.

Information service staff carried out some investigations (and researchers sometimes wrote abstracts). For example, Jean Stamps, who joined the Institute in 1951, was primarily an editor but undertook identifications of *Pythium* and later was 'allowed' by Grace Waterhouse, who had joined in 1946, to carry out the occasional identification of *Phytophthora*. She said, 'Fungi could be beautiful and this magic attracted many to the profession of mycology – looking down the microscope at sporangia opening and spores "swimming about"'.

Edmund William Mason (1890–1975)[53]

Edmund William Mason was educated in botany and agriculture at St John's College. He was severely wounded in the battle of the Somme, 1916. After the War he became interested in fungi at the University of Birmingham and, in 1921, he joined the Imperial Bureau of Mycology as its first mycologist and remained there until his retirement in 1960. In contrast to Bisby, Mason had great difficulty in bringing any project to conclusion. His publications are therefore not very extensive but they are well written and have been very influential. His rearrangement of the Institute's herbarium set a new standard and he is noted for his contribution to hyphomycete taxonomy and pyrenomycetes. In the words of MB Ellis (Mason's successor at CMI) and SJ Hughes (of Ottawa, who Mason trained) – Mason was 'a great man who did as much for mycology as anybody in this century'. He was an assiduous collector and was usually accompanied in the field by his wife Una Mason, who served a term as Foray Secretary of the British Mycological Society. Mason received a number of honours: OBE, presidencies of the British Mycological Society (1939) and the Yorkshire Naturalists Union (1953), and Linnaean Gold Medal (1961).

World War II slowed identifications

In 1940–41 the number of specimens received fell to 230. However, during the War, Ainsworth and Bisby took advantage of night-time fire-watching duty to scour the institutional library for information for their *Dictionary of Fungi* (see opposite) while on the lookout for incendiary bombs. *An Introduction to the Taxonomy and Nomenclature of Fungi*[54] published in 1945 was the first practical textbook on the nomenclature and taxonomy of fungi, a central function of CABI since the establishment of the Institute – and of CABI since. The textbook was to be superseded in 1974 by Hawksworth's *Mycologist's Handbook*.[55]

A 1943 review committee noted that the Institute had little contact with medical mycologists, even though the *Review of Applied Mycology* contained abstracts on medical mycology. A committee of the Medical Research Council was eventually appointed to coordinate the medical mycology activities of the Institute and the more directly involved Bureau of Hygiene and Tropical Diseases, at that stage outside the remit of the Imperial Bureaux. In the same year, the publication of medically related abstracts was separated off into the *Annotated Bibliography of Medical Mycology*.

History of CABI: reminiscences

The evolving culture at the Institute is evident in the reminiscences of staff, particularly from a section of the book *IMI: Retrospect and Prospect*,[56] entitled Reminiscences and written by some 26 former staff members or associates.

An odd collection and elements of the Raj and Empire

The staff of the Institutes and Bureaux were not without their quirks and idiosyncrasies. Ainsworth says of the Mycological Institute around 1939:

> " *The staffs were then rather an odd collection. The Institute Director DT Ashby was very remote. If he had to be consulted, one knocked on his door, went in and then waited to be noticed. Ashby, who was dominated by his forceful wife, lived at the Priory Guest House in Kew to which staff were invited in batches to afternoon tea on a Saturday. A set of page proofs of the* Review of Applied Mycology *was always laid on his table for 24 hours. He never made any comments.* "

Colin Booth (mycologist, 1953–69 and Assistant Director, 1969–85) relates that, when he arrived in 1953, 'an element of the Raj still existed'.

Mason and Bisby

Mason, according to Ainsworth, 'could never make up his mind' and 'his method of writing a *Mycological Paper* was unique. Rough drawings would be sent to the Oxford University Press, where they would be redrawn and proofs made. These proofs then lay about on Mason's table for a year or more while the text of the paper was slowly compiled'. Mr Mason, as he was always known, smoked one of the five or six pipes that also lay on his desk and suggested that pipe smoking was part of the make-up of a mycologist. But Mason was, according to Martin Ellis, a 'remarkable man who had a deep and genuine interest in fungi, which he passed on to those he mentored. He liked collecting them, looking at them, growing them and working on their life histories'. Anthony Johnston called him 'the kindly mycologist'.

Guy Richard Bisby, in contrast, came from a very poor family and told Ellis that 'he often had to walk miles to school barefoot. Later he worked his way through high school and university but was always short of money'. Bisby could 'always make a quick working decision and dealt with his identifications promptly' according to Ainsworth. Bisby was a chain-cigarette smoker. He was, however, according to Howes, a great favourite, a lovely man renowned for his beautiful handwriting who could send handwritten manuscripts direct to the printers. Both Ainsworth and Ellis said that Mason and Bisby were hardly on speaking terms.

SP Wiltshire: meticulous editor and careful shopper

Wiltshire was a meticulous editor of the *Review of Applied Mycology* and, in 1940, he succeeded Ashby as Director but continued as editor with the help of HA Dade as assistant editor. Jean Stamps said that he was very tall, remote and a strict Baptist teetotaller. When she was being soaked by a summer downpour he offered his umbrella to shelter some books Stamps was carrying rather than to shelter her.

Accounts by others describe Wiltshire as 'not particularly sociable' and as someone whose 'thrift was legendary'. According to Booth, Wiltshire insisted that index cards (for records of specimens received) 'were used four times, the top line on both sides and by reversing the card, the bottom gave two more top lines'. All reports and research notes were written on the back of proofs of the *Review of Applied Mycology*. Incubators and culture cabinets were either purchased second-hand or made by a local handyman.

The impact of War

Apart from military service, many Institute staff were Air Raid Wardens and 'dug for victory' on allotments on the Institute grounds. Bisby was the keenest gardener in Mycology and took over any plot relinquished by others.

An Executive Council report from 1943 proudly notes that Hitler did not stop CABI journal production:

" The intensification of the War in the Far East and the extended invasion of Russia reduced further the number of subscribers to the journals and cut off certain suppliers of information. The greater calls for National Service in the UK caused constant review and changes in the non-scientific staffs of the bureaux. These were the general adverse conditions of the time. Against those, publications from Empire countries arrived with great regularity and more were received from foreign countries. In this much help was received from His Majesty's Stationery Office and the British Council. The continuity of all the Abstract Journals was maintained and the bureaux, with their reduced staffs, were kept employed. In some cases, in which reductions had gone too far, assistants had to be engaged. "

According to the report,

" Subscribers in enemy and enemy-occupied countries have been temporarily lost, as have many in the countries of the United Nations (UN), with which communications have become very difficult such as Russia and China. So far as is known, the sales to foreign enemy and enemy-occupied countries in Europe and Asia in 1938/39 were 581 and 273, respectively, and to Russia and China 278 and 69, respectively (347). "

In spite of the War, the total circulation of publications to countries of the British Commonwealth and the USA increased. Neave, the Director of the Institute of Entomology, said in his report for 1943–44 that 'the interference in the Institute's work caused by the war has passed its zenith'. There was a significant increase in demands for identifications and for its publications.

After the war, the Executive Council said:

" On the whole the Bureaux have been fortunate. Their casualties have been few in number. The Council greatly regret the loss by enemy action at sea of Dr William Allen, who was their Chairman at the time, and also of Lieut DS Wilkinson RNVR of the Imperial Institute of Entomology. Mr RF Avery also of the same Institute suffered severe injuries whilst serving in the Home Guard [but was able] to return to duty. But the Bureau suffered no air-raid casualties and the damage done to buildings has been repaired. Other problems related to shortage of staffing, the number of copies of journals had to be reduced because of paper restrictions, and the impossibility of civilian travel. "

The Royal Family

The Duke of Edinburgh's visit to CMI, 1955. ©CABI

Agnes Onions (mycologist, 1953–58 and Culture Collection curator, 1964–87) recalled the opening of the 'New Building' at Kew by His Royal Highness the Duke of Edinburgh in 1955, who delighted everyone in the Culture Collection by examining a plate of *Phycomyces nitens* with 'a lovely line of zygospores' (fused sex cells) and saying, 'So the path of true love does not always run smoothly'.

Post-War consolidation and change

Accessions specimens

The names and numbers given to specimens are crucial to enabling identification of harmful or beneficial species. Mason had started numbering specimens in 1939–40, but it was not until 1945 that the title Herb. IMI No. 1 was given to a specimen – in this case, a species now known as *Trimmastostroma scutellare* that was found on a Japanese larch tree. IMI referred to the Imperial Mycology Institute, but it continued to be used in spite of changes in the Institute's name (and its eventual merger into CAB International). Herb is the shortened term for Herbarium.

There is still an accessions book at CABI. Specimens have been logged continuously since then with details such as name, host and location. The entry was cross-referenced to a list of the plant host or substrate (the host book) and secondly to a species list. The species list included the country, host, the collector, the year of collection and the IMI number.

The modern system used in the Institute derives from principles set out by Mason, including that of one fungus, one name. Hawksworth says that the Herb. IMI system is 'so simple in concept, was beautifully thought out – an interlinking database of information well before its time, and one that was easily transferred to a computerized system'. Innovatively, slides of specimens were made, enabling mycologists to view the specimen under a microscope easily and speedily. The careful labelling of slides of specimens on loan increased the value of the collection for identification purposes and avoided further or subsequent borrowing, and further destruction of the specimen and risk of loss or damage in transit. Private collections were also placed in the Herbarium, specimens obtained on exchange and others acquired for the collection. However, by 1943, Mason's lists and annotated accounts were the only tangible scientific research product of the Institute.

From 1947, scientific and information outputs of the Institute grow

In 1947, fungi in the UK National Collection of Type Cultures were transferred from the Lister Institute to IMI to form the UK Collection of Fungus Cultures, still maintained as part of the IMI and CABI Collection, including Fleming's isolate of *Penicillium*. The information service was relatively well resourced and, by 1947, outputs included *Mycological Papers*, the *Index of Fungi* and the *Bibliography of Systematic Mycology*, first published in that year. The series of *Mycological Papers* was supplemented in 1956 with a new series, *Phytopathological Papers*.

Dictionary of Fungi and Fungal Families of the World

The Dictionary of Fungi has been published by IMI from its outset in 1943, and then after centralization by CABI through to the latest edition in 2008. It remains the basic reference work for systematic mycology, an authoritative consensus classification of the fungi, widely accepted as an informing framework for research into pure and applied mycology. Its distinguishing feature amongst CABI publications is its origin in the work of one of the original CABI Institutes, IMI and its reliance on the taxonomic work of CABI scientists.

In 2007, CABI published *Fungal Families of the World*, an illustrative and perhaps more approachable companion to the *Dictionary*, placing in context seismic changes in classification that were driven by modern DNA sequence analysis, and forming a link between phenetic and phylogenetic approaches to fungal systematics; secondly, it provides substantial information on the 536 currently accepted families of fungi, with detailed descriptions and notes on ecology and economic uses, etc.; and thirdly (and, according to the authors, perhaps most importantly) it depicts the extraordinary range of morphological structures found in fungi, celebrating mycodiversity.

Collecting amongst the chimps

In 1963[57] one of the junior mycologists at the Institute, Kris A Pirozynski, went to Tanganyika to collect mycological specimens for the Herbarium. He was invited by the well-known East African archaeologist and human evolution pioneer, Louis SB Leakey (whose son was a member of the Institute's Pool of Plant Pathologists) to become a short-term resident scientist on a project on chimpanzees in a piece of virgin forest near Kigoma. Pirozynski studied the local fungi, particularly species pathogenic on genera of host plants of economic importance.

Pirozynski is remembered in Jane Goodall's book *In the Shadow of Man*.[58] Pirozynski looked after the Gombe Stream Research Centre for 4 months whilst Goodall was away. His experience in dealing with organisms somewhat larger than fungi is recorded thus:

❝ *And the chimpanzees were becoming more and more impossible in camp. JB (one of the chimpanzees) had learned to dig boxes and wires out of the ground, so that Hassan had had to sink the boxes in concrete and lay expensive piping between box and handle for the wire.*

Then JB dug up the pipes, so they had been put in concrete too. Figan and Evered had started to prize open the steel lids with strong sticks – occasionally if the wire was too slack, they succeeded. Even worse from Kris's point of view, more and more of the chimps had followed David's lead and begun wandering into his tent, taking clothing and bedding. Finally he had organized things, stowing material into tin trunks or stout wooden boxes. The Goliath had started a craze for chewing canvas. Little groups of chimps sat around tearing up and chewing chair seats, flaps of tents – even Kris's camp bed had been destroyed. "

The study of even the most exotic fungi may have seemed mundane compared with life with chimpanzees.

Fungal identification and collection on a massive scale

By the mid-1980s,[59] some 9000 identifications were being carried out every year for many countries (120 in 1975–80), chiefly from the Commonwealth. About 70% of the material arrived as living cultures and the remainder as infected material. All groups of microfungi were covered, with the exception of yeasts.

Having a collection of examples of specific types of fungi was hugely helpful in identification. The Institute amassed the largest 'dried' collection of its type for microfungi, with some 300,000 samples (including numerous type specimens), known as the IMI Herbarium. This arose from the receipt of materials, and the addition of specimens deposited by staff and through exchanges of duplicates with overseas collections. Mycologists worked at the benches in the Herbarium until 1975, when a new culture collection building was built.

The identification service was free for all non-commercial submissions until 1977, when charging for non-member countries was introduced as part of an effort to sustain CAB's operations without subsidy and to keep membership contributions down. However, exceptions were made at the Director's discretion for material of value to the Institute's collections and research.

New techniques made the crucial task of distinguishing important fungi easier. A scanning electron microscope (SEM) was installed at the Institute in 1975, and the tunnelling electron microscope (TEM) and chemical facilities at the adjacent Royal Botanic Gardens were made available to Institute staff in 1982 and 1984, respectively. According to Hawksworth, these 'enabled the Institute to develop novel approaches to the systematics of microfungi'. For example, in 1984, the Institute used these facilities in studying critical groups in *Penicillium*, as part of a Science and Engineering Research Council (SERC) programme entitled 'Systematic Studies of Micro-fungi of Biotechnological and Industrial Importance'. The study combined biochemical, metabolic, ultra-structural, growth and other information with traditional morphological characters to produce more soundly based taxonomies.

Sarah Thomas and Emma Thompson working on Green Muscle™ in the Egham labs. ©CABI

In September 1992, the Institute moved to Egham on a site purchased from Royal Holloway College. It housed an industrial and environmental laboratory, the genetic resources collection (the living collection), preservation, bacteriology and yeast investigation laboratories and space for plant protection projects. In 2009, the two staff responsible for the fungal herbarium were seconded to Kew Gardens; CABI will retain ownership of the herbarium.[60] The genetic resource, or living collection of fungi, remains as a core resource for CABI and the industrial and environmental laboratory as a key asset involved, for example, in the development of test kits for the detection of fungi in aircraft and boating fuels.

Sally Lorraine accessing the living fungal collection preserved in oil. ©CABI

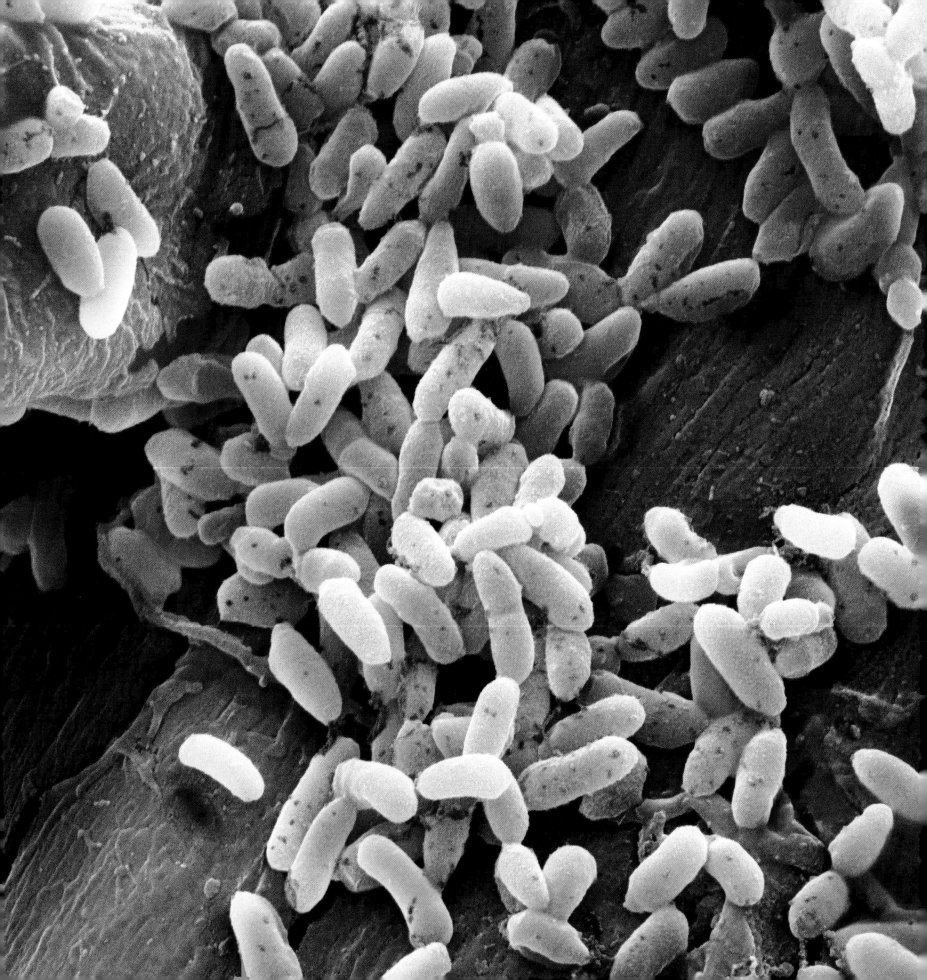

Achievements in bacteriology:
the 1960s and beyond

Christopher Hayward (1959–65)

A unique service for tropical plant-pathogenic bacteria was introduced following the appointment of A Christopher Hayward in 1959 when, by his own account, he started out as the Institute's first phyto-bacteriologist.

Hayward[61] helped develop a diagnostic scheme for the fluorescent *Pseudomonas*, which enables identification of many serious plant pathogens. Ronald Lelliott (MAFF, Harpenden; now FERA, York, UK) and Eve Billing (East Malling) collaborated on this work in the early 1960s, with Lelliott taking the lead. Hayward says that 'this was an early example of quality control in diagnostic methods between different laboratories and the outcome was the LOPAT diagnostic scheme for identifying *Pseudomonas* and other bacteria, which has had a considerable influence and utility for the past four decades'.

The unit also investigated facial eczema in sheep, a major problem in New Zealand in the early 1960s. Hayward recalls 'Martin Ellis being very excited about that work; he was a person who took great pleasure in his work, but particularly when there was a link to some phenomenon of applied importance'. He re-described and renamed the associated fungus as *Pithomyces chartarum*.

John Frederick Bradbury (1965–90)

John Frederick Bradbury was a world authority on the identification and taxonomy of plant-pathogenic bacteria and critical to building CABI's reputation in this field. He wrote the standard text *A Guide to Plant Pathogenic Bacteria* (1986),[62] a massive help to researchers since no comprehensive reference book on these bacteria had been published since 1951.

As Bradbury recounts,[63] however, the task of the bacteriologist was complex given that, unlike fungi, bacteria had few distinguishing visible (even under the microscope) features.

In his landmark *Guide*, Bradbury provided a background to tests sufficient to give plant pathologists the tools to decide whether a bacterial culture is likely to be the pathogen causing observed symptoms and whether organisms isolated from a diseased plant are worth further study. This background proved invaluable to plant pathologists in the field.

Challenging cassava blight

Rob Williams was a research scientist in West Africa from 1969 to 1975, a member of the pioneering team establishing the research programmes of IITA. During this period he says that he benefited greatly from the resources of the then CMI, first using the Institute's herbarium materials to produce a pictorial dossier on the grain legume diseases that had been identified in West Africa and then using the identification service to confirm the presence of certain pathogens in the crops in the region.

Cassava tubers. ©iStockphoto

The expertise of CMI was crucial to the first identification of cassava bacterial blight in Africa in the early 1970s, a disease that threatened the livelihood of countless African farmers. Cassava is a staple food crop throughout the humid tropical regions of Africa, having originated in South America. In 1973, cassava throughout several regions of Zaire was being devastated by *La maladie des cierges*, which Belgian scientists said was caused by an insect, *Pseudotheraptus devastans*. IITA was asked by USAID to investigate, and sent Williams to Zaire in 1973. He set up a temporary laboratory in the bathroom of his room at the Intercontinental Hotel in Kinshasa, took taxis out to the farms outside the city, brought material back to the 'lav-lab' and isolated a bacterium (using the techniques described in Bradbury's *Guide*). This was sent to Bradbury at CMI, who confirmed it as *Xanthomanas manihotis*, the causal agent of cassava bacterial blight, a disease of cassava in South America. Based on the diagnosis and the recommendations for tackling the disease, IITA established a multi-million-dollar programme in Zaire, funded by USAID (the United States Agency for International Development), to bring the disease under control. Careful isolation and taxonomy at CABI underpinned the success of this programme.

On the same visit, Williams found an infestation of cassava mealybug in a field outside the city of Kinshasa, its first identification in Africa. CMI played a key role in the subsequent biological control (see Chapter 6). Williams, after working for ICRISAT and Ciba-Geigy, joined CABI in 1993 as Deputy Director-General and stayed until 2001.

By the mid-1980s the new science of molecular biology was emerging, and Bradbury quickly saw its relevance to bacteriology. Whilst he was successful in obtaining some equipment (in 1970, the Institute purchased a second-hand spectrophotometer echoing Ainsworth's view that bacteriology and mycology were 'cottage industries'), it was not until 1999 that CABI could afford a DNA sequencer.[64]

Opposite: *Pseudomonas aeruginosa* bacteria, SEM, Steve Gschmeissner. ©SPL

Gerry Saddler (1991–2001)

By this time, Gerry Saddler had been appointed as bacteriologist in 1991 to replace Bradbury, arriving with a thorough background in molecular biology. Saddler[65] writes that 'I remember my first few months in the bacteriology laboratory in Kew; by that time the lab had seen better days and the methods used were becoming increasingly outdated. I was beginning to have severe doubts that I made the right choice in coming to work at CABI'.

Using molecular techniques in diagnosis and protection

Saddler was encouraged by Hawksworth, and also appreciated the suggestion from Waller and Jackie Kolkowski that he focus on plant-pathogenic bacteria:

" I also owe a large debt of thanks to Peter Scott, who asked me what I knew about the polymerase chain reaction (PCR) diagnosis and if it would be of any use in agriculture? At the time, the answer to Peter Scott's question was probably very little and I didn't think so! But from this discussion I did some research and was able to win a small grant from the Society for General Microbiology for a PCR machine and some gel electrophoresis equipment in 1991, the Institute's first. PCR has formed a major part of diagnostic work at CABI ever since. "

But could molecular techniques also help protect plants? In 1992 Saddler secured funding from DFID to develop a biological control agent (BCA) for bacterial wilt disease (*Ralstonia solanacearum*), which affects a wide range of plants in the potato family, and recruited Julian Smith and Lisa Offord. The three worked closely together on a number of projects until Saddler left CABI in 2001. This particular project also broke new ground: it was CABI's first foray into the world of genetic modification (GM). Smith developed an attenuated (non-lethal) strain of *R. solanacearum* that protected potato plants against the normal disease pathogen, but the project eventually became lost in the growing public unease over GM in agriculture.

Although PCR was an idea for analysing populations through DNA fingerprinting, at that point it was little used for detection work. Saddler needed a reliable method for the many bacteria that came to him through the Identification Service. He turned from the biochemical tests used routinely by Hayward and Bradbury and persuaded CABI to invest in a gas chromatograph with a dedicated library of bacterial fatty acids (which separated out bacterial samples and compared them against known bacteria). Bought in 1993, it offered a quick, cheap and highly automated means of identifying bacteria. This equipment enabled Saddler to participate in the discovery of a new bacterial pathogen of *Anthurium* spp. in Trinidad, which led to collaboration with a French group and ultimately the description of *Acidovorax anthurii*, which causes bacterial leaf-spot on *Anthurium*.[66]

CABI's natural products programme screening fungi for novel active compounds. ©CABI

The Culture Collection

Thanks to the recent activities of David Smith, in particular, CABI is known internationally for its central role in promoting the importance of Biological Resource Centres (BRCs) and developing guidelines for Quality Control and Assurance. He has ensured that CABI's BRC activities comply with the articles of the Convention on Biological Diversity, maintaining biosecurity. David plays key roles in the UK and internationally. He was President of the European Culture Collections' Organization and now is President of the World Federation for Culture Collections.

From its origin, the Institute maintained a selection of fungi as living cultures. The size of this collection grew dramatically after 1947, when the UK National Collection of Type Cultures at the Lister Institute was dispersed and almost all the filamentous fungi transferred to the Institute. Some UK departments and agencies provided some additional funds. The 760 cultures transferred had increased to 11,000 by the mid-1980s. The culture collection was by then housed in the so-called New Building at Kew and a temporary structure. With the move of the Institute to Egham, it is now located in the purpose-built Ainsworth Building.

The fungi were originally kept by subculturing on nutrient agar slopes, but this gave way to freeze-drying in 1966 for appropriate fungi and these are stored at 15°C in cabinets. In 1968 low temperature storage using liquid nitrogen was introduced for those organisms that do not survive freeze-drying. The Institute has studied preservation methods and the effects of storage at low temperatures and of thawing. The genetic resource, or living collection of fungi, remains a core resource for CABI. According to the *CABI Science Review 2009*, in this collection 'CABI possesses one of the most prestigious living fungal collections internationally, including capacity for cryopreservation'. The collection was derived from the Mycological Institute but 'has successfully made the transition from an old to a new identity and practice'.

Cryopreservation of the fungal living collection at Egham. ©CABI

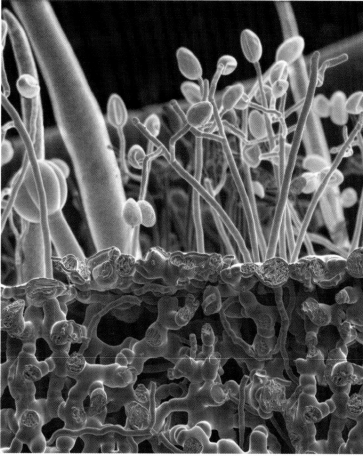

Potato blight fungus, SEM, Power and Syred. ©SPL

Industrial services

Butler had, in the Institute's early days, identified a role for the Institute in 'technical manufactures and trades or industrial mycology'. Investigative work was carried out sporadically in the 1960s and 1970s, but in 1983 this was placed on a more organized footing with funding from the UK Department of Trade and Industry. New staff offered improved industrial services, including the laboratory testing of materials, contracting research, consultancies, enquiry-answering services, preparation of specialist bibliographies and online database searches. In 1984 the National Testing Laboratory Scheme approved the Institute for conducting microbiological testing of materials to UK and foreign standards. These services continue to be provided by CABI.

Commercial products

The mid-1990s saw the emergence of fungal biopesticides, potentially providing CABI Bioscience with a new revenue stream based on the production of biopesticides or the licensing of technology to commercial partners. Similarly, in 2005 CABI launched Conidia Bioscience and FUELSTAT, a real-time test for the presence of *Hormoconis resinae*, a fungus that thrives in aviation and marine diesel fuel.

IMI Scientific Contributions

Systematics

Identifying fungi is crucial to understanding and controlling diseases. However, when the Institute began, few critical works on tropical microfungi in particular existed, meaning that each identification could become a mini-research project. It was vital that these pioneering studies were shared widely, so the lengthy letters of the Institute's first mycologist, EW Mason, evolved into the prestigious *Mycological Papers* series (1925–2001). But Mason, ever the perfectionist, was loath to publish major revisions of different groups of fungi himself. Fortunately, his attention to detail was infectious and two young assistant mycologists, MB Ellis and SJ Hughes, caught the 'bug' and a series of critical accounts of diverse microfungal genera started to appear.

Institute scientists revolutionized the identification of fungi. In 1953 Hughes, just after leaving Kew for Ottawa, published a paradigm-shifting paper on differing types of conidiogenesis (asexual spore formation), which became the basis of classification of these fungi.[67] Ellis (1971)[68] applied this to dark-spored hyphomycetes, and Sutton (1980)[69] to coelomycetes. In 1982–83 Sutton, together with two recent recruits, Paul M Kirk and David W Minter, used transmission electron microscopy to show exactly what these differences meant at the developmental level.[70] Sutton, with Belgian mycologist GL Hennebert, devised a scheme that has become the basis of descriptions of these fungi worldwide[71] – and has been applied to all conidium-forming genera from the 1995 edition of the *Dictionary of Fungi*.

Phytophthora, which causes diseases such as potato blight, is responsible for enormous damage worldwide. GM Waterhouse's work was very influential; in 1963 she distinguished six groups within the genus, still critical in their identification.[72]

Lichens are a fascinating combination of a fungus and either an alga or a cyanobacterium (historically blue-green algae). In the 1960s, scientists realized that the evolutionary relationships of ascomycete fungi could only be interpreted if considered together with the lichenized groups. In cooperation with OE Eriksson in Sweden, Hawksworth set up a new kind of journal to work out these relationships for the largest fungal phylum, *Systema Ascomycetum*. The journal was published by CABI from 1986 until 1998, when it was succeeded by the online-first *MycoNet* journal.

From 1940, the Institute published indices of fungal names in supplements to the *Review of Applied Mycology*, soon evolving into a separate journal, the *Index of Fungi*, which remains the authoritative international source of reference. A computerized production system introduced in 1986 became the online database *Index Fungorum* which, through collaboration with the Mycology Reference Laboratory of the US Department of Agriculture (USDA) in Beltsville, and much keyboarding at the Institute both inside and outside official time, went live free on the Internet in 2000 with over 300,000 fungal names. The database now has over 454,000 named fungi, and is supported by a partnership of CABI, the CBS-Fungal Biodiversity Centre (the Netherlands) and Landcare Research (New Zealand).

Institute scientists were curious to see how conidial (i.e. asexual) fungi related to sexual stages, with cultures being left for long periods to see whether any sexual structures formed, or making cultures from single sexual spores to see whether an asexual stage developed. Booth studied hypocrealean fungi in this way, publishing accounts of *Nectria* in 1959,[73] and *Fusarium* in 1970.[74] A Sivanesan was published on *Venturia* in 1977,[75] and on all known ascomycetes with so-called bituricate asci in 1984.[76]

The *Aspergillus* genus includes moulds that can contaminate food with deadly aflatoxins. Institute mycologists had a special interest in *Aspergillus* and *Penicillium*, most notably Onions and JI Pitt, and later the Institute used biochemical and cultural methods adapted from bacteriology to classify species. This was funded by SERC from 1984 to 1988, the team including five mycologists, including Kozakiewicz (seconded from MAFF), Bridge and RRM Paterson; the latter two went on to form the Institutes' Biochemical and Molecular Laboratory. The work led to a computerized identification system, issued as a CD in 1992. Kozakiewicz, who carried out scanning electron microscopy of spores for this project, also used that method in a comprehensive study of *Aspergillus* species on stored products, published in 1989.[77]

Biochemical and molecular approaches to solving systematic problems became an increasing feature at the Institute, after its move to Egham in 1992 afforded appropriate laboratory facilities for such work for the first time.

Trametes versicolor. ©CABI

Fungal diversity

How many fungi exist on Earth? Bisby and Ainsworth estimated that only around one-third of the fungi were known – implying that there were probably around 100,000 species in total. Also in 1943, Bisby forecast that there were twice as many fungi as plants – implying 500,000 species. Ainsworth was more modest, commenting in 1968 that a figure of 260,000 could be conservative. Most undescribed fungi were thought to be in the tropics. Pirozynski, a tropical microfungi specialist, estimated in 1972 that the microfungi alone outnumbered the plants by at least 3:1, and perhaps by as much as 5:1.

Hawksworth decided to revisit the issue for his Presidential Address to the British Mycological Society in 1990 as biodiversity fever started to grip the world. He used several independent lines of evidence to estimate with a conservative figure of 1.5 million species.[78] This implied that only 5–6% of the fungi on Earth were known, and around six times as many fungi as plants, which caught the attention of *Nature* when published in 1991.[79] The estimate has stood the test of time, especially as molecular approaches have revealed numerous so-called cryptic species in almost any group when studied in sufficient depth.

Key staff had been keen field mycologists from the earliest days at the Institute, foraying into Surrey woodlands, joining excursions of the British Mycological Society (BMS) and other groups. Hawksworth became fascinated by the new and unusual fungi he was finding in Slapton Ley National Nature Reserve in South Devon and, with collaborators and BMS meetings there, 2500 species had been found by 1998, then by far the largest number known anywhere in the world – with over 30 species new to science. That is until Kirk, working with BM Spooner of the Royal Botanic Gardens Kew, had by 2001 grown the total known from Esher Common in Surrey to 2900.

Several staff developed passions for relatively unexplored fungal habitats, discovering numerous genera and species new to science. Deighton and Pirozynski focused on evergreen leaves in the tropics, including the fungi parasitizing or dwelling on leaf-inhabiting fungi; Hawksworth on the fungi occurring on lichens, with keys and monographs of the conidial representatives in particular; Sutton on fallen eucalyptus leaves and the fallen cupules of *Castanea*; Minter on microfungi associated with *Pinus*; and Kirk on fallen laurel leaves.

Bisby and Mason started a tradition of UK checklists with one of the pyrenomycete fungi in 1940. With an SERC grant, Hawksworth prepared an ascomycete fungus checklist in 1978, on which Paul F Cannon was employed prior to joining the Institute staff. Minter catalogued fungi of the Ukraine and the Caribbean with UK Darwin Initiative funding. In the early 1990s, Kirk, assisted by JA Cooper, developed a Fungal Records Database for the UK and Ireland for the BMS – now on the Web with over 1.5 million records by 2010.

The Institute's contribution to global biodiversity in general was demonstrated by workshops it held in the 1990s, in association with UNEP (United Nations Environment Programme), UNESCO (United Nations Educational, Scientific and Cultural Organization), IUBS (International Union of Biological Sciences) and IUMS (International Union of Microbiological Studies). Two sections of the UNEP/GEF (Global Environmental Facility) Global Biodiversity Assessment (1995) were coordinated by the Institute, and involved workshops at Egham. Many important publications on biodiversity priorities and methods emerged.

Environment and climate change

The Institute showed that lichens could be used to measure the cleanliness of the air in cities. Ainsworth's nephew, OL Gilbert, then at the University of Newcastle upon Tyne, had written a note on this in *The Plant Pathologist's Pocketbook* (1968). Hawksworth knew Gilbert and developed this concept further with F Rose (University of London), mapping lichen zones throughout England and Wales, and then correlating them with measured smoke and sulphur dioxide (SO_2) values. The study became a *Nature* cover article in 1970,[80] causing an explosion in lichen biomonitoring studies. Experimental studies supported the correlations and, by the mid-1980s, the subject was included in secondary school teaching. Following the resultant fall in SO_2 levels from the Clean Air Acts and closure of 'dirty' power stations, reports of lichen recolonization around London were the subject of a follow-up *Nature* letter in 1981, and a more detailed analysis published in 1989.

Global warming and elevated levels of carbon dioxide are an increasing concern. When the Institute moved to Egham, it wasn't far from the Natural Environment Research Council (NERC)-funded 'Ecotron' climate control chambers at Silwood Park. Institute staff monitored changes in populations of soil fungi with elevated carbon dioxide levels, leading to contributions to a paper in *Science* in 1998.[81]

The application of molecular biology

The Institute made critical discoveries about combating plant disease by combining biochemical and molecular biology techniques. *Ganoderma* basal stem rot is the most damaging disease of oil palm in South-east Asian plantations. CMI researchers looked at isozymes (proteins) from isolates from several countries and showed the pathogen to be a unique functional group, distinct from isolates on other hosts. A high degree of variability in mitochondrial DNA within the oil palm group, even from fungi from adjacent trees, indicated that spores from the fruiting bodies are much more important in disease spread than previously thought, and root-to-root contact less important; this has major implications for stopping the spread of the disease.

1971, The Plant Pathology Unit:[82] CABI's role in plant health in developing countries

The Institute had always provided advice and services to CABI's member countries, especially developing countries. For example, the service for tropical plant-pathogenic bacteria introduced in 1959 was aimed at developing countries with a tropical climate. It was not until the 1970s, however, that such work attracted increased funding from development assistance agencies. In the mid-1980s, CABI's role in development received increased attention with the establishment of the Partnership Facility, and this focus steadily increased in subsequent decades as described in the Modern CABI in Chapter 11. Nevertheless, plant protection has always been a feature of CABI's scientific work.

The foundations for this plant health and developing-country emphasis were strengthened in 1971, when ODA appointed a number of Liaison Officers attached to CABI Institutes and to ODA Institutes, including the Centre for Overseas Pest Research, the Tropical Products Institute and the Land Research and Development Centre.[81]

Jim Waller was Liaison Officer for Plant Pathology, attached in 1971 to the Mycological Institute. His duties were to develop technical cooperation projects in developing countries, provide technical support to plant pathologists engaged in such projects and to contribute to the activities of the Institute. Barbara Ritchie joined IMI in 1970 and moved to work with Jim in 1973, providing technical support to overseas plant pathologists especially with regard to diagnostics. This period also marked the beginning of a great partnership with John Bridge (appointed to the Institute of Parasitology) and Harry Evans (who began with the Mycological Institute on a Central America pine pathology project but moved to the Institute of Biological Control, where he started the weed pathology programme). These three formed a powerful combination that enabled cross-Institute links in crop protection, which in turn served CABI well and led to its Crop Protection Programme in the mid-1980s. The three remain friends today and continue to serve as CABI Fellows; they can usually be found at Egham on a Wednesday.

At this time Chris Prior joined CMI/IMI, initially to work on a Dominica tree crops project and then on pest distribution maps. He moved to IIBC, tasked with combining pest and disease distribution maps on a crop basis, using cacao as a prototype. The maps were forerunners of the Crop Protection Compendium and Plantwise.

In 1989, ODA formulated an Integrated Pest Management Strategy Area within its Natural Resources Research Department, leading to a rapid expansion of research contracts to the Institutes at CABI and to the recruitment of Mark Holderness and Mike Rutherford. The move to Egham in 1992–93 enabled further expansion and, with the recruitment of Julie Flood and Eric Boa, the unit had seven scientists. This fertile base stimulated CABI's work in coffee, cocoa and other commodity crops; Plantwise and its global plant health clinics; and it strengthened linkages with CABI Research Stations, NARS and regional initiatives such as ASARECA (Association for Strengthening Agricultural Research in Eastern and Central Africa) and CORNET.

Some of the activities of the Unit are described in the box opposite (Advisory Scientific Contributions of the Plant Pathology Unit).

Advisory Scientific Contributions of the Plant Pathology Unit: 1973–95

The Unit focused on eliminating plant disease constraints to crop production, principally on small farms, and through training scientists in NARS and in institutional development.

Projects included:

Clove diseases research in Indonesia (1974–89). The 'Sumatra disease' of cloves destroyed many clove gardens in Sumatra and subsequently in Java. The Unit's work helped in the discovery that the disease was caused by a pathogen new to science spread by an obscure insect vector. Control options were explored and recommendations made for overcoming the problem.

Banana diseases in the Windward Isles (1976–80). Proper control of Sigatoka leaf spot is essential for the production of export-quality bananas by small farmers in the Windward Isles. A technical cooperation project established effective control by use of a forecasting system and aerial spraying.

Cashew diseases: Tanzania (1988–95). Cashew production by small farmers in Tanzania fell from 140,000 to 20,000 tons in the period 1975 to 1985, with powdery mildew disease a major factor. A technical cooperation project in collaboration with a World Bank-funded tree crops programme developed control strategies suitable for resource-poor farmers based on improved agronomy and resistant germplasm, with an option for spraying, which was taken up by many village groups.

Surveys by the Unit were central to introducing effective control measures for crop diseases in Antigua, Kenya, Oman, Gambia and Bolivia. They improved targeting of research efforts and the establishment of local crop protection services and plant health clinics as part of Plantwise. The Unit also investigated and advised on triticale diseases (with CIMMYT (International Maize and Wheat Improvement Center)); coffee rust in Central America and the Caribbean (part-funded by FAO); plant quarantine services in Cameroon and Yemen; coffee diseases in Malawi, Zimbabwe, Kenya, Uganda and Thailand (part-funded by the CDC/EU (Centers for Disease Control/European Union)); banana diseases in Uganda and Zanzibar; and other crops in Egypt and Indonesia.

In 1998 the Institute was merged with the three other Institutes to form CABI Bioscience

Whilst some mourn the merger, it is arguable that it was inevitable and that, by circling the wagons, CABI was able to survive and to strengthen a multidisciplinary focus on plant health without losing its capabilities in mycology, bacteriology and plant pathology, supplemented by new skills in molecular biology. Importantly, provided funding is sustained, CABI's microbial genetic resources collection remains intact and its industrial mycology work continues.

The story continues in Chapter 11, The Modern CABI.

Banana leaves with black sigatoka. ©CABI

PARASITOLOGY: LIFE AMONGST THE HELMINTHS

Parasitology is the study of organisms that live on or in organisms of another species, from which they obtain nutriments and to which they cause some degree of harm. Parasites are frequently considered aberrant organisms, following an exceptional lifestyle. In fact, parasitism is a common life strategy. Parasites are a mega-diverse group with an overall species richness that could easily top 10 million species, assuming conservatively that every animal and plant species has at least five host-specific parasites.[83] Parasitology is of particular importance to veterinary science, medicine, plant pathology and agronomy, and features significantly in the pharmaceutical and plant protection industries. Whilst the Institute covered a wide range of the parasitology literature in its information services, its taxonomic focus was much narrower and concentrated mainly on helminths (flukes, tapeworms and roundworms).

The early years

The Imperial Bureau of Agricultural Parasitology was initially attached to the UK's Institute of Parasitology. As the *British Medical Journal* reported at the time:

"This institute, an integral part of the London School of Hygiene and Tropical Medicine (LSHTM), is located at St. Albans, and there is no need to emphasize the importance to medicine, as well as to agriculture, of much of its work in the sphere of comparative parasitology. Few of man's parasites are exclusively human, and information as to the behaviour of these forms and their relations in animals is of fundamental importance to a complete understanding of how they affect man. Accordingly the collating of all the available current literature is of more than passing importance." [84]

The Bureau provided a valued service. Hugh McL Gordon writes:

"In our earliest days [in the 1930s] in the McMaster Laboratory of CSIR (now CSIRO) in Australia, among the first additions to the embryo library were copies of the 'Bibliography of Helminthology' and then Helminthological Abstracts. *We began to receive coloured slips of paper with the titles and references to papers on helminthology – so tantalizing when the originals were so often beyond our reach because of time, distance or language. These slips of paper we mounted on cards, and that was the beginning of the card index, which still continues at the McMaster Laboratory.*

This was my introduction to that source of information, which grew and blossomed and fruited into that unique institution which has changed its name a few times but continues to keep us informed on what goes on amongst the helminths.

[In those days of the] early 1930s at the McMaster Laboratory, how we looked forward to those little slips of paper from the Imperial Bureau of Agricultural Parasitology, each telling us of something new and exciting among the helminths. The arrival of the Helminthological Abstracts *was truly a 'red letter day'. One could read each issue at a sitting and learn of the current progress of helminthology in an hour or so."*

The Imperial Bureau of Agricultural Parasitology is established. Initially attached to the (British) Institute of Parasitology, the Bureau rents premises at Winches Farm, St Albans, a field station of the London School of Hygiene and Tropical Medicine (LSHTM).	1929
Bernard G Peters is Chief Officer, while the eminent helminthologist Professor Robert T Leiper, being Director of the (British) Institute of Parasitology, is Consultant Director of the Bureau.	1929
The Bureau publishes the first volume of *Helminthological Abstracts*.	1932
AE Fountain is Deputy Director (Chief Operating Officer).	1936
Leiper retires from the Chair of Helminthology at the University of London and is appointed as Director of the Bureau (Chief Operating Officer).	1946
The Bureau is renamed the Commonwealth Bureau of Agricultural Parasitology (Helminthology).	1948
The Review Conference agrees that the Bureau should include taxonomic and identification services, a crucial step towards Institute status, although that is not conferred until 1971.	1955
'The White House' is purchased as the new headquarters for the Bureau, which is renamed the Commonwealth Bureau of Helminthology.	1956
JM Watson is appointed as Director, with AR Stone as Consultant Director.	1958
Sheila Willmott is appointed as Director and Peters becomes Consultant Director.	1961
Helminthological Abstracts is divided into two volumes: *Series A, Animal Helminthology* and *Series B, Plant Nematology*.	1970
The Bureau becomes the Commonwealth Institute of Helminthology, in recognition of its identification services and taxonomic research.	1971
A new journal, *Protozoological Abstracts*, appears.	1977

Opposite: light micrograph of adult female (mauve) and male (red) *Schistosoma mansoni* parasitic flukes, cause of the disease bilharzia, NIBSC. ©SPL

43

Eventually, Gordon visited the Bureau itself:

❝ I first visited the Bureau in 1949 with my New Zealand colleague and ex student, Lloyd Whitten. What joy and excitement to meet 'the great man' of helminthology (Leiper) and with him that quite remarkable character, Piet Le Roux. Tucked away among the rambling buildings of Winches Farm was the Bureau – source of all helminthological knowledge. ❞

Robert Thompson Leiper FRS (1881–1969) – Founding Consultant Director and then Director.

Leiper, elected FRS (Fellow of the Royal Society) in 1923, was considered by some as the father of modern helminthology. His early interests were in helminth infections in humans, but later he published on topics such as teaching in helminthology and preventing the spread of 'potato sickness'. The following abstracts illustrate some of his research, and also his character: he describes one paper as containing 'useless lumber' and in another abstract alleges a 'lamentable ignorance of facts and principles of helminthology to be a failing common among medical officers of health'.

A comment on two recent articles on helminth infections in Man. Leiper, RT (1913) *British Medical Journal*, 15 November, 1302.

In the article by Kay, bodies are described which were believed to be the ova and miracidia of a new trematode. From the figures and description, Leiper has not the slightest hesitation in affirming 'that the bodies do not bear any resemblance or relation to either ova or miracidia of a trematode and that they are certainly not even of helminthic origin. The figures and portions of the description might best be accounted for by the presence of Rotifers in the water used to dilute the urine'.

He also refers to the recently described, supposed indigenous case of filariasis in Devonshire, published in the *British Medical Journal* (see this Bulletin, Vol. 2, p. 103). On examination of the slides he found that the supposed filariae were minute filaments of cotton wool, which had contaminated the freshly made blood films.

He expresses the hope that the above cases will not find their way into the textbooks and quotes '*Filaría gigas*' as a familiar example of the manner in which such records may become stereotyped in spite of repeated repudiation by workers on helminthology: 'If the editors of medical journals were to submit such papers to experts before accepting them, we should be spared much useless lumber'.

Present-day teachings on helminthology in relation to public health. Leiper, RT (1924) *British Medical Journal*, 19 July, 110–113.

Leiper alleges a lamentable ignorance of facts and principles of helminthology to be a failing common among medical officers of health. He puts the blame upon those teachers and textbooks of hygiene that profess to deal with the subject, and as a public duty he condemns out of their own mouth these blind leaders of the blind. But to guard them all from the ditch he here provides a useful summary of those generalities concerning helminth transmission that are of constant and fundamental significance for the public health. He briefly illustrates and expands the established propositions that: (a) parasitic worms do not increase in the body of a human host, though they produce a multitude of eggs or embryos there; (b) these eggs or embryos must, as a necessary prelude to any prospective infection, be discharged from the host in which they were produced; (c) these eggs or embryos, after their discharge, must undergo certain developmental changes in the external environment before they attain a stage infective to man; (d) these developmental changes can go on only under certain definite conditions of this environment, the necessary conditions varying with the different species and sometimes being protracted and recondite; (e) the infective form may enter the body of the prospective host in various ways proper to the particular species; (f) after effecting an entry into the proper host the immature infective form may have to undergo a circuitous journey before it reaches the particular site where it can attain sexual maturity; (g) many of the parasitic worms of man are common to him and certain domestic animals; and (h) the control of helminth infection depends upon a knowledge of the specific life-cycles and their vulnerable points.

The potato eelworm problem of today. Leiper, RT (1940) *Journal of the Royal Agricultural Society of England*, 100 (Pt III), 63–73.

In reviewing the problem it is mentioned that some of the potatoes collected in Mexico and S. America on the expedition financed by the Council of the Imperial Agricultural Bureaux show considerable resistance to eelworm infection. The possibility of breeding resistant commercial types is therefore indicated.

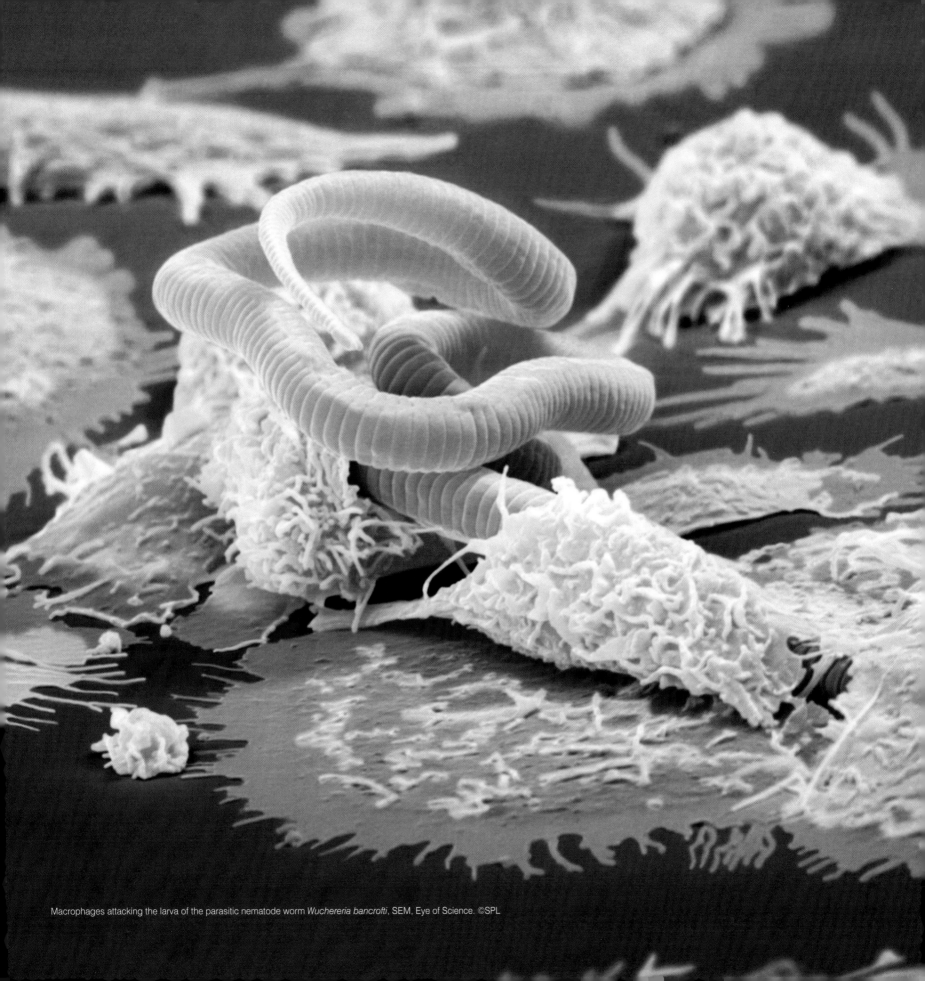

Macrophages attacking the larva of the parasitic nematode worm *Wuchereria bancrofti*, SEM, Eye of Science. ©SPL

A war between two scientific giants

Relations between the Animal Helminthology Unit at the Bureau, and then Institute, and the Parasitic Worms Division of the British Museum (Natural History) (**BMNH**) suffered from the antipathy between two scientific giants: Leiper and HA Baylis, head of the Division. The following is based on an account by David I Gibson, then Head of Parasitic Worms in the Department of Zoology at the Museum.

Baylis, an Oxford graduate, was one of the all-time greats of nematode systematics, but a loner, difficult to get along with and an inveterate moaner. Leiper was a wheeler-dealer, ambitious, competitive, much more politically aware, often surrounded by conflict and yet much venerated, but also one whose scientific integrity had been questioned or alluded to on more than one occasion.[85]

In 1924, Dr LW Sambon of the LSHTM, the same institute as Leiper, was studying the epidemiology of cancer. The British Empire Cancer Campaign (BECC) funded him to visit the 'cancer houses' of northern Italy, a region with a high prevalence of carcinoma. He invited Baylis along to help investigate any link between the nematodes of the genus *Gongylonema* and carcinomas. The BECC also appears to have financed Leiper, who took with him the young Thomas WM Cameron to do the same! On their return, the BECC requested that Sambon and Baylis place their material and unpublished reports in Leiper's hands.

Sambon and Baylis published some of their work in the *Journal of Tropical Medicine*, although publication of their report to the BECC was delayed (apparently by the BECC). Yet Leiper, in public meetings, reported in the press, heavily criticized their work. His report to the BECC, published in 1926, castigated the work of Sambon and Baylis, concluded that there was no evidence of a link between nematodes and cancer and questioned Baylis' systematic judgement.

The dispute grew to include some personal exchanges, each side questioning the other's work: a claim that Leiper must have known that Baylis and Sambon, in their report to the BECC, had cast doubt on the nematode–cancer link and that it was wrong of him not to temper his criticisms accordingly; and other charges including one suggesting that Leiper's discoveries on the life histories of African schistomes 'were not exactly original, being based on Baylis' own work and that of Japanese workers on *Schistosoma japonicum*'. Relationships deteriorated to the point that all correspondence had to be channelled between Institution heads. Resentment towards Leiper continued, fanned by S Prudhoe, Baylis's successor, who had worked for him for almost 20 years.

Importantly, 'this resentment was not only directed at Leiper but also at his conceptions, the Imperial Bureau of Helminthology and subsequently, *Helminthological Abstracts*, which were seen in some quarters as having been founded in competition to Baylis and the Museum, where the Vermes Section of the Zoological

Record was compiled for many years'. When RC Anderson encountered Leiper at the BMNH in the rotunda of the museum, Leiper asked him whether he was visiting 'that fellow upstairs' – meaning Baylis.

John Farley writes, 'He enjoyed controversies—probably because of his ability to outsmart most people—and was not afraid of making enemies; indeed he seemed to believe that people worked better when social frictions existed'.[86]

After Prudhoe's retirement at the end of 1975 the reasons for the antipathy were no longer relevant or remembered, and relations between the Division and the Institute normalized. In Gibson's time the two groups had an excellent relationship, including several joint ventures, notably the co-editing of the CIP keys to the cestode genera.

Leiper retired from the Chair of Helminthology of the University of London in 1946 and took up the post of Director of the Bureau, a position he held until 1958. The Institute's global reputation was due in no small part to his leadership as Consultant Director and then Director.

Commonwealth Bureau of Helminthology. ©CABI

The 'White House' years

The Bureau came under threat in the early 1950s, when the UK funding that had supported the British Institute of Agricultural Parasitology was divided between the Rothamsted Experimental Station and the Central Veterinary Laboratory near Weybridge. Staff members were transferred to other institutions. Alternative accommodation for the Bureau of Parasitology was sought, and the Review Conference of 1955[87] noted that member countries were unhappy with the restricted and poor condition of its current premises. While some suggested buying new premises, Australia and Canada much preferred 'the then present system whereby most of the Bureaux occupied premises at nominal rent', and others suggested delaying until the next Review Conference. However, the matter was referred for urgent consideration to the Executive Council.

It was perhaps during the uncertainty caused by this delay that Leiper apparently offered to purchase the 'White House', a rather imposing Georgian building in the centre of St Albans, from his own resources. His ploy worked, and CAB's Executive Council agreed to the Bureau buying the building in 1956.

Review Conference defines the Institute's mission and changes its name

In spite of disagreement over the building, the 1955 Conference was clear on the need for taxonomic and identification services in helminthology, recommending that 'provision should be made immediately to meet these new requirements'. This would include producing reference books and reference collections of parasites, and local surveys. The Conference also changed the name from 1956 to the Commonwealth Bureau of Helminthology.

Leiper retired in 1958 and a new Director, JM Watson, was appointed. By 1960, a taxonomic unit had been established that 'provided library and laboratory facilities and technical help to scientists of Commonwealth countries who wished to continue or complete their helminthological investigations whilst visiting the UK'. Reference collections and bibliographical support had 'aroused considerable interest throughout the Commonwealth, particularly in African territories'. Also, a three-volume work on parasitic Nematoda was under way.

However, controversy arose over whether the Bureaux should offer taxonomic services. A range of options, such as placing animal helminthology with Animal Health and nematology with Mycology and Entomology, were considered. The 1960 Conference felt that the expected demand had not emerged, and that there were other reference collections in the UK and elsewhere. Some delegates felt that taxonomic services were not required at the Bureau, others that they were essential to the developing needs in many African territories, where helminthology had been neglected. The Conference asked for a committee of experts to examine the issues. The experts recommended that the Bureau of Helminthology and *Helminthological Abstracts* should continue, and that the taxonomic work of the Bureau 'should be developed'.

Sheila Willmott takes charge

After JM Watson left, Sheila Willmott, who had been Deputy Director since 1954, was appointed Director in 1961, and served until 1980. This coincided with a growing recognition of the importance of helminthology in agriculture, medicine and biological sciences. There were, for example, 40 new books published on helminthology from 1961 to 1964. In 1971, the Bureau was renamed the Commonwealth Institute of Helminthology, reflecting its position as a world centre of excellence in the broad field of parasitology, embracing parasitic worms and protozoans.

By the mid-1960s the information explosion had begun, with increasing numbers of abstracts and portents of computerization and centralization. However, requests for information and identification services were not onerous; during 1963–64, these totalled 61 and 26, respectively – the latter number being well below that at the Institutes of Entomology and Mycology, but covering nematodes from such diverse crops, hosts and countries as sugarcane in Pakistan, coconut in Ceylon, insects in India and Ghana, ginger rhizomes and Chinese cabbage in Fiji, plant-parasitic nematodes in Southern Rhodesia, soil and root samples from cotton in Thailand, potato roots crops in Gambia and tomato, tobacco and lentil in Ceylon.[88]

The 'fish boys' set sail

Peter Gooch, who joined in 1968, recalls that the Bureau's main scientific activity was the Fisheries Helminthology Unit under Pete Young, set up and funded by the National Environmental Research Council (NERC) around 1964. Locating the Unit at the Bureau reflected its outstanding reputation in helminthology, for it 'could not have been much further from the sea and cases of herring for cod worm candling would arrive by train every so often'. John T Davey, a member of the Unit, said it focused on the parasitological problems of commercial fisheries (turbot, herring and cod).[89] The idea was that, 'as a small group of scientists starting from scratch, it would be helpful to begin work in the one place in the country that could provide the most comprehensive and concentrated source of parasitological literature and information': a 'sort of hot-house' where the 'tender young shoots of our endeavours could be nurtured until we were all strong enough to be transplanted into the harsher, sterner environment of the East Anglian coast'.

Fish parasitology had a unique aroma. Davey's work was on the anisakine nematodes whose life cycle includes marine mammals as well as fish like herring and cod. He used to extract the eggs of nematodes from seal faeces for culture to help identify the earliest larval stages of different species. The extractions done at the St Albans laboratories became part of the 'smells associated with our research', which were 'worst when a freezer full of fish samples failed'. A deep pit was dug at the bottom of the garden to dispose of the waste, but when 'summer came someone discovered an incredible seething mass of maggots coming to the surface!' The work involved trips to sea on research trawlers of the Ministry of Agriculture, Forestry and Fisheries (MAFF), including 'a dreadful little trawler with almost no concessions to scientific research use'. Davey 'never got used to going to sea because of sea-sickness', cured only by a potent brew from a local pharmacy.

'The fish boys' made 'considerable progress in elucidating the life cycle and ecology of cod worms, *Anisakis*, *Contracaeum*, *Terranova*, etc., at a time when wormy fish were of considerable economic significance'. Members of the Unit visited the Suffolk coast and western approaches to Scottish waters to collect ganoid fish and sea parasites, sometimes going as far as the Arctic on trawlers.

Lotfi Khalil began his career in this Unit.[90] He boasted that he was the first 'Arab in the North Sea' (though Barbary pirates may have got there first). Nevertheless, he went on to develop and lead the Animal Helminthology Unit at the Institute until his retirement in 1992, after 26 years. He was appointed as a Research Associate so that his expertise was not lost, particularly in teaching and maintaining links with South Africa at the University of the North.

The NERC unit moved from the Institute in the 1970s to join the Institute for Marine Environmental Research in Plymouth.

Sheila M Willmott (1921–98)[91]

Sheila Willmott entered University College in 1944 for a two-year specialization in parasitology, before starting a PhD at the LSHTM supervised by Professor JJC Buckley. After postdoctoral studies at University College South Wales and Monmouthshire, she was recruited to the Bureau by RT Leiper in 1951 as a Scientific Assistant (later to be known as a Scientific Information Officer or SIO). In those days, information transfer between the upstairs and downstairs offices was achieved using a large wicker basket attached to a stout rope through the windows. In 1954, she was made Assistant Director responsible for the abstracting and indexing of *Helminthological Abstracts*, which included plant-parasitic nematodes.

Mary B Burton, who worked with Willmott at the 'White House' in the mid-1960s, recognized her as 'a person who made a profound impact on the evolution of information retrieval with regards to parasitology'. Others[92] remember Willmott as a great defender of the Institute. In the spring of 1975, Institute staff members were told that the Institute was to be closed. However, those wishing to close the Institute had not realized the energy and fight that Willmott would mobilize in an effort to save 'her beloved Institute'. The scientific community worldwide was alerted, and responded with letters of outrage and support. A memorable dinner party was held at the 'White House' for the Review Conference Members on a warm summer evening. All staff members were involved 'in cooking and serving the food and wine'. The Institute was to survive another 23 years as an independent entity, until it merged with the other three Institutes into CABI Bioscience. The tradition of staff holding dinner parties and cooking and drinking on special occasions, sometimes with distinguished visitors, also survived.

The family atmosphere in the 'White House'

John Bagenal, who worked at the Institute from 1970 to 1973, said that the 'cloistered life of the White House was a world apart'. Bagenal was allocated 'a tiny office between the dustbins and the toilets'. In contrast, the Director's office 'projected into the garden and was kept delightfully, not like an office at all'. She [Willmott] 'worked at an antique oval gate-legged table – looking, for all the world, like a distinguished writer of detective novels'.

Gordon, writing about the same period says:

> *Come into the White House and there you will find a dedicated and devoted group of workers which somehow always seems more like a family than a miscellaneous staff of directors, librarians, abstractors, taxonomists, typists, helminthologists. Elevenses on the lawn or in the library was more like a family gathering, with the visitors soon one of it. When we foregathered in July 1975 at the party following the first Commonwealth Helminthological Meeting what a family was there, Robert Thomas Leiper would surely have approved and been happy in the achievement.*

And in this happy, active, crowded place, helminthology flourished. Alan Pike was working on schistome cercariae, which he maintained in snails in small aquaria in the only available space – the WC. In a similar vein, David Hunt recalls tiger mosquitoes, escapees from the Institute's colony, flying up and down the corridors. And the old wine cellar was damp-proofed and converted into a place to store the helminth collection. Nothing was impossible.

The flourishing 1970s

In 1970 Willmott reviewed the achievements of the Bureau over its first 41 years, noting that 'in recent years the scope of the Bureau had broadened and the size of the journal had more than doubled, by then being issued in two series, one for animal parasites and the other for plant nematodes'. They contained 'abstracts and titles of about 6000 papers per annum and the corresponding number of author and subject index entries'. She also noted that 'some taxonomic research is carried out by Bureau staff' and that 'the NERC Helminthology Unit, engaged in research on the parasites of economically important marine fish', had been attached to the Bureau since the Unit's establishment in 1964. The Bureau had 'been involved to an increasing extent in its capacity as one of the consultants to the Inter-African Phytosanitary Commission in advising on problems in plant nematology with special relation to control and plant quarantine regulations'.

From the 1930s to 1959 the number of scientific papers cited and abstracted had risen from about 1300 to 2800 (with 38 occasional papers), and by 1969 to 6000. Willmott noted that the only increase in staff was one laboratory assistant. There was increasing financial pressure, Willmott noting that the Governments supporting CABI expected sales to cover much more of publication costs and that

Opposite, clockwise from top left: *Schistosome cercaria* parasite, SEM, NIBSC; *Trichinella spiralis* nematode worms, SEM, Biomedical Imaging Unit, Southampton General Hospital; Asian tiger mosquito, SEM, Susumu Nishinaga; nematode worm egg, SEM, NIBSC. ©SPL

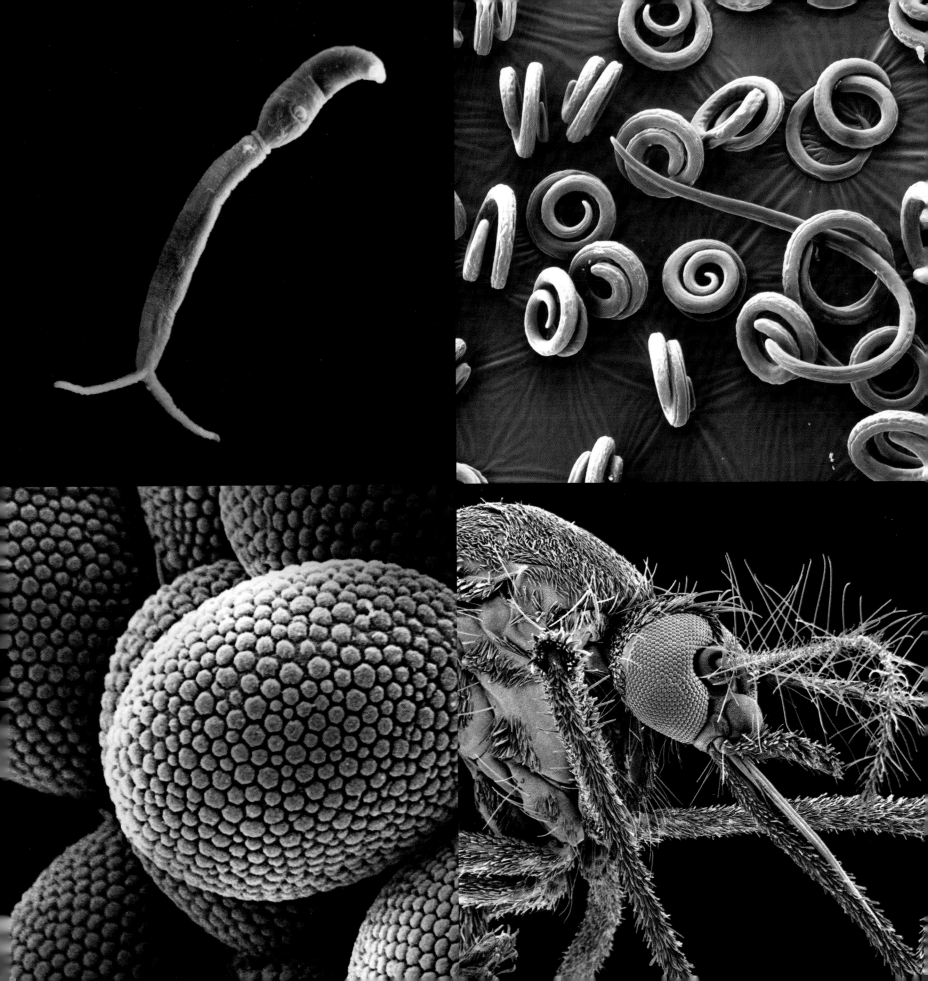

subscribers in non-contributing countries should not be subsidized. She could 'see no possibility that the Institute' would be able to implement the Review Conference's wish that it 'should increase the number of Review articles [or that it] should prepare and offer for sale, as an additional service, annotated bibliographies on selected topics'. However, over time, CABI increasingly saw developing new products for sale as an opportunity to deliver its mission in a profitable way.

In the 1970s the Institute launched into several ambitious activities. *Plant Nematology Abstracts* was split from *Helminthological Abstracts* in 1970 and *Protozoological Abstracts* appeared in 1977. Volumes of *The CIH Keys to the Nematode Parasites of Vertebrates* began to appear, to large acclaim. Indeed, this was 'a stimulating and exciting period during which the taxonomy units grew'. Willmott served as editor of three journals respected internationally: *Transactions of the Royal Society of Tropical Medicine and Hygiene* (1976–86), *Systematic Parasitology* (1978–86) and the *Journal of Helminthology* (1980–87).

The Institute, whilst enjoying its gracious Georgian accommodation at the 'White House', found itself, according to Willmott, 'once more short of space, especially adequate accommodation for the library', which had grown to 'more than 7000 volumes of journals and reference books and nearly 30,000 reprints'. These were 'the vital basis of the Bureau's life and work'. She lobbied hard for new premises, and finally obtained agreement from CAB central office to erect a new building for the Institute at the LSHTM Field Station at Winches Farm in St Albans. Unfortunately, due to poor health, Willmott had to retire in 1980, before the move took place.

The Institute returns to Winches Farm

In 1981 the Institute moved, and was renamed the Commonwealth Institute of Parasitology (CIP), with Ralph Muller as Director, AR Stone as Consultant Director, Gooch as Assistant Director, six taxonomists and nine SIOs. According to Gooch[93], the 'planning of the building at Winches Farm was a considerable undertaking' and required 'much guile to circumvent the periodic cold feet of Central Office (no doubt concerned over the costs involved) and the ambivalent feelings of the LSHTM'. Eventually, the work was done and staff moved into the new premises in the spring of 1981 in 'deep snow, which tested the heating arrangements to the maximum'. On the actual moving day, arrangements were also tested when the Institute received a Desist Order from the School. Fortunately, because of Muller's knowledge of the School Administration, this final unexpected obstacle was overcome.

Commonwealth Institute of Parasitology building, Winches Farm. ©CABI

Ralph Muller (1933–2007)

Ralph Muller was a distinguished parasitologist, and served as Director of the Institute of Parasitology from 1981 to his retirement in 1993. Following graduation in zoology from Queen Mary College (University of London) in 1955, he moved to King's College (London) and obtained his PhD in 1958, continuing as a research fellow until 1960.

He first obtained 'hands-on' experience of parasitology in the tropics in 1960–62, as a scientific officer working for ODA on the control of the human disease schistosomiasis (also known as snail fever). Based in London, his work involved visits to Kenya, Tanzania and Uganda, all then part of British East Africa. Muller then became lecturer and chief of the sub-department of Parasitology in the University of Ibadan in Nigeria from 1962 to 1966. Here, he developed a lifelong interest in the guinea worm, *Dracunculus medinensis*, one of the longest nematodes affecting humans. In 1966 he joined the Department of Parasitology of the LSHTM, where his work drew attention to the importance of this worm and, ultimately, to methods for its control. Muller served as a Council member of the Royal Society of Tropical Medicine and Hygiene from 1982 to 1985. From his retirement in 1993 until the end of his life, Muller continued to put his wide knowledge of helminthology at the disposal of students as a Visiting Lecturer at Imperial College in London and an Honorary Senior Lecturer at the LSHTM. In addition to editing Advances in Parasitology for many years, he edited the *Journal of Helminthology* from 1972 to 1980, and again from 1987 to 1995.

The new building 'allowed for the true development of the Institute as an Institute, and the systematic services benefited greatly from the new opportunities for collaboration in research, teaching and training'. The first major training course, The Identification of Animal Helminths of Economic Importance, was run in the summer of 1982, followed in 1983 by The Identification of Plant Nematodes of Economic Importance, and the 6-week courses continued in alternate years. With 10 to 18 students per course, from all over the world, they added a distinct buzz.

The Institute was 'one of the first to demonstrate online searching techniques' (despite having to try 17 times to make a good connection at the first public display at a British Society for Parasitology meeting in 1977), says Gooch. The cumulative index, some 300,000 entries on paper slips, was microfilmed and sold to a drug company for £500. With the help of the Institute's facilities, Muller continued to write on guinea worm and onchocerciasis.

The 1982/83 Annual Report provides a feel for the active research programme conducted by the six scientists:

- a comparison of the nature of infection and worm burden of domestic and wild ruminants in the Jonglei area of Sudan; filariid nematodes of domestic animals (Dr Khalil);

- a comparative study of nematode parasites of rodents; SEM studies of the internal structures of the buccal capsule and genital cone and other external features used in the taxonomy of Strongylida; *Oesophagostomum* from artiodactylids; and preparation of an SEM atlas of nematodes (Dr Gibbons);

- examination of the hemurid genera *Gastrodiscus, Gastrodiscoides and Homalogaster*; continuation of the studies of taenid species parasitic in East African carnivores and their larval stages in ruminants, using morphological and immunological techniques (Dr Jones);

- preparation of the book *Tylenchida, Nematode Parasites of Plants and Insects*; phylogenetic relationships of the plant-parasitic Dorylaimida and Triplonchida (Dr Siddiqi);[94,95]

- monographic studies of the Dorylaimida (Dr Jairajpuri); and

- new taxa of nematodes from Papua New Guinea; SEM studies of entomophilic nematodes; pathogenicity studies of insect nematodes; and biocontrol and culture collection of entomophilic nematodes (Dr Hunt).

These scientists were all internationally renowned taxonomists. MR Siddiqi, who described some 600 new species of nematodes, was, according to David Hunt, probably the outstanding plant nematode taxonomist of the 20th century. Few would disagree. His book provides the basis for plant nematode taxonomy. He retired in 1994, returning immediately as an Honorary Research Associate, continuing his work without interruption until the Institute was subsumed into CABI Bioscience. He continues to work from home.

Identifications were an important but fluctuating focus of the Institute. By 1978/79 the number of identifications had grown to over 3000. This number fell in the following year to just over 1000, grew in the following 2 years and fell back again to just over 2400 in 1982/83. Hunt,[96,97] for example, completed a large number of high-quality identifications, lending critical support to surveys funded by external agencies.

Insect-killing nematodes emerging from a rusty tussock moth larva, a serious orchard pest in Chile. ©CABI

Shelia Willmott (left), Lotfi Khalil (centre) and MR Siddiqi (right). ©CABI

Willmott sought additional resources to meet growing demands on the Institute's information services. She noted that, by 1970, graduates specializing in information science competed with retired field scientists for prominence as abstractors. But many people associated with the Institute took pride in the fact that 'abstracts were written by taxonomists, in a form and with sufficient detail, so that they could be used by other nematologists'.[98] This was one reason why the journals achieved such international prominence.

Gordon, 'one of the official correspondents of the Institute in Australia', agreed with Willmott that taxonomy should not be divorced from bibliography. He emphasized the value of the breadth of coverage of the scientific literature in the abstract journals:

“ *Nowadays a considerable amount of scientific literature, especially reviews and contributions to symposia and conferences, appears intermittently in, or as, publications, which are outside the regular range of journals. The information in these 'casual' publications is of inestimable value, not only to the working helminthologist, but also to a great many scientists who are engaged in disease control and extension. It is easy to overlook these publications if one is confined to a range of scientific reading. Access to* Helminthological Abstracts *ensures an awareness of this great and important mass of information.* ”

Centralization went ahead in 1987, separating the information component from the Unit, despite Gordon's concerns, but *Helminthological Abstracts* continues to be made available through CAB Abstracts in an even more accessible form through the Internet. The space that was vacated was already filling up with initiatives in Tropical Plant Nematology and Tropical Parasitic Diseases, so that it again became an issue in the 1990s.

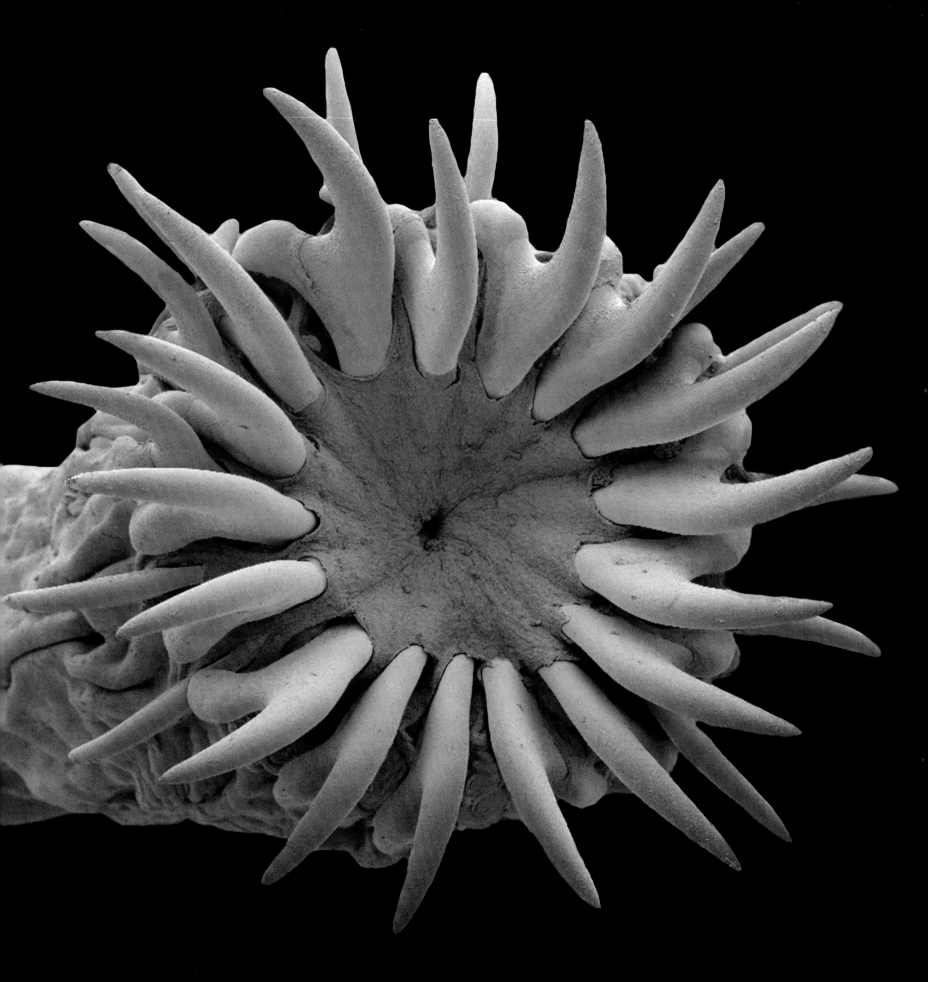

The Institute's information resources and diagnostics services were ideal for training students and researchers; it had always welcomed visiting students and researchers from the Commonwealth and beyond. The Institute's library was seen as being without equal by Scrivenor,[99] especially due to the donation of a large number of Russian publications that were not then easily available elsewhere. However, after the 1990 Review Conference, CABI's Member Countries no longer paid for information or services through their membership, which altered the dynamics of funding for the scientific services.

Muller encouraged postgraduate opportunities in both Animal Helminthology and Plant Nematology. Under his directorship, the WHO Onchcerciasis Unit was also established at the Institute. He was said to be particularly sympathetic and empathic to students, with a gift for explaining the complexities of parasitology, which showed through in his lecturing and the many textbooks he worked on.

This was, in many ways, a golden era for the Institute. However, severe pressures on CABI finances were becoming apparent and, in 1992, the LSHTM closed its once-thriving field station at Winches Farm, leaving the Institute isolated, its future location uncertain. Muller retired in June 1993, before the turmoil began.

Some idea of the research under way at the Institute can be gleaned from a list of books published by CABI in the 1990s.

Tropical Plant Nematology Unit

The Tropical Plant Nematology Unit (TPNU, established 1983), led by John Bridge, undertook (with specialists from other CABI Institutes or external advisers) some 60 surveys and studies of plant-parasitic pests in developing countries.[100,101] Projects funded a new glasshouse in 1988, essential for growing tropical host plants to culture their parasitic nematodes for research and training purposes. By the mid-1990s, over 400 species/strains were being maintained. The Unit helped increase productivity in crops as diverse as banana, coffee, sugarcane and numerous vegetables in subsistence agriculture. It was a new focus for the Institute's work, using the expertise of the plant nematode taxonomists and also attracting substantial funding from the UK aid programme. The team involved Institute biosystematists MR Siddiqi, David Hunt, Janet Machon and Audrey Godman, and fieldwork by Richard Plowright, Nigel Price and Sam Page.

Plant-parasitic nematodes of coffee in Tanzania

In the mid-1980s, root-knot nematodes threatened to cut African coffee yields by 20%, and Bridge from the TPNU was brought in to advise. These nematodes had been recognized in Tanzania from the early 1960s, but there had been little further study. He found more than 30 genera and species of plant-parasitic nematodes associated with coffee. African coffee root-knot nematodes were very serious pests in many areas of the north of Tanzania and, while full control was impossible, Bridge saw that 'good management' could reduce losses. He recommended 'continued uprooting in the most seriously infested sites followed by planting to pasture, maize or other crops', and then replanting after 2–10 years when the nematodes had gone. The nematodes 'were absent from all the coffee shambas and estates sampled in the south of the country' and they would 'only occur if

Entomopathic nematode laboratory. ©CABI

introduced', meaning that following his advice would dramatically limit the spread of the disease. Bridge saw a clear need for a nematologist at the relevant local research centre.

Protecting sugarcane in Papua New Guinea

In 1986 Bridge undertook a 2-week visit to Papua New Guinea, at the request of the multinational sugar producer Tate and Lyle, to investigate the sudden failure of a sugarcane crop in the Ramu Valley. In a seminal research achievement, Bridge identified a new genus of nematode that was attacking the crop. This enabled other researchers to breed a new variety resistant to that nematode.

The Tropical Parasitic Diseases Unit

About 18 million people worldwide suffer from river blindness or onchocerciasis. The Institute's Tropical Parasitic Diseases Unit (TPDU) was originally established in 1984 by Simon Townson as the Onchocerciasis Research Unit, with a grant from the World Health Organization (WHO) to carry out research on the chemotherapy of the disease. In the period 1988 to 1990,[102] it had doubled its personnel to nine (eight full-time, one research associate) and became the TPDU. Its research focused on filarial infections (by threadlike nematodes) of man and animals and, to a lesser extent, their arthropod vectors. By 1990 the Unit had five outside-funded projects on various aspects of drug and vaccine development for onchocerciasis and lymphatic filariasis, and was also studying the basic biology of the parasites and their vectors.

The Unit was testing compounds that might control the parasite. They screened compounds, supplied by industry and others in the WHO network, using bovine parasites (as models for human parasites) collected from abattoirs. Fieldwork in Guatemala tested the Unit's newly developed cryopreservation techniques and new drugs against the human parasite, *Onchocerca volvulus*. Another project looked at the *in vitro* cultivation of the filarial nematodes *Acanthocheilonema viteae* and

Opposite: tapeworm (*Taenia pisiformis*) head, SEM, Steve Gschmeissner. ©SPL

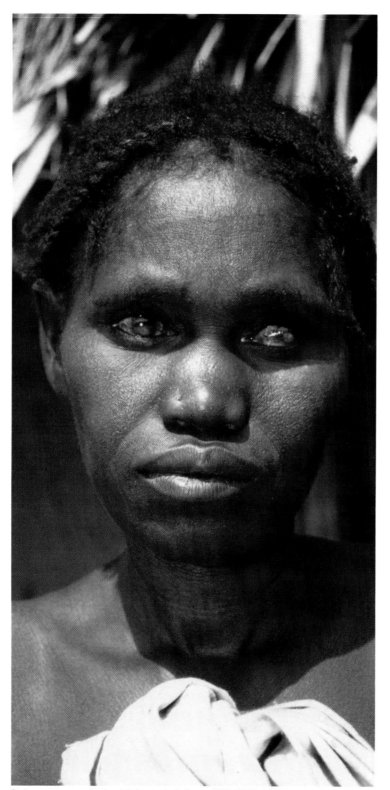

Sudanese woman with river blindness, Andy Grump, TDR, WHO. ©SPL

Onchocerca lienalis. The Unit identified several promising compounds with good anti-*Onchocerca* activity, which were then developed outside of the Institute. Townson initiated a contract with Cyanamid in the early 1990s to work on the veterinary drug Moxidectin; the very promising results led to WHO adopting this drug for human development – it is now in phase 3 of human trials in West Africa, where it appears to be a good candidate for mass treatment.

By 1993,[103] the Unit had a project-funded Malaria Unit headed by Emeritus Professor Wallace Peters – an eminent malariologist who was appointed Honorary Research Fellow at IIP in 1992.[104] The group operated an externally funded international reference centre for the evaluation of malarial drugs on behalf of WHO. They examined candidate compounds for activity against a broad spectrum of strains of malaria resistant to malarial drugs in current use. Derivatives of artemisinin, a drug isolated from the Chinese wormwood plant (*Artemisia annua*) and used in Chinese traditional medicine, were promising. WHO now recommends that artemisinin combination therapies should be the first-line therapy for malaria worldwide.

The final years: location, location, location

In 1993 Hominick replaced Muller as Director of the Institute. Three of the four Units established in Muller's time were renamed better to reflect their functions: the Animal Helminthology Biosystematics Unit (AHBU), the Plant Nematology Biosystematics Unit (PNBU) and the Tropical Plant Nematology Research and Advisory Unit (TPNRAU). TPDU kept its name, and two more units were added: the Entomopathogenic Nematode Biosystematics and Research Unit and the Molecular Biosystematics Unit. These were brought over with Hominick when he left Imperial College. There were 31 full-time staff and, although IIP was the smallest of the four scientific institutes, the breadth of coverage of parasitic worms was unique. Plant nematology, animal helminthology, tropical parasitic diseases and insect-parasitic nematodes are disciplines that rarely interact – the specialists usually attend different scientific meetings and publish in different journals. A delight and strength of the Institute was being a place where the pathways of these disciplines crossed.

Once again, the location of the Institute and its inadequate facilities was a key issue. Indeed, some staff were housed in two Portakabins with restricted planning permission. The LSHTM had closed Winches Farm, to sell the site for housing, which left the Institute scientifically isolated, in a crowded building, with the prospect of being located in the middle of a residential development. Also, shared facilities with the LSHTM were lost, and there were differences of opinion with the School as to what CABI could and should do. Consequently, Hominick was tasked to search for a more suitable site (the building was owned by CABI with more than 80 years remaining on the lease at a peppercorn ground rent). Meanwhile, since CABI Central Office was understandably reluctant to invest in the current site, but any move was several years away, Hominick decided to maximize its usefulness with minimal costs. Staff pitched in with ideas and a willingness to relocate parts of their facilities, a local builder and the resident handyman provided the expertise and labour, and inexpensive kitchen furniture flat-packs were used to build benching and laboratory furniture. The outcome

Antimalarial drug extraction from wormwood plants, Andy Grump,TDR, WHO. ©SPL

Bill Hominick

Bill Hominick is a Canadian who became Director of IIP in November 1993. Following his education in Canada, in 1973 he came to the University of Newcastle upon Tyne to work on potato cyst nematodes. He became a Lecturer in Parasitology at Imperial College London in 1975, and a Senior Lecturer in 1990.

At Imperial, Hominick's research involved a broad range of nematodes, from plant, animal and human parasites to those parasitic in insects. His major interest is entomopathogenic nematodes (EPNs), which can be produced commercially for control of insect pests in agriculture. Two isolates discovered by his research group during a contract to survey UK soils were commercialized by Agricultural Genetics Company, and sold under the names Nemasys and Nemasys H, and still marketed by Becker Underwood. His research on EPNs focused on their biodiversity, biogeography, in-country production and population dynamics and characterizing species and strains with DNA technology. This work carried over to IIP, where he established an EPN programme and a laboratory using DNA technology to characterize species and strains of nematodes.

Hominick was Director of IIP until it merged with the other institutes into CABI Bioscience. During that period he provided the leadership, good humour and corporate awareness to keep IIP's science and teaching programmes functioning while managing the process of merging into CABI Bioscience and relocation from St Albans to Egham. In 1998 he became Director of Biodiversity and Biosystematics at CABI Bioscience, thereby inheriting a three-site operation (Egham, St Albans and Queensgate/NHM) that required centralization at Egham. He took early retirement in 2000 and was appointed an Emeritus Fellow of CABI Bioscience. He then worked on several assignments for CABI, including provision of the Secretariat of an EU project, the European Biological Resource Centre Network, from 2001 to 2004. In 2006 a new bacterial species, *Xenorhabdus hominickii*, was named[105] after him, in recognition of his contributions to the systematics of entomopathogenic nematode–bacterium complexes.

was a molecular biology laboratory, an entomopathogenic nematode laboratory (in a Portakabin), the Wallace Peters' Malaria Chemotherapy Unit (Portakabin) and a teaching/visiting scientist laboratory. A much-needed procedures laboratory and insectary for the TPDU were built by converting the darkroom and AHBU laboratory. These were rebuilt from the staff room, which was relocated to the library. New displays, built by each Unit illustrating their work, livened up the corridors.

The official opening of the renovated Institute was celebrated on 18 March 1994, when a number of distinguished guests attended a special lunch. The cutting of the 'ceremonial tapeworm' was by Prof Lord Lawson Soulsby, a distinguished veterinary parasitologist and friend of the Institute. This was a happy occasion, and sent a clear message to the scientific community that the Institute was very much open for business. It also demonstrated to CABI that, while IIP might have been the smallest of the institutes, it was making significant contributions to research, training and information for the international parasitology community. It was also willing and able to help itself.

The International Institute of Parasitology was a happy and active place that always welcomed visitors and made them part of the family. Even the occasional outbreak of hostilities arising from an unwanted visit from CABI headquarters – usually to announce more budget cuts – was managed with good humour by the personable Hominick. It is a testimony to the staff that continued growth and success occurred in the face of uncertainty. The 7th International Training Course on the Identification of Helminth Parasites of Economic Importance was held in the new training laboratory. Some of the funded projects at IIP in 1994 included:

- resistance of yams to plant-parasitic nematodes;

- rice nematodes in upland swamp rice continuum in West Africa;

- identification of nematodes from surveys in Belize, Kenya, Uganda and West Africa;

- contributions to an FAO distance learning programme on parasites of livestock;

- parasites of Houbara bustards in the United Arab Emirates;

- drug studies on onchocerciasis in Guatemala;

- evaluation of novel antimalarial drugs and drug combinations in rodent malaria models;

- control of the large pine weevil with entomopathogenic nematodes;

- effect of entomopathogenic nematodes on the dynamics of insect populations; and

- identification of entomopathogenic nematodes from Japan, Belgium, Kenya, Ivory Coast, Costa Rica, Trinidad, Indonesia and the USA.

During 1994 and 1995 CABI's plan was to relocate the entire Institute, with a decision in principle to relocate about 6 miles away to a purpose-built building, Rothamsted Experimental Station. Senior Management at Rothamsted offered a prime, central site, opposite their Nematology Building, and planning permission was obtained. Together, IIP staff planned a new building, sitting around the antique, oval gate-legged table that Willmott once used and that Hominick used for all meetings. In June 1995, the new building cost was estimated at £2.4 million, but CABI's 1995 budget was showing an excessive deficit. Nevertheless, with the strong scientific case to relocate to Rothamsted, CABI Senior Management asked Hominick to continue to plan for Rothamsted, but with reduced costs. In July, IIP began a detailed 5-year Strategic Development Plan to show where growth would occur, to justify CABI's investment in a new building.

The last third of 1995 was more frantic than usual; budgets at CABI and Rothamsted were under great pressure. Rothamsted was concerned by the delay in progress over the IIP move, and was starting to question the wisdom of allocating a prime location to an outside organization. The IIP Strategic Development Plan was completed at the same time as a revised CABI financial plan that allowed for no capital investments until 1999 at the earliest.

Helminthology training course. ©CABI

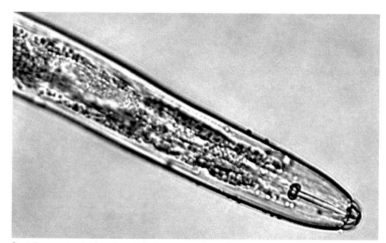

Scutellonema bradys female anterior from yam tuber. ©CABI

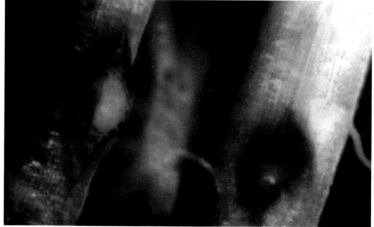

Rice cyst nematode (*Heterodera oryzicola*). ©CABI

In August 1996 Rob Williams, CABI's Deputy Director-General of Science, wrote to Rothamsted to say that IIP could no longer relocate to the site. Instead, Williams and the Directors of the four Institutes were planning the centralization of the Institutes in the Egham/Silwood area to create a CABI Biosciences Centre. This reflected the increasing collaboration between the Institutes and would encourage further possibilities to decrease operating costs by sharing facilities. However, this would be a long-term development requiring considerable planning and capital investment. It also required the sale of the St Albans site at an acceptable price. Once more staff at IIP were in a difficult position, knowing that relocation would occur but with no indication of when.

The IIP Strategic Development Plan showed that AHBU was a high-cost, low-income unit, while TPDU was a high-income, high-cost unit, both outside the focus of CABI Bioscience. Additionally, it relied on a single individual and was therefore vulnerable – only Townson had the ability and experience to lead and generate project income for the Unit. Also, it required licensed animal facilities that CABI could not provide elsewhere. Finally, if the Unit left the St Albans area, Peters would not follow and the malaria unit would cease to exist.

The situation in November 1996 was summarized in a report of the Programme Committee of the Board, headed by George Rothschild. The Committee accepted that running four institutes was uneconomic, and that it could not afford to build a new IIP at Rothamsted. While there were different views on the potential of the human health and animal health work at IIP, the Committee supported the CABI Bioscience themes identified by the DDG-S and Institute Directors for re-focusing the overall science programme, which excluded those areas. Closure and redundancies were inevitable.

Rumours and speculation, coupled with low morale, characterized the end of 1996 and beginning of 1997 for all at CABI, not just IIP. However, the traditional IIP Christmas party showed that staff still had a spirit that would not be broken. They put on a hilarious, witty, sceptical skit about CABI restructuring that pulled no punches. Indeed, senior management had tried to keep discussions confidential because, if redundancies were to occur, strict procedures had to be followed. In addition, the belief was that confidentiality would avoid upsetting staff before any decisions were made. It clearly didn't work. One IIP staff member attended a meeting in Africa in January 1997, and was asked by an African colleague why CABI was closing four Institutes and creating one Bioscience! It was fair to ask: if scientists in Africa had so much information, why didn't CABI staff?

Early in 1997, one fact was very clear – the AHBU would not be a part of the re-focused CABI Bioscience. Hominick tried to find a suitable host organization for it. While the outstanding international reputation of the scientists was unquestionable, all new initiatives at universities required them to be self-sustaining. Attempts to find alternative positions in the Information Division were also unsuccessful. Hence, on 19 February, formal proceedings to make the Unit redundant were initiated.

The AHBU was officially closed on 14 July. As much as possible was done to secure its legacy. The unique animal helminth collections were transferred to other institutions. The type-collections (including the type-collections of the London and Liverpool Schools of Hygiene and Tropical Medicine) are now in the NHM London (curated by EA Harris, Parasitic Worms Division, Department of Zoology). The WHO Filarioid Nematode Collection was transferred with them. The substantial remainder, including probably the most extensive collection in the world of helminths from African animals, was housed in the Royal Veterinary College, Camden, in London. The valuable and rare helminthology books were transferred with the Leiper Collection to the Bioscience library in Egham. Other helminthology books were offered to the University of the North in South Africa, as the AHBU had strong ties with Prof Mashego, Vice Chancellor. The AHBU Training Course was transferred to the Royal Veterinary College, where Lynda Gibbons was made an Honorary Associate with special responsibilities as course organizer. Arlene Jones was appointed a museum researcher at the NHM and was given unlimited access to specimens from the AHBU collection for her research.

The TPDU, which basically supported itself, with a small contribution to CABI overheads, could occupy the building as long as required, until CABI was offered a reasonable price to vacate. In return, the Unit had the facilities it required and also time to investigate options for relocation. Its success in obtaining research grants made it attractive to several universities and research organizations.

On 19 December 1997 the last official function of IIP was held – the Christmas party. It was a remarkable occasion, with 18 staff, dressed formally, sitting down to a complete traditional turkey dinner, with all the trimmings, cooked by Andy Freeman (the animal technician) and helped by staff. There were no speeches, just everyone enjoying the occasion and celebrating the remarkable spirit, laughter and friendship that characterized IIP. It evoked the era of Willmott and the 'White House'.

Winches Farm in the new CABI Bioscience

When CABI Bioscience came into existence, IIP plant nematologists and entomopathogenic nematologists from Egham were to join the plant pathologists and biosystematists. However, they had to remain at Winches Farm until renovated facilities were ready in September 1998.

The TPDU continued working at St Albans for a further year, before closing in October 1999, with Simon Townson having successfully transferred its programme to the charity-based Northwick Park Institute for Medical Research. Just before it closed it had started work using antibiotics to treat filarial infections (the antibiotics kill the bacterial endosymbiont *Wolbachia*, eventually leading to the death of the *Onchocerca* worms). This work led to the unit being partners in a US$23m grant from the Bill and Melinda Gates Foundation to develop new drugs using this novel approach, and the consortium currently has several clinical trial candidates.[106] The following day, Hominick conducted a last tour of the now desolate site, and closed the building. The sale to LSHTM was completed in November, and on 10 December, Hunt watched the last wall come down. It was almost the end of the Millennium, and how ironic that IIP ended at Winches Farm, where it began in 1929 as the Imperial Bureau of Agricultural Parasitology. It had been a wonderful journey.

BIOLOGICAL CONTROL: BEST OF NATURAL ENEMIES

What is biological control? Often shortened to biocontrol, it refers to the use of living natural enemies – including parasitoid insects (as egg, larval or pupal parasitoids), arthropod predators and pathogens (such as fungi) – to attack invasive alien pests and weeds. Natural enemies or biological control agents (BCAs) for alien invasive species are usually obtained from the pest's country of origin. They must be carefully screened to ensure that non-target flora and fauna will not be affected, and then released into the weed- or pest-infested areas where they establish self-sustaining populations at little or no further cost. The aim usually is not the eradication of the pest or weed but rather the reduction to such low numbers that it ceases to be a problem.[107]

Introduction

The idea of using living organisms to control pests is a hugely attractive one. The early 20th century saw a transition from the relatively unsophisticated and haphazard introduction of natural enemies against pests. The history of the Institute reflects and contributed to the evolution of international policy and practice in biological control of alien pests and weeds. The Institute emerged from the Imperial Institute of Entomology, and in particular from the Imperial Parasite Service at its Farnham House Laboratory in 1927, set up with Empire Marketing Board funds. Sheffield Airey Neave, Assistant Director of the Institute of Entomology, was its first Superintendent. He was succeeded, 1 year later, by WR Thompson. The Laboratory, nicknamed 'The Parasite Zoo',[108] through its Institute staff, provided shipments of BCAs, mainly parasites, to Empire and Commonwealth countries and conducted associated research.[109]

However, enthusiasm for biological control has fluctuated over time. Over the following decades, the intensity and spread of work at the Institute was to ebb and flow with developments in global policy and practice in biological control. The emergence of chemical pesticides after World War II, which 'appeared to offer a quick and simple solution to all insect pest problems',[110] created something of an ebb tide. However, the influence of such works as Rachel Carson's *Silent Spring*,[111] which criticized pesticide development that paid too little attention to the effects on wildlife, sustained the flow of work. This was in turn checked by other studies that queried the impact of BCAs on biodiversity. This then led advocates of biological control to encourage stricter rules and more sophisticated

research on areas such as host specificity – in particular, avoiding the introduction of agents that would harm non-target organisms. Research expanded to include the use of pathogens and the development of biopesticides.

The Institute gradually built up capacity and experience through responding to reported pest and disease outbreaks that threatened agricultural industries around the Empire; the search for BCAs through expeditions and more permanent stations; the formulation of more coordinated, integrated responses that drew on the international network of Research Stations and collaborative arrangements that emerged; and the more sophisticated understanding of the science of biological control and its role within IPM. To understand the history we need to retrace the early years, the expeditions, the stories of the research stations and their emergence as elements of an international network.

The early years: a shaky start

Scrivenor[112] says 'The creation of the CIBC was largely due to the initiative of Sir Guy Marshall. He had long thought that more use ought to be made of beneficial parasites and predators, and he was responsible for persuading the Empire Marketing Board to make available a grant of £15,000 for the purchase of Farnham House', 'a dignified English country house, set pleasantly in a rose garden.'[113] The Board also provided £5000 per annum, for the running of the Laboratory, later increased to £7000. It is a remarkable tribute to the foresight of Marshall and his successors that they should have anticipated by many years the current demand for ecologically sound methods of pest control.

Farnham House, 1927. ©CABI

The Laboratory made a good start under WR Thompson, who already had wide practical experience in biocontrol and a considerable reputation as a theoretician. In its first year the Laboratory shipped 6000 specimens. Its work was extended to include weeds as well as insect pests. Australian scientists were posted to the Laboratory, and most of the work was on projects for Australia and New Zealand. David Miller, of New Zealand's Cawthron Institute, said in 1930 that the Laboratory 'was perhaps the most fundamentally important entomological organisation in the British Empire,' noting that half the parasites studied there were shipped to New Zealand.[116]

By 1933–34 shipments had risen to 94 and specimens to 1.2 million. In the same year CIE became part of CAB and, whatever regrets Sir Guy may have had about the Institute losing its independence, he must have been relieved to see some hope for the continuation of the Laboratory at Farnham House, which by then was in a bad way financially. The financial crisis of 1931 had cast a shadow of doubt over its future and when, in 1933, the Empire Marketing Board was abolished, it seemed to be doomed. The Executive Council of CAB, however, managed to secure a grant in aid from the (British) Department of Scientific and Industrial Research, which enabled the Laboratory to carry on.

And carry on it did. In the early years, work was carried out principally in the UK and Europe for Canada, New Zealand and Australia. However, as the demand for long-term exploration studies grew, permanent Research Stations and Sub-stations were established throughout the Commonwealth.

1928–34: The Myers' expeditions: rapids, disease and shortage of food

In 1928 John Golding Myers and his wife (Iris H Myers) were sent by the Institute to the West Indies to study the possibility of biological control for the main pests of agriculture in the British Colonies of tropical America. He undertook tours in the West Indies and Latin America for the Institute in 1928–30 and 1930–34. Afterwards, he was seconded to the Imperial College of Agriculture in Trinidad. His work and recommendations, followed by those of the sugarcane entomologist HE Box, led to a sharp increase in biological control activity, halted only by World War II.

In a report covering 1930–34, John Myers recorded his studies of 19 major pests, mainly of sugarcane, their natural enemies and other factors limiting their spread and control. These investigations followed in the tradition established by Neave and Simpson in Africa, and foreshadow the Institute's Research Stations in Africa, Asia, Europe and the Caribbean, and the extended tours by CABI scientists in the 21st century, sometimes in

John Golding Myers, Farnham House, 1930s. ©CABI

difficult conditions, in Africa, Latin America and Asia. Modern transport and communication technologies, and the limited time available to CABI scientists in the modern era, mean that nowadays most excursions are brief ones from the CABI international centres.

The Myers undertook five trips – along the river networks of Trinidad, Venezuela, Brazil and British Guiana (now Guyana). JG Myers noted that on one of these 'about 800 miles were covered on foot – a method of progression which offers the best condition for entomological work which ought to be adopted more generally if time were available'. In his account of his travels,[117] Myers acknowledged the encouragement of Marshall, Thompson and Neave.

These were obviously extraordinary and difficult tours. Just try to picture this touring Englishman, who no doubt suffered tropical illnesses, and his sometime ailing wife, travelling by boat and dugout canoe along barely explored, turbulent rivers and rapids, walking – where track and time allowed – through jungle and savannah. It must have been hot, humid and unhealthy work.

Thanking his anthropologist wife, Myers wrote of her contribution not only to the official projects allocated to her but also 'in every other direction'. The difficulties they faced were evident: Iris 'was invalided to England at the end of 1931 with severe malaria resulting from the conditions of work in the unhealthy Orinoco Delta'.

The hardships are described in the following extract from his report:

" *Of the three main difficulties in South American travel, namely rapids, disease and shortage of food, the writer has had his share. With a few notable exceptions, involving desertions under difficult conditions, the labour employed, Latin, Negro, East Indian, aboriginal Indian and mixtures of several, after judicious selection, proved trustworthy, hardworking and intelligent and those with aboriginal blood being by far the most efficient in entomological work and attaining a very high degree of skill in particular jobs.*

Grave difficulties and delays were encountered in Brazil, and only there, as a result of recent restrictions on research and exploration by foreigners. Through the kind offices of the (British) Ambassador in Rio de Janeiro, and of the local Consuls, these were finally overcome. On my return journey from Santarem, however, I was permitted to travel up the Rio Branco only on condition that I gave my word of honour to do no scientific work en route. "

On the practical difficulties of transport and their impact on collections, Myers wrote:

" *Means of transport on the Amazon near Santarem, where all the material was collected, are confined almost entirely to water. Practically all the puparia shipped, or from which further supplies were reared in the laboratory, were collected by means of boats or canoes. It was necessary at the height of the campaign, to employ a small fleet consisting of a motor-launch (in addition to that carrying the shipments to Para), a small sailing boat and eleven dugout canoes or montarias. Some of the richest collecting grounds lay ten miles and more from the laboratory, and the frequent* rough water at that season, in stretches of open water three or four miles across, made travelling uncomfortable and at times dangerous. The collecting personnel, save for three Arawak and coloured men from British Guiana, who acted as foremen, was entirely recruited locally, and reached a total at times of forty people. The puparia were handled in the same manner as the Lixophaga, and Mr. LC Scaramuzza ascertained that the same rearing technique could be applied.*

Transport was the most difficult and expensive part of the campaign. The regular airways supplied a weekly service from Para to Georgetown, making the journey in one day. The problem lay in covering regularly, and as frequently as possible, the stretch of some 470 miles of river between the collecting base at Santarem and the airport at Para. The river steamers, of which there are many, are too irregular or infrequent, and the time at our disposal was insufficient for unexpected delays. The parasites were sent as puparia, the normal period of pupation being 9 days, which could be extended to a maximum of 13 days by judicious use of ice. Thus with freshly reared puparia we had a maximum of 13 days and with collected puparia of unknown age, a corresponding shorter period. "

In spite of the difficulties, Myers stressed the importance of sustained observations in the tropics as 'the biological headquarters', saying it was

" *a curious fact that while astronomers and meteorologists go to tremendous expense to establish permanent stations in the most inaccessible regions of the world, where conditions happen to be ideal for their investigations, biologists are largely content to (confine) themselves to the artificial and*

1984	Peter Ooi is recruited to establish project activities in Malaysia at Ebor Research, which would grow to become the CIBC Malaysian Station.
1985	The Institute is renamed the CAB International Institute of Biological Control (also CIBC).
1986	Jeff Waage is recruited as chief scientific officer to integrate the work of the Centres into an overall cohesive science strategy.
1987	The Indian Station is handed over to the Indian Council of Agricultural Research (ICAR) to become the core of ICAR's biological control programme.
1988	A CABI Regional Representative for the Caribbean is appointed and based at the West Indian Station.
1989	MS Swaminathan formally opens the purpose-built new CIBC headquarters and CABI Library Services Centre at Silwood Park. Greathead becomes Director, on the retirement of Bennett. Start of LUBILOSA in collaboration with IITA and DFPV.
1990	CIBC becomes the International Institute of Biological Control (IIBC) with the sub-description 'an Institute of CAB International'.
1991	Waage is appointed as Director on the retirement of Greathead. Chris Lomer is recruited and posted to IITA to collaborate on the LUBILOSA programme.
1992	The Malaysia Station moves into newly refurbished facilities constructed at the Malaysian Agriculture Research & Development Institute (MARDI), Serdang.
1993	Peter Baker is sent from CABI's IIBC Trinidad Station, where he was Scientist-in-Charge, to Chinchina in Colombia to manage a new £1 million 3-year research project.
1995	Additional facilities for IIBC are added at UK headquarters and its research station in Switzerland.
1998	CABI Bioscience is formed through the integration of the four Institutes. Green Muscle® is registered in South Africa to be on the market by the end of 1999, representing the culmination of 9 years of international collaborative research through LUBILOSA.

mutilated animal and plant associations of the older civilized northern countries, eked out by the study of preserved material and by hasty visits to the tropics, often too short to acquire that essential local knowledge so essential to valid ecological work. To this regrettable tendency the Imperial College of Tropical Agriculture and the several biological stations founded in the American tropics present notable exceptions. "

He believed in the 'importance of searching (for parasites) in primitive habitats', a view confirmed by the discovery of the Amazon fly (*Metagonistylum minense*), a parasite of the sugarcane stem borer, and of other tachinid parasites of the froghoppers. He outlined advice he had given to local governments, planters' organizations and individual planters throughout his extended tour. The pests of sugarcane received most attention as the most important regional crop and because of financial support from the sugarcane industry.

These daunting explorations led to real benefits in controlling pests. The small moth borer (*Diatraea*) was the most important pest of sugarcane – as a result of his recommendations the Cuban fly (*Lixophaga*) was introduced into the Leeward and Windward Isles in collaboration with Box; and the Amazon fly into British Guiana in collaboration with a Mr Cleare. Both of these promising parasites, the second of which was discovered during the course of the investigation, were now widely established. He said that specific parasites were needed for *Diatrea canella* in British Guiana and for *Diatrea impersonatella* in Trinidad, noting that *Paratheresia* might serve for the first and *Metagonistylum* for the second.[118]

With the development of the Scaramuzza–Box technique and other rearing techniques instigated during Myers' time, over the next 30–50 years tachinids, such as the Amazon fly discovered by Myers, have been widely used in the biological control of sugarcane borers (and other pests).[119] CABI's Institute of Biological Control was a major element in these efforts. Myers died following a car accident in the Sudan in 1942.

1940: The outbreak of World War II forces a move

Headquarters remained at Farnham Royal until the outbreak of World War II made work in Europe impossible. In 1940 operations were transferred to the Dominion Parasite Laboratory at Belleville, Canada. The Laboratory was retitled the Imperial Parasite Service, but it remained part of the Imperial Institute of Entomology. Subsequently, the name changed again, as it became the Imperial and then the Commonwealth Bureau of Biological Control; and in 1951 to the Commonwealth Institute of Biological Control (CIBC). WR Thompson was Director until 1958, when he was succeeded by FJ Simmonds. Thompson said while the English climate was not particularly suited to parasite studies, 'Belleville offered the access without crossing seas, to climate variation from the Arctic to the tropics in South America.'[120] He also said that early in the war Britain had rejected plans to use insect pests to attack enemy crops.[121]

Dominion Parasite Laboratory at Belleville, Canada. ©CABI

As demand grows, permanent research stations are established

As the demand for long-term exploration studies and procurement of beneficial organisms around the world increased, it became evident, as Myers had argued in the 1930s, that permanent stations in critical areas would be more effective than short-term investigations by staff operating from headquarters. In 1941 an outpost in California was set up with further stations following after the war.

The history and fate of the stations varied considerably. Some, such as those in Europe, California and the West Indies, were established to provide material for distant parts of the Commonwealth. Others, such as those in India, Pakistan and East Africa, were organized at the request of the national governments to assist with the introduction of exotic, beneficial organisms as well as material for other countries. Research stations in California, Canada and India were discontinued or integrated into national systems. Although the network of centres and offices were established incrementally and opportunistically, their reshaping into an integrated scientific strategic framework has endowed the modern CABI with a unique global resource in plant health research and development.

1941: California

In 1941, an officer was transferred from Canada to Riverside in California, and provided with free quarters in the Department of Biological Control of the Citrus Research Station, University of California; and, in 1949 with the emergence of a research programme involving a large number of parasites and predators to control two diapine scale insects attacking the Bermuda cedar, was transferred to a purpose-built laboratory in Fontana, 10 miles from Riverside.

Work at California was focused on: (i) benefits to countries other than the USA; (ii) investigation and shipment of parasites and predators of subtropical crops (initially); (iii) from 1945 to 1965, provision of material for Mediterranean climatic regions; (iv) work mainly for Australia, Canada, New Zealand and South Africa, as well as for other Commonwealth countries; and (v) some work for France, Italy, Mexico, parts of the USA itself and the USSR. Projects included: (i) the potato tuber moth; (ii) an attempt to control the swollen-shoot disease of cacao in Nigeria and Ghana by biological control of mealybug vectors; (iii) other programmes on soft-scale and armoured scale pests of citrus; and (iv) investigations on insects attacking weeds. After David Lloyd's departure for Argentina in 1961, E Alan Cameron continued alone in the California Station as work wound down until closure in 1965. Work continued elsewhere and, through cooperation with the USDA, especially through the European Station.[122]

1946: The West Indies

In September 1946, FJ Simmonds of the Institute was stationed in Trinidad at the Imperial College of Tropical Agriculture (now part of the University of the West Indies), studying natural enemies of the weed *Cordia curassavica*, leading to the establishment of the West Indian Station under the leadership of Simmonds and, from 1958, Fred D Bennett. The Station played a crucial role in the history of the Institute – from 1962 to 1984 it served as headquarters, pioneering biological control in the region including the establishment of a sub-station in Barbados focusing on management of the sugarcane stem borer.

The Station moved to its present location, Curepe, in 1962, with a new laboratory specially constructed at the University with costs being met by a Colonial Department and Welfare grant to the West Indies (75%) and by CAB itself (25%). A larger two-storey building was added in 1975, built with funding from the Cultural Industries Development Association. As headquarters of the Institute, facilities included the headquarters library, brought from the UK via Canada and which, in addition to many books and journal series, had a valuable reference collection of some 12,000 reprints. This library is still in Trinidad. Over the years, an important insect reference collection was built up, particularly strong in the main groups of parasitoids and predators used in biological control.

The Station: (i) obtained, or mass-produced, parasites and predators for various West Indian territories from other parts of the world; (ii) organized the transfer of beneficial organisms from one West Indian area to another; and (iii) carried out surveys of natural enemies of certain pests in the West Indies, eastern South America, Mexico and south-eastern USA, as well as procuring beneficial insects from these areas for shipment to tropical and subtropical countries elsewhere.

Barbados Sub-station and the sugarcane stem borer

Over the years, the Station's experts have investigated a range of insect pests through the use of CBC. These include: fruit flies, leaf-cutting ants, scale insects, mealybugs and whiteflies, sugarcane stem borer (*Diatraea* spp.), cassava mealybug (*Phenacoccus manihoti*), cassava green mite (*Mononychellus tanajoa*) and mahogany shoot borer (*Hypsipyla grandella*).

Amongst those pests, the work on the sugarcane stem borer has particular resonance in the West Indies story because it continued a long-standing focus of the Institute's research; it capitalized on the Institute's broader network of Research Stations and is still important

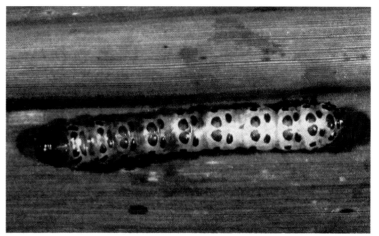

Larva of *Diatraea saccharalis*. ©D.G. Hall

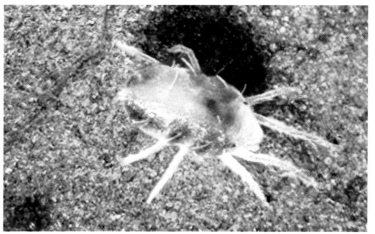

Mononychellus tanajoa (cassava green mite). ©Georg Goergen/IITA Insect Museum, Benin

Phenacoccus manihoti (cassava mealybug). ©Georg Goergen/IITA Insect Museum, Benin

Anagyrus lopezi, parasitoid of *Phenacoccus manihoti*. ©CABI

Water hyacinth. ©CABI

Lantana camara. ©CABI

in the region. It led, in March 1966, to the establishment of a sub-station in Barbados with the Ministry of Agriculture. As Myers noted, the Cuban fly, *Lixophaga diatraeae* (Tachinidae) was introduced from the 1930s up to the 1960s. It began to be consistently recovered from the field in 1966. In 1967 a braconid wasp, *Cotesia flavipes* obtained from the Institute's Indian Station, was established and together the two parasitoids brought the pest under satisfactory control, maintained in Barbados ever since. In later years, *C. flavipes* was introduced into many neotropical countries for control of stem borers, almost always giving at least some degree of control.

The Centre's role in discovering the centre of origin of the cassava mealybug, *Phenacoccus manihoti*, is perhaps the Institute's biggest success.[123] Although identified by the West Indies Station, it depended on the Institute's whole network of centres and/or their local partners and specialized quarantine facilities in the UK (see 'Biological Control in Africa').

The Centre has also been involved in the control of weeds, including water hyacinth (*Eichhornia crassipes*), salvinia weed (*Salvinia molesta*), mile-a-minute (*Mikania micrantha*), Spanish flag (*Lantana camara*) and Siam weed (*Chromolaena odorata*). The Centre also pioneered the introduction of participatory approaches in the Caribbean region through farmer field schools (FFS), and has employed its expertise in using beneficial organisms to combat pests and diseases by passing this knowledge on to farmers.

Following his appointment as Director of CIBC in 1976, Bennett remained as Entomologist-in-Charge until 1981, when Matthew Cock, appointed in 1978 to study the biological control of mile-a-minute weed, took over until 1982. Bennett resumed responsibility until he retired in 1985 and was replaced by Maajid Yaseen, who had been posted to the West Indian Station from the Pakistan Station in 1969.

A highlight of Yaseen's career was the 1980 discovery of *Anagyrus lopezi* in Paraguay, which became the most effective BCA against cassava mealybug. After Yaseen's death, Peter Baker was appointed Scientist-in-Charge in 1989. In 1993 Baker was transferred to Colombia, where, based at Cenicafé, he ran a large IPM research and capacity-building project on coffee berry borer. Roger Hammond then took responsibility for a diminished Caribbean and Latin America office.

1948: The Institute returns to continental Europe

Louis Mesnil. ©CABI

The genesis of CABI's European Station in Switzerland followed soon after the establishment of the CIBC and its early cooperation with Canada: a sub-station opened at Feldmeilen close to Zurich in 1948. Louis Mesnil, an authority on parasitic Diptera, was the first Entomologist-in-Charge and, under his supervision, the station moved to Delémont in 1958 and in 1963 occupied a purpose-built facility on land bought by CAB. Hubert Pschorn-Walcher succeeded Mesnil in 1969. In April 1979, Klaus Carl took over as a Centre Director until he retired in December 1996 after 36 years of service. Dieter Schroeder, who supervised a 50% enlargement of the facility in 1997, succeeded him. In 2000, Schroeder retired after 40 years of service,

Opposite: giant salvinia (*Salvinia molesta*), Science Source. ©SPL

particularly on the CBC of weeds. Matthew Cock took charge in 2000 until he was promoted to be CABI's Chief Scientist, with Ulrich Kuhlmann becoming Centre Director in 2010.

A close link has always existed between CABI in Switzerland and Agriculture and Agri-Food Canada (AAFC) and the Canadian Forestry Service, and has continued despite declining funding, particularly with AAFC. Emphasis has shifted from forest pests in the 1950s and 1960s to weeds and agricultural pests.[124] This collaborative work is well documented in *Biological Control Programmes in Canada*, which CABI published in 1962, 1971, 1984 and 2002.

CABI Switzerland: successes in North America

Successful control resulting from releases of BCAs for forest insect pests in Canada included:

- *Cyzenis albicans* and *Agrypon flaveolatum* against the winter moth, *Operophtera brumata* (1950s–60s);

- *Agathis pumila* and other parasitoids against the larch casebearer, *Coleophora laricella* (1960s–70s);

- *Mesoleius tenthredinis* and *Olesicampe benefactor* against the larch sawfly, *Pristiphora erichsonii* (1960s–70s);

- *Olesicampe geniculatae* against the mountain-ash sawfly, *Pristiphora geniculata* (1980s); and

- *Lathrolestes nigricollis* against the birch leaf miner, *Fenusa pumila* (1990s).

The following releases of BCAs against agricultural insect pests also resulted in successful control with local or regional impact in Canada and the USA:

- *Tetrastichus julis* against the cereal leaf beetle, *Oulema melanopus* (1970s);

- *Macroglenus penetrans* against the orange wheat blossom midge, *Sitodiplosis mosellana* (1980s);

- *Peristenus digoneutis* against *Adelphocoris* and *Lygus* plant bugs (1980s–2000s);

- *Ageniaspis fuscicollis* against the apple ermine moth, *Yponomeuta malinellus* (1990s–2000s); and

- *Lathrolestes ensator* against the European apple sawfly, *Hoplocampa testudinea* (1990s–2000s).

Releases of the following weed BCAs have resulted (or are currently resulting) in successful control of the designated weeds where they occur in North America:

- *Aphthona* spp. leaf beetles against leafy spurge, *Euphorbia esula* (1980s–90s);

- Flower- and root-feeding weevils against knapweeds, *Centaurea* spp. (1980s–90s);

- *Galerucella* spp. leaf beetles against purple loosestrife, *Lythrum salicaria* (1990s);

- *Mecinus janthinus* stem-boring weevils against Dalmatian toadflax, *Linaria dalmatica* (1990s); and

- *Mogulones crucifer* weevils against houndstongue, *Cynoglossum officinale* (in Canada) (1990s–2000s).

Peristenus attacking *Lygus*. ©CABI   *Aphthona* leaf beetle. ©CABI

Since 1990, the training of undergraduate and graduate students has become an important part of the Centre's programmes. Each year, it offers placements to allow undergraduate students of biology and agriculture and postgraduate researchers to assist CABI Europe–Switzerland (E-CH) staff with high-impact practical projects and receive hands-on training in practical aspects of applied biological control research. This has led to relationships being developed, for example, with many Canadian universities, resulting in a total of 90 Canadian student placements since 1995, and many joint peer-reviewed research papers. Several students have subsequently won prizes and prestigious scholarships on the basis of work undertaken in collaboration with CABI.

The Swiss Centre's current role is described further in 'CABI and its Member Countries' (Chapter 9).

Carole Rapo exposing plants, Swiss Centre. ©CABI

1957: The Institute opens Stations in India and Pakistan

The Indian Station was established in 1957 in Bangalore under the Colombo Plan with Canadian support.[125] By the mid-1960s the Station (with its sub-stations and collection centres) employed an entomologist-in-charge, seven junior entomologists, a plant pathologist, 22 entomological assistants, a mycological assistant and 29 laboratory-cum-field assistants. It was, by then, handling more than 25 projects. There were just three scientists-in-charge: VP Rao (1957–73), T Sankaran, (1973–85) and MJ Chacko (1985–89). After 30 years of activity, the Station was formally handed over to the Indian Council for Agricultural Research (ICAR) to become the headquarters of the national biological control programme. After the handover to the Indian Council of Agricultural Research (ICAR) in 1987 CIBC continued to be a presence, working on a survey of mango mealybug natural enemies until the end of 1989.

Suggestions that a Research Station of the CIBC should be established in Pakistan were made by the Pakistan representative at the CAB Review Conference in 1950, AM Shaikh, who 'offered to provide accommodation and equipment in that country'.[126] The Station was supported by Canada as part of the Colombo Plan, and opened at Rawalpindi in 1957. The laboratory, was said to be 'well provided with scientific and office equipment and had a small reference library and collections of both insects and plants'.

The first Scientist-in-Charge was MA Ghani, who retired at the end of 1979 and was replaced by Ikram Mohyuddin, who was based at the East African Station from 1967 to 1969. At the end of 1994, Mohyuddin retired and was replaced by Ashraf Poswal.

In 1965 the technical staff of the Pakistan Station consisted of an Entomologist-in-Charge, six entomologists, eight junior entomologists and two entomological assistants. Because of the lack of basic

MA Ghani. ©CABI

information on insect and weed pests and their natural enemies in Pakistan, surveys on their distribution and biology received priority. Much of this was funded under the US Public Law 480 scheme, which allowed some of Pakistan's financial obligations to the USA to be spent in-country on projects of mutual interest.

The Station's investigations (including those for other countries) identified some serious pests such as aphids on conifers, some fruit flies, scales, mites and seed-cone and wood borers previously unknown in the area. Further study assisted in evaluation and control.[127]

By 1983–84, an agreement with the Pakistan Agricultural Research Council, signed the previous year, was beginning to bear fruit, and Institute involvement in the application of natural enemies as BCAs was increasing. This period was characterized by a focus on practical IPM projects with and for local growers, particularly the large-scale growers of such as sugarcane, fruit and cotton, including IPM services to growers supplying individual sugar mills, based on a scientist at a sub-station at each mill.

Pakistan Research Station sucesses

Chilo partellus *and hybrids*

Mohyuddin investigated the control of a predator of sugarcane, *Pyrilla*, using *Apanteles flavipes* and, by 1984–85, a strain from Indonesia released 2 years before was well established in the Punjab and the North West Frontier Province (NWFP) in cane fields, parasitizing *Chilo infuscatellus* and *Acigona steniellus*. In 1991 CABI released a parasitoid in Pakistan, a hybrid between the Indonesia strain from the sugarcane borer *C. infuscatellus* and that from the local strain, *C. partellus* on maize in the Nawabshah area, for control of sugarcane borers. The parasitoid was well established and had parasitized up to 40% of larvae.

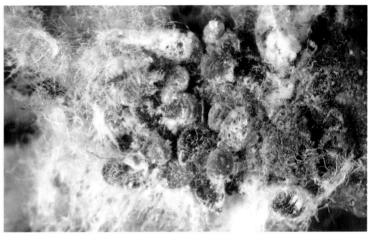

Woolly apple aphid (*Aphelinus mali*). ©FLPA

The woolly apple aphid

By 1987 *Aphelinus mali*, imported from Switzerland, was providing excellent control against the woolly apple aphid. Ten years later[128] it was being trialled against the pest in Afghanistan, where it is an important and serious pest of apple orchards.

The brown peach aphid in Yemen

In 1993 the brown peach aphid, *Pterochloroides persicae*, a lachine pest of *Prunus* spp. crops, was reported for the first time in Yemen. The aphid caused widespread damage to peach and almond crops, which are the mainstay of 200,000 families in Yemen. FAO approached IIBC in 1995 to help implement a Technical Cooperation Project, and surveys for natural enemies were started in Pakistan, where the aphid originated. The parasitoid *Pauesia atennata* was identified, and material sent to the UK quarantine facility, a culture established in 1996 and a dossier produced in support of its introduction into Yemen. Early in 1997 material was taken to Yemen, cultures established by the General Department of Plant Protection with support from the German agency, GTZ plant protection project and releases soon started. Before the end of the year there were high levels of parasitism, aphid populations collapsed and in the Yemen national press over 7 million trees were reported to have been saved. This was the first implementation of biological control of this pest, achieved in just over 2 years and a complete success; the network of IIBC Stations able to respond flexibly to the need was key to the rapid response. The General Department of Plant Protection, Republic of Yemen, was one of two organizations chosen to share the 1998–99 Edouard Saouma Award.

Outposted staff and sub-stations

Rawalpindi Station, Pakistan. ©CABI

Since the establishment of the Farnham House Laboratory, staff members were sent on extended travel or based for a longer term with host institutes or in rented accommodation. Even with the network of Stations, this was still needed, and the bases were referred to as sub-stations, which had a degree of autonomy. This practice continues today on a project needs basis. The locations included Sapporo, Japan; San Carlos de Bariloche, Argentina; Austria; Hungary; Serbia; Monterrey, Mexico; Bangalore, India; Rawalpindi, Pakistan; Bogor, Indonesia; Kumasi, Ghana; and Sabah, Malaysia.

1959: Increasing demand for biological control

By 1959 there was increasing global demand for prospective biological control of insect and weed pests, as shown in an annual summary[129] of the activities of the Institute, which were 'widespread with stations in California (Fontana), Europe (Delémont, Switzerland), India (Bangalore), Pakistan (Rawalpindi) and the West Indies (Trinidad) in addition to the headquarters in Canada'. The 1958 report lists some 27 projects being undertaken throughout this network and notes that some 278 shipments of 48 species of beneficial insects, totalling approximately 440,000 individuals, had been sent to 13 countries during the year.

After the retirement of WR Thompson, FJ Simmonds was appointed as Director and moved from the West Indian Station to headquarters in Ottawa in June 1958. (See Box 'Dr FJ Simmonds'.) He was followed by Fred Bennett.

Dr FJ Simmonds – a professional career in CIBC

FJ Simmonds[130] graduated from Cambridge University in 1939 and obtained his PhD in 1947 and DSc in 1960. His entire professional career was spent in the services of CIBC. Evacuated from France in 1940, where he was studying the codling moth, he proceeded to Canada in 1941. In 1945 he was sent to the West Indies to obtain and screen natural enemies of *Cordia curassavica* to dispatch to Mauritius, where biological control was achieved. His dynamism and enthusiasm for biological control is said to have led to the establishment of a permanent CIBC station in Trinidad. When Simmonds succeeded WR Thompson as Director of CIBC, he moved its headquarters to Trinidad. His work covered the economics of biological control and the biological control of weeds, as well as arthropod and vertebrate pests. He was a founder of the International Organization for Biological Control (IOBC) and served as its Treasurer until his retirement in 1976. He died in the UK in 1985, aged 70.

1962: With air travel facilitating pest invasions, the Institute ventures into Africa

According to Matthew Cock, the desirability of a station in East Africa had long been realized. In 1952, the Assistant Director toured a number of East African countries; the issue was discussed in the Review Conference of 1955, and the Director toured East Africa in early 1960. In 1962 the Institute's East African Station was set up at the Kawanda Research Station in Uganda, some 8 miles west of Kampala, with Greathead as its first Director. The aim was to assist African countries and to find natural enemies of pests for export to other countries. Work was initiated with funding from the Tanganyika Coffee Board, the Kenya Coffee Board, the Uganda Government and a US$10,000 grant from the Rockefeller Foundation.

David J Greathead (1931–2006): a life in biological control

David Greathead was born in London and trained at Imperial College. He was recruited in 1953 by Boris Uvarov to work at the Desert Locust Survey, involving 8 years of fieldwork and research in Ethiopia, Somalia, Kenya and the Aden Protectorate (part of Yemen). It was not a life for the faint-hearted: there was laborious work on the choice of oviposition sites by locust swarms in studies undertaken with George Popov,[131] in Somalia in 1953 and in northern Kenya in 1954;[132] and a systematic survey of the locust recession areas, including Lake Assal, in what was then French Somaliland (now Djibouti). This is the lowest point in Africa, at 155 m below sea level and the most saline body of water in the world. It is set in a glistening white salt flat which they had to cross while maintaining a high speed, because the salt crust, below which lay thick sludge, would have begun to break up if they had slowed down. Worse was to follow: near the port of Assab in Eritrea (at the time federated with Ethiopia) they were surrounded by an Ethiopian garrison and put under house arrest under suspicion of being from the French army.

The locust survey days gave rise to an enduring legend about Greathead. An Ethiopian locust officer accompanying Greathead on a field survey played his radio very loudly in the mornings and, in spite of repeated pleas to turn down the volume, the noise continued until Greathead picked up a .303 rifle and put a bullet through the offending radio.

Greathead joined CAB in 1962, founding the CIBC East African Station at Kawanda in Uganda, but returned to the UK in 1973. One of his first tasks was to co-edit a companion to his review of African biological control, *A Review of Biological Control in Western and Southern Europe*, published in 1976.[133] As the sole staff member of CIBC in the UK at the time, Greathead persuaded CAB that it needed an information officer, a journal to promote biological control, as well as an Assistant Director, a post Greathead occupied. Greathead became Director of IIBC in 1989 on the retirement of Fred Bennett, and continued to develop the UK Centre with strong links to Imperial College. James Ogwang[134] tells how, as a student at Silwood Park, 'Dr Greathead (was) one of the pillars that influenced me to develop interest in biocontrol'. Greathead instilled into his recruits the importance of taxonomy, encouraging them to develop a specific interest. His own interest in Bombyliidae and other Diptera, especially in tropical Africa, was how Neal Evenhuis came across him.

Evenhuis says, 'He generously took me "under his wing" as it were and – in addition to letting me in on his incredible knowledge of African bee flies – he also taught me about the necessities of scientific work: patience, thoroughness, and even diplomacy in dealing with co-workers'. At 60, Greathead stepped down as Director of IIBC. He was awarded an Honorary Senior Research Fellowship at the Centre for Population Biology, Imperial College London at Silwood Park, and remained professionally very active in biological control; and a stalwart support to staff, and as ready as ever to discuss ideas and problems and dispense advice based on his unparalleled knowledge.

One of the first projects tackled from this new base concerned the *Antestiopsis* spp. complex, the main pests of arabica coffee, probably beginning CABI's intimate involvement with the commodity, at least in Africa. The identity of the pest was unclear, but Greathead 'sorted out the *Antestiopsis* spp. complex' in a series of papers. Subsequent work on sugarcane scale *(Aulacaspis* spp.) led to the introduction of the coccinellid, *Rhyzobius lophanthae* (syn. *Lindorus lophanthae*) from Mauritius to northern Tanzania, which was outstandingly successful and brought the pest under control within 18 months of being released.

1973: Escaping from Idi Amin

The Research Station remained in Uganda under increasingly difficult political circumstances during the regime of Idi Amin until 1973. By that date, permission to leave the country even temporarily was difficult to obtain, but Greathead managed to extract a letter personally signed by the Minister of Internal Affairs allowing him to leave, with his wife Annette and daughter Emma, to conduct annual field work in neighbouring Kenya (where their two older children were at school). With the CIBC Station Land Rover filled with laboratory equipment, and what possessions they could fit in once this was all stowed, they set off, arriving at the border after dark. It was, as Greathead recounted in later years, a particularly tense moment when he handed over the letter. They watched the soldier read it, slowly. They were not sure what to expect next – but it was certainly not what happened. The soldier, clearly awed by the signature on the bottom, asked reverentially whether he could keep it. Bemused, Greathead cordially replied that of course he could. And so they were waved through.

1984: With continuing demand and opportunities for biological control, a new Centre is established in Kenya

Although a sub-station was operating in Ghana in West Africa from 1969 to 1978, there was a hiatus in CABI's East African activities following the effective closure in 1973 of the Uganda Station, despite continuing demand for biological control in the region.

The 1970s–80s

Rex Ingram and Richard Markham arrived at the East African Agriculture Forestry Research Organisation (EAAFRO) at Muguga, some 25 km from Nairobi, after driving an old, smoking Land Rover packed with laboratory equipment and some old furniture from Tororo in Uganda to set up what was to become known as CIBC. The Land Rover had a 'chronic hard start' and Markham had to park it on a slope to be sure of a 'kick-start!' They had run away from political upheavals during dictator Idi Amin Dada's early years in power (1977–80). EAAFRO served Tanzania, Uganda and Kenya. By 1983, laboratory work had increased and Ingram requested the then Director of KARI (the Kenya Agricultural Research Institute) in Muguga to second one

Richard Markham. ©CABI

laboratory technician (Peter Karanja) to assist in the rearing of various Hymenoptera parasitoids. Ingram, as the Officer-in-Charge of CIBC's Kenya Station, later left and was replaced by Ian Robertson around 1984. With the increasing number of projects the volume of work also increased, and more staff were seconded from KARI. Moses Kairo, George Oduor and Francis Nang'ayo, entomologists from KARI, joined in 1985, followed in 1987 by Kenyan entomologist Dennis Rangi.

After occupying space provided by KARI for 2 years, a shared biological control research centre was established with the Kenyan Institute, with support from the Canadian International Development Agency (CIDA). The refurbished facility, opened in 1986, housed the Institute's Kenya Station and the KARI Biological Control team, and had offices, laboratories, glasshouses and rearing facilities, and at its peak was occupied by ten scientists.

Robertson left in 1988 and was replaced by Matthew Cock, who was the Scientist-in-Charge until 1991. It was during his tenure at CIBC Kenya Station, as it was by then known, that two huge projects, the biological control of the African bollworm, *Helicoverpa amigera* and the control of conifer aphids, was implemented. Sean Murphy was in charge of the biological control of coffee pests.

Henk van den Berg (who joined in 1988) studied the impact of the indigenous natural enemies of African bollworm with Matthew Cock and George Oduor until 1991, soon after which he moved to work on farmer-participatory research with the Malaysia Station in Indonesia. After Markham left in January 1988, the transfer from Trinidad of Gill Allard was arranged in May 1989, leading to the development of aspects of insect pathology. Building on Markham's foundations, Allard evolved a networking approach to national programmes in a collegial supportive manner to address IPM issues. This was a turning point in CABI's development in Africa, and as a development organization globally.

During the 1980s, the main projects at the Centre were: (i) research on the natural enemies of the tsetse fly; (ii) research and supply of natural enemies of the coffee berry borer for Latin America; (iii) evaluation of the natural enemies of the African bollworm; and (iv) complementary activities and support to the IITA-led programme of CBC on cassava green mite and cassava mealybug.

Some CABI Africa projects from the 1970s and 1980s are listed below.

1. Integrated management (1984–88) of the cassava green mite, *Mononychellus tanajoa* and the cassava mealybug, *Phenacoccus manihoti* in sub-Saharan Africa, with funding from IDRC and IITA.

2. Coffee pests, from 1987: work continued in Kenya under the leadership of Sean Murphy for control of the coffee berry borer, *Hypothenemus hampei* in Latin America. Shipments of *Prorops nasuta*, the bethylid parasitoid, were sent to Silwood Park for screening in quarantine for coffee diseases before being sent on to the German agency, GTZ in Ecuador. The braconid *Heterospilus coffeicola* was collected in western Tanzania and shipped to the UK for screening. Unfortunately it has not yet been possible to breed this parasitoid in the laboratory. Studies on *Icerya purchasi*, for Kenya coffee farmers, revealed two further primary parasitoids, *Oricoruna arcotensis* and a *Parasaphodes* sp., and high levels of hyperparasitism that may limit the

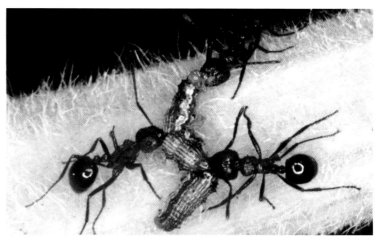
Myrmicaria ants attacking African bollworm caterpillars. ©CABI

main parasitoids, *Cryptochaetum* sp. and *Austroterobia* sp. A release of the predator *Rodolia iceryae* helped to reduce an outbreak of *Icerya pattersoni* on one estate. Shipments of the coffee green scale parasitoid, *Metaphycus baruensis* (called *Metaphycus* sp. nv. *Lounsburyi* in previous reports) were sent for screening in the UK and forwarding to Papua New Guinea. This is one of several important parasitoids of the coffee green scale complex in Kenya studied in previous years that shows potential as a control agent in other regions where the scales have been introduced.

3. *Heliothis* studies, 1988: following Matthew Cock's preparatory work on *Helicoverpa armigera* in Kenya, van den Berg began a 3-year programme, funded by ODA in collaboration with KARI, to investigate indigenous natural control in smallholder crops. Surveys of farmers' fields showed predation by ants to be widespread. Regular sampling sites with a variety of crops were set up in different parts of the country for in-depth studies.

4. *Salvinia molesta* control, Kenya, 1990: with funding from the Australian Centre for International Agricultural Research (ACIAR), and in collaboration with the Kenya Agricultural Research Institute (KARI), a consignment of *Cyrtobagous salviniae* was brought from the Commonwealth Scientific and Industrial Research Organisation (CSIRO) and released on Lake Naivasha, which effectively controlled *S. molesta* in the lake.

5. Biological control of the coffee berry borer (*Hypothenemus hampei*) with funding from the Mexico/IDRC (International Development Research Centre) project started in 1985.

6. Service projects included the collection in Kenya of parasitoids (e.g. *Euvipio rufa*, *Pediobius furvus*, *Dentichasmias busseolae* and *Bracon* sp.) of cereal stem borers and shipping them for control of sugarcane pests to the USA (Texas) and Cape Verde, funded by Texas A&M University and the Cape Verde Government, respectively) in 1985, as well as exporting parasitoids (e.g. *Copidosoma koehleri*) for control of the potato tuber moth in Yemen, funded by the Yemeni Government in 1987–88.

Opposite: tsetse fly, SEM, Eye of Science. ©SPL

CABI Africa regional centre, Nairobi, Kenya. ©CABI

1990–98

CAB International opened its Regional Office for Africa in Westlands, Nairobi in 1995, with Garry Hill now Regional Representative-cum-Scientist-in-Charge and Dennis Rangi as the Deputy Regional Representative, indicating CABI's plan to make its services and products more accessible to African countries, particularly its member countries. The IIBC Kenya Station facility at Muguga, 25 miles from Nairobi, continued to implement biological control projects.

In 1996 Rangi was appointed as the first (African) Regional Representative of the CABI-Regional Office for Africa, which was primarily concerned with CABI's corporate, information and publishing activities. At the same time, Sarah Simons took over as Scientist-in-Charge of CABI's newly established Bioscience Station (Kenya), which was primarily concerned with CABI's bioscience research and development. Together, staff at the CABI-Regional Office for Africa and the Bioscience Station embarked on a period of unprecedented growth and expansion for CABI in Africa.

During the 1990s the major activities were the introduction and evaluation of *Teretriosoma nigrescens* for the biological control of the larger grain borer, and establishing and running a regional network to tackle forestry pests, notably cypress and pine aphids. This latter was established by Gill Allard. When she left in 1996, Roger Day was recruited from Imperial College to continue the work, and he is still with the Centre in 2010.

CABI in Africa was broadening, from a classical focus on biological control towards initiatives on IPM and Information for Development (IFD). During 1996, a suite of new projects was successfully developed and funded, primarily by the UK Government's DFID via the initial tranche of the Natural Resource Institute's funding from DFID (1996–99), with additional funding provided by the IDRC and others. Projects initiated during this period included: (i) peri-urban vegetable production in Kenya; (ii) IPM of coffee (Kenya and Malawi); (iii) biocontrol of water hyacinth; and (iv) use of entomopathogenic fungi to control storage pests, together with a separate, private sector-funded project on biocontrol of sugarcane white grubs and biocontrol of *Leuceana* psyllid under the related Forestry Research Programme (managed by Oxford Forestry Institute).

A rapidly increasing project portfolio, with a wider range of projects, activities and countries, meant that both the Regional Office for Africa and the Bioscience Station (Kenya) needed staff. Thus, more office and laboratory space together with a more reliable communications system quickly became essential to CABI's future in Africa. There was also growing recognition of the need for a more holistic and integrated approach towards addressing development issues in Africa, with IPM projects increasingly incorporating elements of IFD projects and vice versa. Co-location of the Regional Office for Africa and the Bioscience Station (Kenya) to a single, larger and better-equipped site was the next logical step and, in January 1998, CABI proudly opened the doors of its Africa Regional Centre (CABI-ARC) at the ICRAF (World Agroforestry Centre) Campus in Nairobi. At this point, Rangi became Director for CABI Africa, while Simons became Deputy Director. CABI-ARC encompassed all of CABI's activities, namely Information, Bioscience and Publishing, and was, in effect, a flagship Centre for CABI globally.

For the activities undertaken by CABI in Africa from 1998, see Chapter 9.

Biological Control in Africa

Before air travel, invasive species had to survive transport by sea, which could take several weeks and limited the number of exotic arthropod pests capable of colonizing Africa. However, air travel allowed arthropods to arrive within a few hours in planting material, produce and cut flowers for sale or passengers' food, as smuggled plant material or via adults hitch-hiking in the body of the plane. Many of the new pests that reached Africa after World War II and have been targeted for biological control arrived in this way, including the cassava pests *Mononychellus tanajoa* and *Phenacoccus manihoti*, introduced from South America on illegally imported planting material;[135] *Liriomyza trifolii*, which reached Kenya on chrysanthemum cuttings from Florida[136] imported for multiplication; and *Pineus boerneri*, which is believed to have reached Africa on pine twigs imported for grafting. *Prostephanus truncatus* arrived by sea in maize sent as famine relief. The South-east Asian banana skipper, *Erionota thrax* almost certainly arrived in Mauritius during civil disturbances when troops were flown at night from Malaysia to help keep order.[137] Such new arrivals are prime targets for CBC.

After World War II, the work of the Institute in developing countries was expanded. The Institute opened an East African Station in 1962 in Uganda and a West African Sub-station in Ghana in 1969,[138] to assist African countries and to find natural pest enemies for export to other regions.

Highly successful control resulted from the campaign in Mauritius to control black sedge (*Cordia curassavica*), an invader from the Caribbean, which had developed dense thickets that were displacing pasture and natural vegetation. Research in Trinidad by the CABI Institute's FJ Simmonds resulted in the introduction of two leaf-feeding chrysomelid beetles in 1947. One of these, *Metrogaleruca obscura* (Degeer), became established and, by 1950, much of the scrub was dying and continued defoliation was reducing its competitive power. To combat re-colonization, seed-destroying insects were studied, after which *Eurytoma attiva* was introduced and successfully established. These two agents have reduced *C. curassavica* to a minor roadside weed.[139] This success was subsequently repeated in Malaysia and Sri Lanka.[140]

The first of a new generation of international collaborative biological control programmes developed following the discovery of the mite, *M. tanajoa*, on cassava in Uganda in 1971 and the mealybug, *P. manihoti*, in 1973 in the Congo. The Institute was funded to research their natural enemies in Trinidad and South America, with IITA implementing the biological control, the largest programme ever undertaken. Outstanding control of *P. manihoti* across a range of climates was obtained with the encyrtid parasitoid *Anagyrus lopezi*, shipped to IITA in 1981 through the Institute's newly established quarantine facility in the UK. The most successful species, *Typhlodromalus aripo*, is confined to shoot tips and so allows persistence of the host population and is also better able to survive on alternative sources of food when *M. tanajoa* is scarce. It is now established in some 20 countries and has reduced mite damage by more than 50%.[141]

The floating waterweed, the water hyacinth *Eichhornia crassipes*, which originated in South America and has been spread by horticulturists throughout the tropics on account of its showy flowers, has long been present on the African continent. This weed had been controlled successfully on the River Nile in the Sudan during the 1970s by BCAs from CABI's West Indian Station.[142] It did not attract international attention until it invaded West Africa (Côte d'Ivoire, Ghana, Bénin and Nigeria) and Lake Victoria, down the Kagera River from Rwanda. Its rapid spread in the lake threatened fisheries, transportation and the hydroelectric power station at Jinja in Uganda, where the River Nile leaves the lake. The Kenya Station was also involved with the FAO in developing an international campaign against it. Although action was delayed by international disagreements, it is now achieving very promising initial results. Later, the Kenya station became part of the International Mycoherbicide Programme for *E. crassipes* Control in Africa (IMPECCA) to complement the action of insect agents; this programme also includes South Africa, Malawi, Nigeria, Bénin and Egypt. Insect control agents had already been established in these countries, but had not always been as successful as had been hoped.[143]

Biological control of pests of medical and veterinary importance has seldom been successful, but stable flies that were a serious constraint to dairy farming in Mauritius have been substantially controlled by introduced parasitoids. Studies in Uganda, started as part of a worldwide survey of filth fly natural enemies, showed a spectrum of *Stomoxys* spp. breeding in rotting vegetation from that found in dung pits. When the parasitoids from puparia in rotting vegetation were introduced during 1975–78, a substantial drop in stable fly numbers took place and their level remained acceptable during most of the year.[144]

Biocontrol by mail-order

By 1981 the Director of the Institute, Fred Bennett, hailed the 'first major success' of CBC when 'cottony cushion scale *Icerya purchasi* was brought under control by the importation of the Australian coccinellid *Rodolia cardinalis*'. This insect also provided 'an excellent example of the mail-order type of service (of the Institute) wherein proven natural enemies can be supplied readily to other countries'. Since 1980, when success was apparent in California, *R. cardinalis* had 'been distributed to over 35 countries'. The Institute had participated 'on several occasions'. In Peru, where rufous scale was a key pest of citrus, the Institute supplied the parasite *Aphytis roseni* from Kenya. This 'led to satisfactory

Rodolia cardinalis. ©Edu Rickes Produções Fotográficas

control and also provided an essential component for the integrated control of citrus pests in Peru'.

The banana skipper, *Erionota thrax*, a South-east Asian leaf roller, following its appearance in Mauritius was brought under control by the egg parasite *Ooencyrtus orinotae* and the larval parasite *Apanteles erionotae*.

The Biocat database

The Biocat database was initially a card database, kept by Greathead, of all introductions of insect natural enemies (parasitoids and predators) for biological control of insect pests worldwide; his wife, Annette took over running it when it was computerized. Greathead recognized that 'the results of introductions of agents of CBC are of great interest, not only to biological control practitioners, but also to ecologists interested in biogeography, and the process of colonization by invading species, to taxonomists who may encounter unfamiliar species and to conservationists concerned with their impact on native biota'.

CIBC/IIBC addressed the challenging task of cataloguing all published records of natural enemies, and published these in two multi-volume series, each covering 25 years, building on the abstracting activities of the IIE. The first 25 years covered 1913–37, and were published between 1943 and 1965 (edited by WR Thompson). The second 25 years, 1938–62, were published between 1971 and 1982 (edited by B Herting). After this the task proved too great and, although an update was produced in 1989 for publication in 1987, the lack of financial support or return meant that the effort had to be abandoned. Nevertheless, the 50 years that were catalogued remain valuable.[145]

1982: The mealybug pest of mango and citrus – another hidden virtue?

Research by CABI scientists helped to control the mealybug, *Rastrococcus invadens*, a serious pest of mango, citrus and other fruits in West Africa. The biological control of *R. invadens* is one of the most successful examples over the last 30 years. Analysis showed that the savings in a very poor part of the world greatly exceeded costs. The project demonstrated excellent cooperation between organizations and countries, and has produced some very good science to support the concept of CBC.

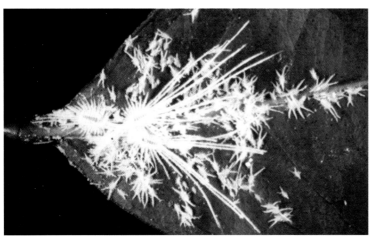

Rastrococcus invadens colony. ©CABI

Gyranusoidea tebygi. ©CABI

In 1982 the mealybug, later to be described as *Rastrococcus invadens*, was discovered in the West African states of Ghana, Togo and Bénin, where it was a serious pest of mango and citrus. Breadfruit, banana and species of *Ficus* were also being severely attacked. Although indigenous predators and a small parasitic wasp attacked the mealybug, they had little impact. Mealybugs reached vast numbers on the leaves and fruit of hosts, coating them with the white of their massed bodies; they weakened plants by direct feeding, puncturing the plant cells and consuming sap, and produced large amounts of honeydew which dropped to the leaves below, promoting the growth of saprophytic fungi. The thick, black layer of sooty mould caused a drastic reduction in photosynthetic capability, worsened by the premature drop of mature leaves. Yields of mango and citrus plummeted, effectively to nothing in some areas. These crops provided energy and vitamin A and C sources, especially valuable for children living in an area where up to 20% of infants die before the age of 5. In fragile economies where locally produced mango and citrus fruit supplemented income for many, the economic impact was devastating. In Togo, and many other West African countries, village life is centred on particular trees, and the mango tree is also used for medicinal purposes.

Biological control appeared an obvious measure. IIBC was contracted by FAO to search for suitable natural enemies, with the aim of releasing them in Togo. This collaborative work involved IITA in Bénin, amongst others.

The mealybug was presumed to have been introduced, but was then an unknown species. When found previously in India and South-east Asia, it was mistaken for *Rastrococcus spinosus*, a closely related species. Scientists from the CABI station in India began work in mid-1986, finding *Rastrococcus* spp. to be widely distributed, but only of local importance and short duration. The complex of natural enemies seemed to maintain good control over the mealybugs. Two primary parasitoid species were supplied to CABI Bioscience for further study in the UK; both were new species and were named *Gyranusoidea tebygi* and *Anagyrus mangicola*.

Following assessment in the laboratory and in the field, *G. tebygi* was shipped to Togo in October 1987 for mass rearing. In November 1987, the first releases were made; by May 1988, parasitism was recorded up to 15 km from the release sites and the mealybug was effectively controlled in the immediate area of the release. During 1988 the parasitoid was released and established in four other experimental sites and, within 12 months, the parasitoid had spread 100 km from the initial release point, where *R. invadens* was under control. Soon after the introduction of *G. tebygi*, 50–90% of the mealybugs in the release area were parasitized. After 8 to 9 months, low densities of the pest confirmed that the parasitoid had successfully adapted to the environment and was controlling the mealybug. Before the introduction of *G. tebygi*, *R. invadens* had attacked many species of plant but, following introduction, reduced population densities resulted in fewer food plants being used by the pest, with only mango, citrus, *Ficus* spp. and the ornamental bush, frangipani remaining as major hosts.

The project proved a major success, rapidly controlling the mealybug. It still occurs, over a wide area, but has been kept at economically acceptable population levels by *G. tebygi* and *A. mangicola*. Losses in citrus and mango production in Togo alone were estimated at between US$2.0–3.5 million per annum, and this loss was mostly reversed within 3 years of the introduction of *G. tebygi*. The original project cost around US$175,000: over 20 years this represents a cost–benefit ratio of over 200:1 for one country alone.

The science of biological control was evolving. Insect parasites and, to a lesser extent, insect predators had an excellent record as BCAs and were still in 1982–83 the most widely used beneficial organisms. They were crucial in the control of the cassava and mango mealybugs.

By that time, progress was being made with other categories of biotic agents, most notably pathogens of insects and weeds. In the light of this trend, in 1984 a pathologist, Harry C Evans, was appointed to develop projects against both invasive weeds and arthropod pests. Evans had wide experience in tropical plant pathology, having carried out screening for *Parthenium* rust in Mexico in 1982, and had a personal interest in insect-attacking fungi. He investigated plant pathogens as weed BCAs and assisted CIBC entomologists encountering insect diseases. It was the beginning of a brilliant career with CABI.

Work by the Institute in 1982–83 focused on coffee green scale in Papua New Guinea (PNG). There were a 'surprising number of parasites and predators' in East Africa, believed to be the area of origin of scale pest. Contacts with the Kenya Coffee Research Foundation led to a request that CIBC assist in the study of a new scale insect pest, *Icerya pattersoni*, which was causing concern. A German technical team on Cape Verde was supplied with parasite cultures from Trinidad, where excellent results in control of the diamondback moth, a pest of *Brassica* crops, had been reported. Nevertheless, the moth has proved to be a stubborn pest. A virus active against the moth has been investigated.

Datuk Rahman Anwar Syed (1932–2009)[146]

Datuk Rahman Anwar Syed was born into a Muslim family in the village of Alawalpur, Punjab, India. His father, Major Dr Abdul Majeed, was a doctor in the British Indian Army and a renowned malariologist. After the 1947 Partition of India his family moved to Pakistani City. Syed played a leading role in the Pakistan television drama, *Lagan Apni Apni*.

Syed's first job, in 1962, was teaching zoology at Gordon College, Rawalpindi. In 1968 he joined CIBC to work on the biological control of fruit flies. After his doctoral studies, Syed was posted by the CIBC to Sabah, Malaysia, where he gained a measure of notoriety for his work that led to the doing away with certain insecticides through the use of a virus to control palm leaf-eating nettle caterpillars. Leslie Davidson, then Chairman of Unilever oil palm plantations in Malaysia, hired Syed to investigate the possibility of oil palm pollination via insects rather than, as conventional wisdom had it, solely by wind or by hand. Syed's field and laboratory research in Cameroon showed that the most efficient pollinator of oil palm was the weevil species, *Elaeidobious kamerunicus*. It was approved for importation and brought to the plantations of Malaysia in 1981, and dramatically improved palm oil production, ending the costly and time-consuming practice of hand-pollination, and speeding plantation expansion. A colourful account of Syed's character and travels to West Africa is provided in an extract from *Planters Tales*.[147]

For his contribution to Sabah and Malaysia's economic and social well-being, the Malaysian state of Sabah bestowed upon Rahman Anwar Syed the honorary title of Datuk. In its first post-release year alone, *E. kamerunicus* was calculated to have increased Malaysian oil palm production by approximately US$370 million. It is now used throughout the world.[148]

Syed remained active in entomological consulting and in business until his death, founding, owning and chairing Nourbiz Pvt Ltd, a Pakistani snack food company responsible for the well-known Korneez brand. He died at his home in Islamabad after a long battle with cancer.

Dr Rahman Anwar Syed Rises to the Occasion: an extract from *Planters Tales*, by Mahbob Abdullah

" As I stood in the laboratory in Cameroon where Dr Rahman Anwar Syed did his study, I knew that work worth millions would be lost if he blew his temper. I had seen him flare up before, although he was all right as long as he had his way. Now I had brought two entomologists and the Malaysian plant quarantine chief to check on his work. He had spent many months studying the insects in the Unilever oil palm plantation. Would the insects be safe enough to bring back to Malaysia? I watched as the entomologists peppered him with questions. "

Dr Rahman Anwar Syed was a famous entomologist. He had left his home in Pakistan to work for CIBC, based in London. For several years his work took him to Sabah, where he showed how to use a virus to kill nettle caterpillars that ate the palm leaves. The planters were grateful because it did away with insecticides. Now Unilever had engaged him through Leslie Davidson, the Vice-Chairman of Plantations, to study the role of insects in pollination of oil palm. He was asked to find out why natural pollination of oil palm was bad in Peninsular Malaysia, and worse in Sabah, while in Cameroon in West Africa the bunches were big.

In turn, Unilever was acting on behalf of the East Malaysia Planters' Association, which had agreed to pay for the study. If all went according to plan, and if the government agreed, the insects could be brought to Malaysia. I had persuaded Leslie Davidson that I should go to Africa with the scientists.

'The visitors need my help', I wrote. Two of them were ladies, Mrs Kang Siew Ming, head of plant quarantine in the Ministry of Agriculture, and her colleague Mrs Zam Karim. The third was Dr Tay Eong Beok, the Deputy Director of Agriculture in Kota Kinabalu.

Leslie Davidson was not convinced that I should go until I wrote, 'There is also the issue of Dr Syed and Dr Tay'. This was the clincher. Many planters believed that the two did not get on. Dr Syed was a big figure, with thick hair and a clipped moustache, and when he was upset he would stop smoking his pipe and stare for a long time at you. He could be very cutting. Dr Tay was a tall, taciturn man who was a very private individual. Slow to anger, he could be as hard as the Sabah billian wood. He was also an entomologist, and he could stop the project.

Dr Syed was a handful when he started the study in Pamol Kluang during the time I was estate manager. He did not compromise on anything, from the brand of microscopes and torchlights to the size of the car he wanted for his use. I met Dr Syed only rarely. He was often up in the palms at night. He said to me one day, 'There is an insect that already pollinates your palms in Peninsular Malaysia. It is *Thrips hawaiiensis*. But it is a weak flier.'

'What were you doing up in the trees all night?'

'To see if there are any other creatures. Only earwigs, ants and rats.'

Elaeidobius kamerunicus adult male. ©CABI

'Cobra?'

'No. They are scared of me.'

He went on to do the study in Sabah, and his next stop was Lobe estate in Cameroon. There he did several months of work and completed his report. Now in the laboratory, he explained about the *Elaeidobius* insects. They ate only oil palm pollen and when they landed and fed on the male flowers, the grains would also stick to their bodies. Often these insects would also land on female inflorescence, which had the same aniseed smell. While looking for food they would crawl and leave a trail of pollen. The result was an excellent bunch development that no manual pollination could match. 'The best insect we can use is *E. kamerunicus*', Dr Syed said, 'although there are two other insects, *E. subvittatus* and *E. plagiatus*. We can see them in the field.'

We saw a male flower in anthesis. The weevils were there, covered in pollen like gold dust. Then Dr Syed took us to the tall palms, and climbed a ladder to a receptive female flower, and came down again. 'You can see them.'

Mrs Kang was the first to climb, a lady of energy and determination, and supported by a couple of fronds, she watched the weevils landing on the flower. Zam followed her. She was a silent listener, and preferred to take notes and form her own judgement. Dr Tay climbed and took photographs. Dr Syed showed the team that the insects did not feed on coconut or cocoa or any crops. Sweeps were made over bushes for the presence of the weevils. None were found. 'It is clear the insects are host-specific', Dr Syed said. Dr Tay remarked, 'We have not seen other types of palms'. Dr Syed said, 'At Bamenda in the highlands, there are other palm species. But it is a long way away.'

'I want to see them.' I looked at Dr Syed. 'We will go there', he said.

The next day we drove on a hard road to Bamenda, a cold and muddy place. My body ached. After Dr Tay was satisfied that there were no insects on those palms, we journeyed back to Lobe again the next day. Over lunch in a roadside restaurant, at Ngkongsamba, we were tired and getting edgy. Dr Syed gave us another glimpse of his nature;

'I have always learnt that you should insist on what you want. Unfortunately, the Managing Director at Lobe thought I should settle for less. He gave me an old car. It did not work well. So l used a bicycle. When he was having breakfast every morning on his veranda I cycled in front of his house, very slowly. After three days he gave me a new car. But my office was small. So I sat under a tree. It took only two days and l got the office I wanted.'

Dr Tay smiled, even though it was not the way he would have played it. But even as they shared a big red mango after lunch, I could sense the tension between the two men. It did not lead to any explosion between the two, however, even up to the time we completed our programme in London.

Dr Syed had arrived in Kuala Lumpur with a box of *E. kamerunicus* for quarantine by Mrs Kang. The insects were finally released, the first batch being in Mamor Estate, Kluang, and supervised by Mrs Kang. In Sabah Dr Tay and the Director of Agriculture, Dr Aripen Ampong gave their permission, and the insects were released in Pamol's Tungud Estate. The insects multiplied rapidly. Fruit set improved and palm oil and kernel production increased. A year later, the pollination teams were disbanded. Costs went down. The East Malaysia Planters' Association refunded Unilever the costs of the study; and presented a gold Rolex watch, studded with diamonds, to Dr Syed at a dinner in his honour.

When I next met him, Datuk Dr Syed was ebullient. But he was still not satisfied. 'We have more work to do', he stared at me, 'if we can find the funds. The *subvittatus* and the *plagiatus* are still in Africa. We should reunite them with our oil palm here. They complement the *kamerunicus*. You will get even better fruit set.'

1984: The Institute's headquarters relocate to Silwood Park in the UK

Greathead, who was then Assistant Director, moved from Farnham Royal to Silwood Park in 1981, and the centre started to grow under his leadership. There was a technical assistant and a visiting scientist, Richard Hill from New Zealand's Department of Scientific and Industrial Research working on the biological control of gorse. The UK unit was also managing staff posted to detached project duties. Dave Moore was recruited and posted to St Lucia to work on coconut mite, and then Peter Ooi was recruited to work on cocoa pod borer in Malaysia, leading in due course to the Malaysia Station. The LUBILOSA programme, which started in 1991, was run entirely from the centre,

Institute of Biological Control, Silwood Park, Ascot. ©CABI

and in the 1990s project programmes in Colombia (Peter Baker) and West Africa (Charles Williams) were also run from the UK.

A belief that good science was the way forward lay behind the recruitment of Jeff Waage from Imperial College as Chief Research Officer in 1987. The aim was to evolve the Research Stations programmes within a more integrated science strategy – one that, according to Waage,[149] 'enabled the Institute to build its own solid strategic research programme while remaining able to service the evolving of long-term sponsors like Canada, USA and New Zealand, [and to] build the underpinning activities that allowed us to become independent of this fire-fighting activity and to grow'. The Leverhulme Fellowship scheme, was established in 1925 to support research and education scholarships. The scheme produced useful research with applications to biological control. An inclusive approach to the integration of biological and non-biological control technologies (IPM) led to links with the experts in pesticide application in tropical countries at the College's International Pesticide Application Research Centre (IPARC). CABI invested in the building and greenhouse infrastructure in order to handle both low-risk and high-risk pathogens, allowing the Institute the opportunity to further enhance its role as a third-country quarantine centre. High-profile pathology projects could be undertaken, including those against the desert locust and the rubber vine weed described below. The quarantine facilities at Silwood Park also meant that staff and students based at a UK university were able to study tropical pests.

The new building was completed in 1988, comprising the Institute offices, laboratories and quarantine facility, together with CABI's Library Service based on the combined Imperial College and IIE libraries, creating arguably one of the three most important entomological libraries in the country, later renamed the Michael J Way library. In the 21st century, in one of CABI's more regrettable decisions, the IIE library was disposed of as a cost saving – although a portion was moved to the new Bioscience site at Egham; some was sold, but much was simply thrown away.

Also in 1988, Nick Mills was transferred from the European Station to be the first Scientist-in-Charge of the UK Centre. Greathead became Director of the Institute in 1989, on the retirement of Bennett, and continued to develop the UK Centre with strong links to Imperial College. Professor MS Swaminathan opened the new building and glasshouse complex in 1989. Mills left in 1990 and Matthew Cock was transferred back from the Kenya Station in 1991 to replace him.

1984: The Institute opens in Malaysia

Whilst the Institute operated a sub-station in Sabah from 1969 to 1974 (see above), a Permanent Station in Malaysia opened in 1984 with the recruitment of Peter Ooi. It evolved into an important regional centre for CABI with responsibility for CABI's relationships with its member countries in the South-east Asia and Pacific region; special relationships with donors in the region, including Australia; and it had a development responsibility for CABI's links with China.

Its research history reflects a typical pattern: growing its own biological control portfolio with support from the Institute's headquarters; exchange of BCAs with other centres and partners in the Institute's network; and trials of natural enemies, parasites and parasitoids. It

Participants identifying thrips and leafminer pests, Universiti Putra Malaysia (UPM), Malaysia as part of APEC's Re-entry Workshops to build capacity and knowledge in diagnosis and surveillance. ©CABI

built expertise in the field of IPM and FFS – with staff from the UK and Kenya, it helped to transfer the FFS concept from Asia to Africa. Some of its staff had particular expertise in biological control of the white fly and diamondback moth.

In 1986 the Malaysian Station had three scientists: Ooi (Entomologist), LG Kirton and MW Tan (both Assistant Entomologists). Three projects were under way:

- investigations on natural enemies of the cocoa pod-borer (*Conopomorpha cramerella*) in South-east Asia for the East Malaysia Planters' Association – began in 1984;

- introduction of the oil-palm pollinating weevil (*Elaeidobius kamerunicus*) to Sri Lanka for the Sri Lanka State Plantations Corporation, a project started in 1986, following the Institute's earlier success with the weevil's introduction to Malaysia (see above); and

- control of *Rastrococcus invadens* in Togo for FAO, in partnership with CIBC UK and India.

The Station helped farmers develop more cost-effective and environmentally sustainable practices. In 1994–96 it ran an Asian Development Bank (ADB)-funded technical assistance project on farmer-participatory IPM of highland vegetables (mainly cabbages) in Luzon Island, Philippines. Lim Guan Soon was the Project Coordinator, and FM Laigo was the local project leader. Farmers adopting the recommended practices reduced their pesticide use by 80%, while obtaining similar or better crop yields and higher profits compared with those who did not.

By 1995, the focus of the Malaysian Station was testing and implementing IPM methods for cotton in China, India and Pakistan through benchmark surveys, on-farm research and demonstrations. Results in all three countries indicated that IPM plots yielded higher than farmers' practice plots, and that high levels of insecticide applications induced higher populations of whitefly, and also sometimes cotton bollworm.

Weighing and loading cotton in Pakistan. ©CABI

Plans were also being finalized in 1995 to improve and extend the facilities of the Institute's station at the Malaysian Agricultural Research and Development Institute (MARDI) campus near Kuala Lumpur. The building was partly funded by FAO, and the CABI Institute was to provide facilities for an FAO crop protection specialist. Personnel included the Scientist-in-Charge, Lim Guan Soon, an IPM Coordinator, S Ramaswamy, a scientist (Janny GM Vos, taking over from H van den Berg), a research assistant and two clerical officers.

In 1996, the Station was involved in an IPM component of a World Bank-financed Agricultural Rehabilitation Project in Vietnam. It included evaluation of the role of natural biological control of pests in vegetables, especially Brassicaceae, which led to the use of a biological control method for *Plutella xyostella* on cabbage and the development of curricula for the training of trainers and FFS in IPM of vegetables.

More details on the Centre's activities are given in Chapter 9.

A network of international linkages

The Institute created an enduring network of international linkages. SP Singh (formerly Director, Project Directorate of Biological Control, Bangalore, India) describes the evolution of CABI's links with India. From when he was a postgraduate student in Russia, Singh had harboured a desire to meet the 'stalwarts of biological control from CIBC'. His opportunity came in 1984 while working in Bangalore as a Project Coordinator of the All India Coordinated Research Project on Biological of Crop Pests and Weeds, as he describes:

" *When I met Dr Greathead, then Assistant Director, CIBC, I eagerly explained the activities and the progress of work and also put forth the expansion plan of the project to coordinate research, transfer viable technology on biological control of important crop pests and weeds and to serve as a nodal agency for introduction, exchange and conservation of BCAs at national level. He listened carefully and offered several suggestions, and told me that such a type of expansion requires a lot of public funding.* "

In the years that followed, 'collaboration and interactions with CABI improved' and continued to flourish after the formation in 1993 of the Project Directorate of Biological Control, with its 16 coordinating centres and laboratories. The association led to joint CABI–ICAR workshops and many other meetings and seminars involving CABI staff – indeed, some became regular visitors and collaborators.

The views of Singh reinforce those of Waage, who describes the Institute, its network of Research Stations and their 'secure and supportive' partners such as the Indian Directorate, as a 'beautiful and unique international system', a network which enabled the Institute to 'do exploration in one part of the world, quarantine in the UK or with partners who had it, and introductions in another part of the world using our Stations or local partners'. And according to Waage 'this was because the Institute was a flexible, un-bureaucratic, intergovernmental organization – and very unique as such'.

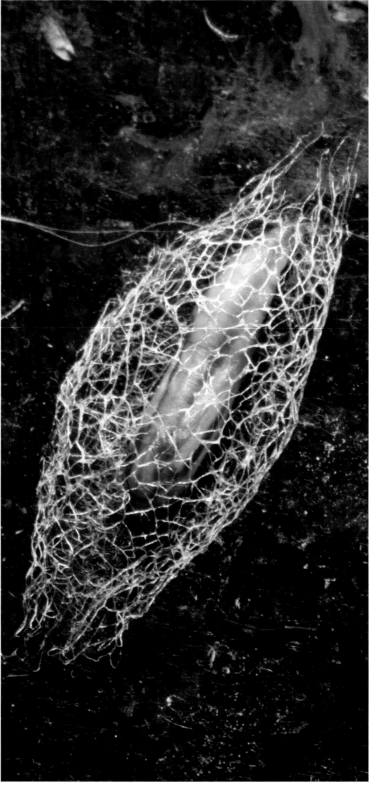

Diamondback moth (*Plutella xylostella*) pupa in its cocoon, Courtesy of Crown Copyright FERA. ©SPL

Environmental awareness: a double-edged sword for biological control

Increasing environmental awareness had had a double-edged impact on biological control: potential environmental as well as economic non-target effects of introduced BCAs were seen as significant; meanwhile, the emergence of IPM, in response to the overuse of pesticides, was leading to increased adoption of biological control as its cornerstone. Thus countries with little experience of biological control were starting to make introductions of BCAs, both for CBC and formulated as biological pesticides. However, there was a risk of all this getting out of hand. A warning bell was rung in 1983 by Francis G Howarth, who pointed out[150] that the euphoric press coverage of CBC of the early 1980s was analogous to the coverage of broad-spectrum chemical pesticides of the 1940s and 1950s. Howarth's main concerns were with biological control projects of the earlier part of the 20th century, and also some continuing practices in his own State of Hawaii. CABI's standing as a leader in biological control and expert on invasive species with the environmental community, including the IUCN, helped it to meet Howarth's concerns head on.

The late 1980s and 1990s: The Institute scientists champion properly regulated biological control

Following a seminar given by Bennett at the World Bank in 1981, CIBC was commissioned to review opportunities for biological control in developing countries. This was done by Waage, who was then at Imperial College, and Greathead. They say[151] that they presented the case at a London IUCN meeting in 1988 for the introduction of adequately screened biological control to 'an audience inclined to consider all introductions as undesirable'.

Institute staff presented their case at a range of conferences and seminars. In January 1990, Greathead participated in a UNDP/NORAGRIC (United Nations Development Programme/Department of International Environment and Development Studies) Workshop on Health and Environmental Impact of Alternative Control Agents for Desert Locust Control, specifically presenting on the regulation of pathogens. Waage, whose intellectual strengths are renowned, in October gave a keynote address on the future of biological control in Canada, heralding the formation of the Canadian Forum for Biological Control. He also spoke at a workshop on Ecological Foundations of Sustainable Agriculture, organized by CABI at the Royal Society, for policy makers and donors.

They recognized that there were real dangers from the indiscriminate movement of BCAs across national and ecological boundaries. The cactus moth, *Cactoblastis cactorum* had been successful in the biocontrol of cacti in St Kitts Nevis, and was subsequently and deliberately introduced to other Caribbean islands and spread on its own, or accidentally to others, until in 1989, when it became established in Florida. Here it was considered a pest, threatening indigenous *Opuntia* spp. cacti. It was already spreading through Georgia to Mexico, an important centre of endemism for *Opuntia* spp. (i.e. some cacti are unique to that area). Introducing the moth was the right decision for St Kitts Nevis at that time (1950s), but today the risk of spread and potential non-target damage would be carefully evaluated before any introduction.

The Institute took the lead in introducing rules for safe biological control. Around 1989, the Institute and the International Organization for Biological Control (IOBC) approached FAO to propose an international code of conduct. FAO commissioned the Institute and Michael Way, an advisor to FAO on IPM, to prepare a discussion document. A worldwide consultative process led to the development of the code as an International Standard for Phytosanitary Measures (ISPM) of the International Plant Protection Convention (IPPC: an international treaty for protection of plant resources), under the guidance of Gerard Schulten of FAO and with support from Greathead, culminating in its endorsement by FAO member countries at the end of 1995 and formal publication in 1996 as ISPM No. 3.

An assessment of ISPM No. 3, by Kairo, Cock and Megan Quinlan in 2003[152], described its publication as timely: in many developing countries the economic and social factors influencing biological control decisions tended to be more concerned with economic and food security issues than impact on indigenous species. They wrote:

> *It is those mostly developing countries that had recently started or have an opportunity to use biological control who benefited most from ISPM No. 3. Previously, there was little guidance available to these countries and none with the international authority. It gave them increased confidence to proceed, based on the assurance that they were following international standards and procedures. It has provided a good basis for facilitation of regional projects and dialogue between countries facing similar problems.*

ISPM No. 3 was revised and republished in 2005.

CABI's eventual success in obtaining approval in 2010 for the introduction of a BCA against Japanese knotweed vindicated its persistence in arguing the case in careful scientific terms. A scoping study entitled 'The potential for the biological control of aquatic and riparian weeds in the UK' for the Environment Agency identified the knotweed

Japanese knotweed emerging through tarmac in the UK. ©CABI

(*Fallopia japonica*) as the target with the most potential for CBC. It is worth noting the long time frame associated with this and other biological control projects is an issue of concern to organizations such as CABI without the assurance of long-term funding beyond contributions from member countries and promises of core support from aid agencies that, between them, account for just 10% of CABI's costs.

IPM training and implementation

A number of IPM projects were initiated by the Institute throughout the 1990s. For example, a regional cotton IPM project in China, India and Pakistan trained 437 plant protection staff and about 1000 farmers and, on farm research, showed that 'cotton yield and net income can be significantly increased and toxic chemical insecticides reduced substantially when IPM practices are adopted'.

Weed biological control in Australia

Australia has a long and successful history of biological control, with BCAs released against over 60 weeds since 1920. CABI claims a role in one of the biggest success stories for CBC in Australia in recent years: control of the rubber vine (*Cryptostegia grandiflora*) following the release of the rust pathogen, *Maravalia cryptostegiae* in 1995.[153] Before the release of the rust pathogen, rubber vine was described as the single biggest threat to natural ecosystems in tropical Australia. The plant was threatening the biodiversity of Australia's unique tropical riparian flora, quite literally smothering native eucalyptus forests and severely degrading pastureland.

It proved to be one of the most successful biocontrol programmes ever carried out against an invasive weed. Originally predicted to take 10 years, the rust delighted farming communities and CABI bioscientists, who led the project, by bringing most of the weed under control within 7 years. Benefits to agriculture have conservatively been put at US$300 million.

Although this made headlines in Australia, it followed many successes over the years, including water weeds such as salvinia (*Salvinia molesta*), water hyacinth (*Eichhornia crassipes*) and water lettuce (*Pistia*); rangeland weeds such as Paterson's curse (*Echium plantagineum*), the giant sensitive plant (*Mimosa invisa*) and ragwort (*Senecio jacobaea*); and weeds of cropping systems including skeleton weed (*Chondrilla juncea*), which had invaded wheat-growing regions of south-east Australia.

Madagascan rubber vine. ©CABI

Carpet of rubber vine over Eucalyptus forest, Australia. ©CABI

1998: The Institute is merged along with the three other Institutes into CABI Bioscience

Waage, who had been appointed as Director of the Institute on Greathead's retirement, believed that as a result of the merger the work of the Institute would be 'substantially enhanced by closer coordination with biosystematics expertise in nematode, fungal, bacterial and insect BCAs, and by the addition of groups involved in biological management of plant disease and nematodes and the management of insect pests by entomophilic nematodes'.[154]

His confidence appears to have been vindicated by the view of the Science Review in 2009, that some 10 years later CABI had 'an excellent reputation for its expertise in identifying and for developing biologically based systems for the control of invasive species, pests and diseases'. CABI's continuing work in biological control is described in 'The Modern CABI' (Chapter 11).

With the merger of the four Institutes in 1998, the Bioscience Centres were endowed with wider responsibilities: to represent CABI Bioscience and to support its field research. In 2001, these CABI Bioscience Centres were created as 'profit centres', with delegated authority over their own revenues and expenditures, encouragement to seek out new, self-funding programmes and charged with an objective to generate contributions to CABI's overhead costs. After 2005, they became known as CABI Regional Centres. As we shall see in Chapter 11, the challenge became one of how to ensure the retention of the best features of the centrally led, science-based programme and, at the same time, to benefit from the undoubted advantage of freedom and enterprise that derives from delegated authority.

Biological control in the service of conservation[155]

In the 1990s gumwood (*Commidendrum robustum*), the endemic national tree of St Helena (i.e. found only there), was in danger of extinction because of an alien insect, Orthezia scale (*Orthezia insignis*), which is native to South and Central America, but is now widespread through the tropics. It was accidentally introduced into St Helena in the 1970s or 1980s, and became a conspicuous problem when it started feeding on gumwood in 1991. Gumwood once formed much of the extensive woodland that covered the higher regions of the island, but was by then restricted to two stands of around 2000 trees.

At least 400 gumwoods had been lost by 1993. *Orthezia* damages its host primarily through phloem or sap feeding, but the colonization of the honeydew that it excretes by sooty moulds has a secondary effect through reduction of photosynthesis. Because *Orthezia* can feed on many plants, and large populations could be maintained on other hosts such as lantana (*Lantana camara*), it spreads easily to the relatively rare gumwood tree. Gumwoods are susceptible to *Orthezia* and, if nothing had been done, it is most probable that gumwood would have become extinct in its natural habitat.

CABI Bioscience assisted the Government of St Helena in carrying out a biological control programme against this pest. The predatory coccinellid beetle, *Hyperaspis pantherina* had been released for the biological control of *O. insignis* in Hawaii, four African countries and Peru. Substantial control was reported after all releases. Accordingly, *H. pantherina* was obtained from Kenya, which was then cultured and studied in CABI Bioscience's UK quarantine. When subsequently released in St Helena, it rapidly established and did indeed control *Orthezia* on gumwoods. This is probably the first case of biological control being implemented against an insect in order to save a plant species from extinction.

Biological control in support of the economy

It is generally accepted that biological control programmes can have a high economic return on investment. Support for this proposition is provided in the following CAB Abstract.

Hyperaspis pantherina. ©CABI

Return on investment: determining the economic impact of biological control programmes. McFadyen, R (2008) In: *Proceedings of the XII International Symposium on Biological Control of Weeds, La Grande Motte, France, April 2007*, pp. 67–74.

In 100 years of weed biological control, few economic impact assessments of biological control programmes have been undertaken, and all were successes. Yet, biological control is still largely paid for by governments, who need proof of the return on their investment. Cost/benefit analyses can also be used to rank biological control against other management methods. A recent economic impact assessment of all weed biological control undertaken in Australia since 1903, including successes and failures, demonstrated annual benefits of $95.3 million from an average annual investment of $4.3 million, a cost/benefit ratio of 23:1. Even with the enormous economic impact of the prickly pear success excluded, the cost/benefit ratio of all other programmes was 12:1. The benefit came from 17 successful programmes: two, which are usually considered failures, in fact returned strongly positive benefits because small reductions in the weed problem nevertheless resulted in considerable cost savings. The scarcity of economic studies has many causes: long period from commencement to full field results; difficulties in assigning monetary values to biodiversity and social impacts; and difficulties in assessing impacts of biological control. The Australian study demonstrated the importance of obtaining baseline economic data before starting biological control and at intervals during the agent release period. Seeking advice from economists at all stages of a programme must become as routine as consulting statisticians.

Prickly pear cactus. ©iStockphoto

Biological control of pink hibiscus mealybug in the Caribbean[156]

Pink hibiscus mealybug (*Maconellicoccus hirsutus*) is native to parts of Asia, but has been introduced to other parts of the tropics. It was first reported from Grenada in 1994, and subsequently spread to at least 25 territories in the Caribbean region. The mealybug attacks a wide range of plants, particularly those in the family Malvaceae. Important hosts include ornamental hibiscus (*Hibiscus rosa-sinensis*), blue mahoe (*Hibiscus elatus*, an important indigenous watershed tree in Grenada), samaan (*Samanea saman*), teak (*Tectona grandis*), soursop (*Annona muricata*) ochro (*Abelmoschus esculentus*), sorrel (*Hibiscus sabdariffa*), cotton (*Gossypium hirsutum*), cocoa (*Theobroma cacao*) and citrus (*Citrus* spp.). Damage to these crops was often substantial, including loss of fruit, defoliation and death.

Hibiscus mealybug was the subject of a successful biological control programme in Egypt, is the target of ongoing augmentative efforts in India and was fortuitously controlled in Hawaii when it was introduced with its natural enemies. CABI Bioscience worked with the Government of Grenada to introduce a narrowly specific encyrtid wasp (*Anagyrus kamali* Moursi).

The risk of non-target impacts associated with the introduction of *A. kamali* was seen as minimal, in contrast to those of a ladybird predator of mealybugs, *Cryptolemus montrouzieri*. The programme planned by CABI Bioscience and FAO with the Ministry of Agriculture, Grenada, focused on *A. kamali*. However, it soon became apparent that the political and social pressures to solve the hibiscus mealybug problem were so great that other BCAs, including *C. montrouzieri*, were being demanded irrespective of the greater associated risks. Other agencies moved to introduce *C. montrouzieri*, and Grenada immediately agreed to this. Both BCAs became established and good control in most situations was rapidly achieved. The programme was considered an outstanding success.

The experience in Grenada facilitated a regional programme with support from FAO and the affected countries, which enabled CABI Bioscience to work with other Caribbean and mainland countries to rapidly implement biological control when the pest reached them, thereby minimizing the impact on their economies. Biological control, in the context of IPM tools, is now an accepted strategy for pest management in the region.

Biological control: the published record

From 1961 to 1977, 18 volumes of *The Commonwealth Institute of Biological Control Technical Bulletin* were published, a house journal of research results. These were printed in India under the editorial guidance of Simmonds.

Between 1960 and 1989, ten *Technical Communications* of the CIBC were published, covering Australia (two volumes), Canada (four volumes), South-east Asia and the Pacific, Africa, western and southern Europe, the Commonwealth Caribbean and Bermuda, and New Zealand. The reviews were compiled by scientists from partner organizations or by CABI staff. These reviews remain key literature for biological control practitioners.

An irregular series of Miscellaneous Publications of CIBC was started in 1969 with the *Proceedings of the First International Symposium on Biological Control of Weeds*, held at the Europe Station in Switzerland. There were eight such publications until the series ceased publication in 1975.

The First International Symposium on Biological Control of Weeds was largely instigated and organized by Helmut Zwolfer and Dieter Schroeder of the CIBC Europe Station, having been held in Delémont, Switzerland in March 1969. This series of symposia has evolved into the 4-yearly cycle of International Symposia on Biological Control of Weeds. In April 2007 the 12th Symposium was held at La Grande Motte, near Montpellier, and once again CABI published the proceedings. This time, four CABI staff were on the scientific committee, two on the editorial board, 16 attended and gave ten papers, eight posters, were involved in organizing two workshops and won the prize for the best poster. Modelled on the Symposia on Biological Control of Weeds, a similar series of symposia was started on the biological control of arthropods in 2002 in Hawaii. The second was organized by CABI Switzerland at Davos, Switzerland in 2005. They have, in turn, become central to the science of arthropod biological control.

Following the closure of the East African Station and Greathead's appointment as Assistant Director, the intention was that David Girling – also from the former East African Station – would run a new Kenya Station. In 1979, however, while negotiations on the Station continued, Girling became Information Officer, initially based at CIE in London, and then at the UK Silwood Park centre. *Biocontrol News and Information* (BNI) started in 1980. Following Girling's retirement in 1996, it continues today under the freelance editorship of Rebecca Murphy (ex-IIBC Kenya Station), and includes review articles, news and abstracts.

Opposite: pink hibiscus flower. ©iStockphoto

THE INFORMATION BUREAUX

The adventures in the first decades of the 20th century of CABI's founding entomologists, mycologists and parasitologists and the voluminous research outputs of the new breed of biologists of which they were part, demanded new approaches to publishing of research findings. These were made possible by the information science and communications technology revolution that began with paper abstracts in the first decade of the century and had become an Internet phenomenon in its last decade. Throughout the last 100 years, CABI has faced the challenges at the leading edge of that revolution. It has also found innovative ways to make information available to those who need it most in developing countries.

Introduction

At the centre of CABI's history is the abstract of published research findings, carefully worded, using controlled terms, written by experts. An abstract is intended to tell the story of a published research paper and, in a single paragraph, provide background, the essence of the article (or its main findings) and its implications for further research and potential application. CABI's abstracts illustrate the history of the applied life sciences since 1910, providing: the backdrop to CABI's story over the one hundred years; the context for CABI's research and development services over the period; and they also point to the value of CAB Abstracts as an historical record. As the science progressed, so did CAB Abstracts' recording of it: some new inventions such as the electron microscope, and developments in molecular biology, enhanced CABI's experimental research. Seminal abstracts are shown throughout this chapter, both to display the changing art of abstract writing as it has been practised for 100 years and to illustrate the changing science. In some cases only the title of the abstract is given.

Neave drew attention to the need for improved uniformity in nomenclature in biology, which highlighted the critical importance of ensuring that scientists were talking about the same species by giving it a unique name. The following text is an abstract of one of his papers, published in 1919, retrieved from CABI's archive. CABI's early experience in abstracting and using controlled language gave it a competitive edge over other databases.

The use of scientific and popular names in economic biology. Neave, SA (1919) *Annals of Applied Biology*, April, 5, 274–275.

Lack of uniformity in nomenclature with regard to both popular and scientific names is the frequent cause of one or the other being omitted in works on economic biology. To alleviate this difficulty it is suggested that a central body be formed, the duty of which would be to collect data as to all recognized popular names throughout the English-speaking world. A list, reducing these names to a minimum, should be compiled, to which as far as possible all authors should agree to adhere. To make comparisons of results possible between those who speak different languages the use of scientific names as well as popular ones is essential. If objected to in the text they may be given as a footnote, as is done in some of the publications of the USDA. An appeal is made for final decision as to the accepted scientific names of the principal animals and plants of economic value, and this would remove one of the chief objections to their use. Care should also be taken in the selection of popular names, and these should be as informative as possible.

1913: The first Bureau – the Bureau of Entomology

The Bureau of Entomology published the first abstracts in the *Review of Applied Entomology* in 1913, a periodical which aimed to give 'a brief summary of all current literature, both British and foreign, dealing with noxious insects whether agricultural pests or disease carriers'. The story of this Bureau and its information services has been told in Chapter 3.

This abstract journal was later split into the *Review of Agricultural Entomology* and the *Review of Medical and Veterinary Entomology*.

1922: The Mycological Bureau

The *Review of Applied Mycology*, modelled on the *Review of Applied Entomology*, was first published in 1922. An early record on mycology related to the discovery of *Penicillium* is given below.

Opposite: early database input. ©CABI

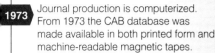

1973 Journal production is computerized. From 1973 the CAB database was made available in both printed form and machine-readable magnetic tapes.

1975 Review Conferences look to self-sufficiency in information services.

1977 A new online service for researchers, DIALOG, is launched.

1978 A CAB Abstracts Word List of indexing terms is produced, which leads to the development of the CAB Thesaurus.

1979 A comparative study[157] of CAB Abstracts and AGRICOLA, a database produced by the US National Agricultural Library, reports an overwhelming preference (70%) for CAB Abstracts.

1987 Centralization of information services at the new CABI headquarters in Wallingford, ending the association of the individual Bureaux with British research institutions, and with CABI's Entomology, Mycological and Parasitology Institutes.

1989 CABI, CTA (the Technical Centre for Agricultural and Rural Co-operation) and FAO co-organize an International Crop Protection Information Workshop, which leads on to the Crop Protection Compendium and subsequently to further compendia in forestry, animal health and production and aquaculture.

1990 As scientific interest in biotechnology grows, CABI introduces a new series of books on biotechnology in agriculture, adding to the already extensive list in the CABI books programme.

1993 CABI acquires the Bureau of Hygiene and Tropical Diseases.

Alexander Fleming discovered an antibacterial substance in the fungus *Penicillium notatum*. This was the first antibiotic discovered and is still in use today. Before this time there were few effective therapies against common bacteria, and many people died from infections we regard as trivial today. The filamentous fungi have yielded several important classes of antibiotics, including the cephalosporins.

On the antibacterial action of cultures of a *Penicillium*, with special reference to their use in the isolation of *B. influenzae*. Fleming, A (1929) *British Journal of Experimental Pathology*, 10, 226–236.

The author records a series of observations on a strain of *Penicillium rubrum*, which produces a filterable substance with well-marked antibacterial properties, active against some bacterial species, but not against others. Among the sensitive species are staphylococci, haemolytic streptococci, the pneumococcus, the gonococcus, and bacilli of the diphtheria group: among the insensitive species are *Bact. coli*, *Bact. typhosum* and other members of this group, *B. anthracis*, the enterococcus (*Str. faecalis*) and the influenza bacillus. A striking series of results are recorded showing the usefulness of this substance in obtaining relatively pure cultures of *Haem. influenzae* from nasopharyngeal swabs. The antibacterial power of a culture of the *Penicillium* in ordinary nutrient broth reaches its maximum in about 7 days at 20°C. After 10 days its activity diminishes, and almost disappears after about 4 weeks. The active substance ('penicillin') is relatively thermostable; it is not affected by boiling for a few minutes, but its power is markedly reduced by boiling for 1 hour in alkaline solution; autoclaving for 20 minutes at 115° C practically destroys it. For use in selective media, the substance is used in the form of a crude broth filtrate. This may be incorporated with the melted agar, or other medium, immediately before plates are poured; or a few drops may be spread over the surface of the plate, after it has been inoculated from a swab. The crude filtrates lose their activity after being stored for 10–14 days at room temperature; but if the alkaline reaction, which develops during the growth of the mould (pH 9), be adjusted to pH 6.8, the filtrates are far more stable (exact figures not given). W. W. C. Topley.

The story of this Bureau, and its information services and colourful characters, is described in Chapter 4.

The *Review of Applied Mycology*, first published in 1922, was later split into the *Review of Plant Pathology* and the *Review of Medical and Veterinary Mycology*.

1927: The bureaux blossom

In the early 20th century, the volume of research output from the Institutes, and from science generally, grew beyond what a specialist researcher could readily keep up with. The success of the abstract journals in entomology and mycology led, in 1927, to agreement that eight new Bureaux be established: soil science; animal health; animal nutrition; animal genetics; plant genetics; pastures and forage crops; horticulture; and agricultural parasitology (helminthology). The individual stories of these and three later bureaux, their contribution to science and their characters will be told shortly.

The Imperial Conference considered whether the eight centres should be at one place or at different research institutes involved in the particular subjects. They chose the latter, so that officers of the bureaux would not become 'detached abstractors'. According to Norman Jones,[158] this was an 'excellent way to start an activity, relevant to the particular science [and was] sized and financed to purpose'.

Governments accepted this recommendation, agreed financing and set up an Executive Council, responsible directly and equally to member governments, which started work on 1 April 1929 and the eight bureaux in the following months. These arrangements did not immediately affect the older Bureau of Entomology and the Mycological Bureau, which both took on the title of Institutes. However, an Imperial Committee on Economic Consultation recommended the transfer of administration of the two Institutes to the Executive Council, which happened in 1933. The Bureau of Dairy Science, and the Forestry Bureau were established in 1938, with the Bureau of Agricultural Economics following in 1966.

The Bureau of Agricultural Parasitology

One of the first of the eight new Bureaux, the Bureau of Applied Parasitology, closely followed the models of Entomology and Mycology, as discussed in Chapter 5.

The first volume of the *Helminthological Abstracts* appeared in 1932. It was divided in 1970 into *Animal Helminthology* and *Plant Nematology*. A new journal, *Protozoological Abstracts*, first appeared in 1977.

An early record, digitized in CABI's Heritage project, on the work of the founding Consultant Director (and later Director) of the Institute, RT Leiper is shown below.

Leiper discovered the snail host of the parasite that causes schistosomiasis, allowing the life cycle of the parasite to be pieced together. *Schistosomiasis* is still an important tropical disease today, affecting 200 million people worldwide. This is the first 1915 entry for the discovery of the causative agent of bilharzias, part of a sequence of four records/reports.

Observations on the Spread of Asiatic Schistosomiasis, With a note on '*Katayama nosophora*'. Robson, GC, Leiper, RT and Atkinson, EL (1915) *British Medical Journal*, 30 January, pp. 201–203.

The authors note that from 1852, when Bilharz announced the discovery of *Distomum haematobium* down to 1904, no progress was made in the elucidation of the aetiology of schistosomiasis. At the end of 1913 it was reported that Miyairii of Kiushu had found a reproductive stage of *Schistosoma* in a *Lymnaeus* species. The Commission formed by the two authors left England in February 1914 and was engaged in the work until the outbreak of war in August. The headquarters were at Shanghai. 'The Looss hypothesis of direct infection was set aside in favour of one to the effect that the schistosome conformed in essentials to the life cycle of other digenetic trematodes'. The method employed was 'to submit all likely hosts to an overwhelming infection; the proper host will show a marked, even a fatal susceptibility, while other even closely allied hosts will remain uninfected'. It was necessary first to obtain an animal with such a heavy infection that the eggs could be separated from the faeces with little contamination. After a search of three months a suitable dog was found, the motions consisting almost entirely of mucus and blood crowded with eggs. Our second necessity was to localize a small village with a fairly high percentage of infection amongst the inhabitants, and then study the local molluscan fauna and submit the various species to the 'blunderbuss' test.

The Institute of Biological Control

For details of biological control journals, see Chapter 6.

Working together, apart

The separate Institutes and Bureaux began to work together, under the Imperial umbrella of the Executive Council, in spite of their dispersed locations. For example, the Imperial Parasite Service continued to rely heavily on the support of the Institute of Entomology; and as it evolved beyond insect parasites into an Institute of Biological Control and to embrace pathogens, it worked increasingly with the Mycological Institute. The information Bureaux began to develop common methods and, particularly from the late 1970s, a shared, controlled language from which the CAB Thesaurus emerged. Staff often met under the aegis of their professional union.

Schistosomiasis snail (*Bulinus globosus*), Sinclair Stammers. ©SPL

Placing individual Bureaux within relevant scientific research institutions had its advantages. The CABI Institutes and Bureaux were set to act 'as effective clearing houses for the interchange of value to research workers in agricultural science throughout various parts of the Empire'. They were, according to the Hankey Review (see below), not to be 'detached abstractors supplying the bare bones of information', but people who could easily engage with researchers in their specialist fields. Initially, the heads of the host research institution were made the Directors of the information centres or Bureaux. Eventually, as the Bureaux grew in stature, dedicated Director posts were created and the Directors of the host research centres were designated as Consultant Directors of the Bureaux.

1943: The Hankey Review – the little-understood bureaux system, its characteristics and recommendations for change

Lord Hankey. ©Library of Congress

An insight into the thinking behind the information bureaux, CABI's place in the agricultural world and issues that were to recur until the 1980s, is given by the Hankey Review. In the autumn of 1942 the Executive Council, instead of convening a Review Conference, because of the War, invited a special committee chaired by the Right Hon. Lord Hankey to consider how the Bureaux could be of better service to the British Commonwealth of Nations and, in general, to the UN. It dealt with issues of centralization and subject coverage, which subsequently grew in importance. The reference to the UN was important given the development of the UN FAO for which, contentiously, functions were envisioned that overlapped those of CABI's Bureaux.

The Bureaux's virtues were deeply hidden

The Hankey Review noted that the Bureaux system was little understood even amongst those who regularly received the journals. It observed that Bureaux were added as the need for them was felt; they did not reflect a comprehensive plan, but covered 'nearly the whole range of science in its application to agriculture'. As constitutional relations between governments of the British Commonwealth of Nations changed, the Bureaux had too, thus becoming 'an organized system under one administrative control'. However, this 'unity in control and general purpose was not so obvious as it would have been had all the work been started at one time under one organization operating from one centre'. According to the Review, 'emphasis has lain on each Bureau, a centre of information in its own subject, rather than on the whole as an organization covering science in its relation to agriculture'. This emphasis on individuality had 'yielded several practical advantages',

and the links between individual Bureaux and recognized groups of scientists was a 'valuable feature of the system that should be preserved'. However, the Hankey Review also recommended closer working relations between the Bureaux.

The place of the Bureaux – general boundaries of subject areas were clear but should not be watertight

The review considered the place of the Bureaux in the supply of agricultural information. It pointed out that 'Science is not divided into watertight sections in how it affects agriculture, medicine or industry', and so it made sense for one Bureau to cover both human and animal nutrition. In defining scope it argued that 'the general boundary of activities is fairly clear though precise definition is difficult and inadvisable. It is a matter of establishing contacts between groups of centres where their subjects touch'. It concluded that covering the application of science to agriculture and forestry was a sufficiently large and distinct task to justify the existence of the Bureaux, and they should link up with relevant organizations for agricultural economics, medicine or industry as they emerged.

The Committee considered suggestions for new Bureaux in agricultural economics and statistical interpretation of experimental data; plant physiology; and in general husbandry and farm systems. It recommended positive action in the form of a study only on the last of these. On agricultural economics it recommended only that contact should be made with any relevant organization.

The Bureaux should remain co-located with relevant research institutions

The Committee regarded the location of Bureaux at relevant research institutes as 'fundamentally sound', noting these were likely to be visited by scientists interested in those subjects. While in principle 'a Bureau does not form part of the institute at which it is located, and can be transferred to any country, [the Committee had] no transfers to suggest'. It did say that the publications branch of the International Institute of Entomology 'must remain close to the British Museum (Natural History) (BMNH), its host organization'.

Bureaux staff members should interact with scientists to boost exchange of knowledge

The Committee said that each Bureau was 'meant to be a live centre for the interchange of information in its subject' [and that] its officers 'by their work in the Bureaux should obtain an ever-extending knowledge'. This meant that the more opportunities there were for discussion (between Bureaux staff and researchers in the field of work) and seized upon, the more their capacity for help and live interest would develop. It cited examples of links with the Agricultural Research Council, which brought information scientists into contact with researchers from other Institutes; the South American potato expedition arose through contacts made by Penrhyn Stanley Hudson of the Plant Breeding and Genetics Bureau (with the South American Potato Collection) and meetings where he raised awareness of other work on the genetics of potatoes; favourable results on the nutrition of camels in Somaliland arising from a discussion between the Deputy Director of a Bureau and an officer from that country. The knowledge made available to a particular enquirer 'quickly becomes available to others. The information on camels has been used in India; the Indian need for new strains of potatoes has led to them being available for all countries of the British Commonwealth; the close knowledge of work in progress in the UK, which Bureaux officers are getting, should aid them in answering questions from other Empire countries.'

Because of the public benefit, Bureaux should receive journals for free

Because of this public benefit, the Bureaux expected to receive agricultural papers and journals from around the Empire freely. Even though departments of agriculture had from time to time been 'inclined to withhold their publications unless an exchange had been agreed', such difficulties were rare once the mutual benefits were appreciated. Sometimes with foreign countries an exchange had to be agreed but, as Bureaux journals gained a reputation for quality, accuracy and promptness, 'authors and editors tend, of their own volition, to send to the Bureaux copies of their papers and journals'. Sometimes, however, receipt of journals, such as those from Russia, was spasmodic. The Committee urged greater use of microfilm as a means of distributing abstract journals.

The Hankey Review and the three Institutes

The Committee made just three recommendations on the Institutes: (i) the Publications branch of the Imperial Institute of Entomology might best be relocated to the Imperial Institute's Building; (ii) the liaison in medical mycology between the Imperial Mycological Institute and the Bureau of Hygiene and Tropical Medicine should be brought to the notice of agricultural, medical and scientific research organizations in the Empire; and (iii) the identification of helminths should not become a function of the Bureau of Agricultural Parasitology, nor should the scope of the Bureau be extended to cover protozoology.

Greater service to the UN and the risk of duplication by the FAO

The Committee noted that the UN Conference on Food and Agriculture allotted functions to a proposed new organization that appeared very similar to Bureaux roles, and a Commission was asked to plan a comprehensive abstracting service covering all agricultural research. In strong language the Committee recommended:

1. The Executive Council (should) approach governments represented (on the Commission), to ensure that the history, work and scope of the Bureaux be brought prominently to the notice of the Commission.

2. Duplication [of the Bureaux] by another official service of information is obviously wasteful. To replace it by a new and untried organization is to throw away its experience and to break that continuity in the methodical compilation of scientific information, which so greatly increases the usefulness of any intelligence service. The obvious course of action is to preserve it as an organization for this particular purpose, retaining its machinery, its characteristics and its administration, linking it up, in whatever way may be most convenient, with the (proposed) Permanent Organization.

Despite the Committee's comments, FAO was endowed with a substantial information function that duplicated some Bureaux functions. CABI's relationship with FAO was characterized by competition and cooperation.

The Bureaux, the Empire and the wider world

The Committee noted that the Bureaux were organized on 'an Empire basis' but operated internationally, as they collected worldwide information; and that its journals were on general sale (i.e. outside of the British Commonwealth). In 1942, most copies of journals were sold to the USA and the Soviet Union. However, services were not available to the UN as much as to the Empire. Publications worth £9000 were distributed to Empire countries, compared with £5300 to 'foreign countries'. It recommended that the Executive Council 'make the Bureaux system better known in foreign countries', especially to achieve sales in the USA, USSR, China, South America and the Middle East. The Committee recognized the limitations of publishing in English, but publishing in other languages was deemed too expensive.

1950s: The Bureaux were expected to generate surpluses for reinvestment

The Bureaux were funded by agreed contributions from several cooperating governments and by sales income from Bureaux publications. There was consistent pressure to decrease the former and increase the latter. For example, the 1946 Review Conference noted that 'Abstract Journals are still priced at pre-war levels' and recommended consideration of the 'advisability of raising all or some of these rates to accord more nearly to present levels'. The standard price for the *Review of Applied Mycology* in 1949 was 40 shillings, the Empire rate 32 shillings and the departmental concession rate (for bulk orders) was 25 shillings (1 shilling = 5 UK pence in today's currency).

By the 1950s, income from the sale of Bureaux publications prompted Review Conferences to seek further sales beyond the Commonwealth. In the early 1960s, however, the full cost of producing the journals was considerably higher than the price being charged to non-member countries, and Information Services' costs were higher than the abstracting services of others in the biological sciences, including BIOSIS and IRL. The differences had many causes, including the higher proportion of title-only abstracts, the percentage of abstracts that were simple copies of author abstracts, the lower number of journals scanned and the lower percentages of foreign-language journals covered by the rival services.

The search for revenues extended to advertising

On the recommendation of the 1955 Review Conference, the Bureaux experimented with advertisements from commercial firms. Advertisements in CAB journals during the years 1955–56 to 1959–60 yielded £3407, and mostly appeared in *Dairy Science Abstracts*.

Information for developing countries

The founding principle of the Bureaux was to make information available to users across what was then the British Empire, and later the Commonwealth. By 1936, *Nature*[159] noted that 'abundant illustration is afforded of the value now attached to them by the number and diversity of the inquiries sent from all parts of the Empire, quite apart from their regular work of preparing and distributing abstract journals'.

The organization continued to review how to do this effectively. The *New Scientist* magazine, commenting in advance of the 1965 Review Conference said:

" *There will be discussion about how the Bureaux can render better service to the less developed countries of the Commonwealth. Some critics have suggested that the information contained in the abstracts and bulletins emphasizes the science of interest primarily to the agriculturally advanced countries. If they do, they merely reflect the distribution of effort in research in progress around the world. It is in any case important that agricultural scientists in developing countries should be informed about sophisticated lines of research. The meeting will however consider whether more cannot be done in the Bureaux to train scientists on secondment from Commonwealth countries in information work.* **"** [160]

The work of more recent initiatives in this area is considered in 'The Modern CABI' (Chapter 11).

Bureau of Animal Health

The Bureau of Animal Health was one of the original eight Bureaux established in 1929 at the Central Veterinary Laboratory at Weybridge. Within 3 years it was publishing the *Veterinary Bulletin* and, 2 years later, the *Index Veterinarius*. Its first Director was William Arthur Pool (1889–1969). By 1955 he had been replaced by AW Stableford, Consultant Director, and M Crawford, Director.

The *British Medical Journal* noted in 1934 that *Index Veterinarius*' 'careful designing has ensured that any particular reference can be traced quickly … So painstaking an effort should need no special commendation to those concerned with diseases of animals who desire information about the literature relating to the subject.'[161]

The importance of the Bureau was emphasized by Sir Bryce Burt, Chair of the India Board of Agriculture and Animal Husbandry, in a report in 1939: 'The abstracts published by the Imperial Bureau of Veterinary Science gave a good summary of recent veterinary researches in all countries … There really was no reason why any veterinary worker should now be unaware of the results of recent research.'[162] In the same year, Edward F Peck, Director of Veterinary and Agriculture Services, British Somaliland (now part of Somalia), wrote:

" *Of the greatest assistance to one working single-handed are the Imperial Bureaux in England. It is not generally recognized that the various Imperial Bureaux have immense resources and knowledge available, and that between them they abstract the agricultural and veterinary literature of the world. A publication of particular veterinary value is the journal of the Imperial Bureau of Animal Health, from Weybridge, England, which will keep anyone, be he G.P., or Government servant,* au fait *with the latest world advance in veterinary science.* **"** [163]

The Bureau was not limited to producing journals. A report on the First Imperial Veterinary Congress in a Canadian journal noted that, as the Bureau received support from the Empire – 'Scientific workers in all parts of the Empire have the right to ask them for information on the particular subjects they study'.[164]

The Review Conference of 1960 asked that the Bureau 'examine the relatively simple methods used by other bureaux for the production of indexes [sic]', given concern over the complexity of approaches at Animal Health'.

Roy Mack's[165] first contact with the Bureau was in 1950, when he became a freelance abstractor while working in veterinary practice. He was appointed as an SIO in 1953 under Pool, and retired as Director of the Bureau in 1987, before the move to Wallingford. He finally stopped abstracting in 2003, in order to concentrate on dictionary compilation. In 1972 he implemented computerization at the Bureau, which 'worked very well'. At that time the Bureau was dealing with 14,000 items of literature a year. As a member of an Expert Panel for Veterinary Information of the European Commission (Directorate General XIII) in the 1970s, Mack proposed a veterinary multilingual thesaurus (English, French, German, Italian; 5000 terms) and oversaw its creation, with publication in 1979. George Philips succeeded Mack in 1987 and served until 1993.

International Bee Research Association[166]

Apicultural Abstracts emerged from a research committee appointed in 1945 by the British Beekeepers Association. Eva Crane was the secretary of this committee. In 1949 the Bee Research Association, with individual and corporate membership priced at £1 and £5, respectively, was formally established with Crane as its Director. She initially produced *Apicultural Abstracts* in her own home and was unpaid. In 1952 *Bee World* became an Association Journal. In 1953, when Mount Everest was climbed for the first time – by a beekeeper, Sir Edmund Hillary – he was given a collection of apiculture books by the Association.

By 1955 the fledgling Association had accumulated over 4 tons of publications. At this point, 53% of its members were from outside the UK and, in 1958, members from other countries were appointed to the Governing Council. The 1960 CAB Review Conference granted £1500 per year to the Association for the abstracting and indexing service in

return for a supply of copies to member countries and the maintenance of 'a proper standard of abstracts'. By 1965 this had been raised to £3500 to allow for the appointment of a full-time qualified assistant to help Crane. The Association also bought Hill House at Gerrards Cross as a headquarters. In 1969 the journal was computerized.

1973 saw 'advances in the computerization of data in cooperation with the Commonwealth Agricultural Bureaux', the beginning of a relationship that would last until around 2000. CABI took over the compilation, digitization and production of the printed version of *Apicultural Abstracts*, and was given permission to add 36,000 records to CAB Abstracts. For the years 1972 to 1996, bee research was averaging around 1200 citations per year. CABI itself has always covered bee research, with around 22,000 records spanning the years from 1912 to 2010.

At the end of 1983 Crane retired after 35 years as Director. She was followed by: Margaret Adey; Vince Cook (1987), who died suddenly a year later; David Francis, who took over as a temporary Director for a fixed period of 2 years; Andrew Matheson (1991); and Richard Jones (1996).

In 2000 *Apicultural Abstracts* became available on CD-ROM. It was at about this time[167] that, because of changes in workflow and in indexing and coding, CABI and the Association agreed to part company. In 1998, financial pressures had forced the Association to cut back on staff. In 2005, further difficulties meant that *Apicultural Abstracts* and *Bee World* were suspended.

1949 *Apicultural Abstracts* first published.

Bureau of Pastures and Field Crops

The Bureau began life in 1929 as the Imperial Bureau of Plant Breeding (Herbage Plants) at the site of the Welsh Plant Breeding Station in Aberystwyth, but moved to the Grasslands Research Station at Hurley in 1949. In 1936 it became the Imperial Bureau of Pastures and Fodder Crops, when all plant genetics was transferred to the Plant Breeding and Genetics Bureau at Cambridge. In 1948 it was retitled again, as the Imperial Bureau of Pastures and Field Crops, expanding its scope to cover all cereals, field root crops, pulses, groundnuts, cotton and other fibre crops grown on a field scale, sugarbeet and sugarcane.

The 19th Annual Report of the Executive Council, 1947–1948, gave in-depth consideration to proposals for new Bureaux, including those on General Husbandry or Farm Systems. *Field Crop Abstracts* was published from 1948, but there was 'undoubtedly an audience, a specialist and scientific audience, interested in general husbandry'. The subject was covered 'pretty completely', by *Soils and Fertilizers*, *Herbage Abstracts*, the *Veterinary Bulletin*, *Horticultural Abstracts* and 'now *Field Crop Abstracts*'. The Council felt, however that it was 'unreasonable to expect anyone to read six abstract journals', suggesting they be collected in a *General Husbandry Abstracts* journal.

Bill Russell joined the Bureau in 1964, learning Japanese so that he could translate agricultural books into English. Previously a psychoanalyst, Russell also wrote science fiction novels, and introduced the concepts of replacement, refinement and reduction into animal welfare research. He could set almost anything he said to a Gilbert and Sullivan tune, and was a panellist on BBC Radio's *Round Britain Quiz*.

Peter Boyle was Director of the Bureau from 1970 to 1985, Robin Lewington in 1986 and Peter Wightman from 1986 to 1993. In 1997 the Bureau's journal *Potato Abstracts* received the accolade of being 'guest publication' on the BBC satirical TV show *Have I Got News For You*, but none of the panellists successfully guessed any of the abstract titles when presented with versions with key sections blocked out.

1948 *Herbage Abstracts* and *Field Crops Abstracts* first published

1952 *Weed Abstracts* first published.

Bureau of Soils

Commonwealth Bureau of Soils. ©CABI

One of the original eight Bureaux, it was established in 1929 at Rothamsted Experimental Station as the Imperial Bureau of Soil Science, but developed slowly. Its journal was operational by 1937 and, in 1938, its total sales from its technical communications, *Soils and Fertilizers* Abstracts, bibliographies and miscellaneous items just exceeded £555. Sales fell to a low of £308 in 1942–43 because of the War, but they had picked up to £1482 by 1946–47; in 1939–1940 a beginning was made in overhauling its 100,000-term index and it prepared a 'very comprehensive subject index which greatly expedites the tracking of information'.[168]

Bureau staff did much to highlight the risks of soil erosion. In 1937, Deputy-Director Graham V Jacks wrote to the *Daily Telegraph*: 'In the United States, where soil erosion is a dominant factor in national life, a recent survey showed that 110,000,000 acres had been converted to desert by erosion,' citing similar instances in Canada, Australia and South Africa.[169] *The Times*[170] noted that 'the lack of literature dealing with the problem has made it difficult for the layman to gather information. This lack has now been made good' by the report 'Erosion and Soil Conservation', published jointly by the Bureau of Soil Science and the Bureau of Pastures and Field Crops.[171]

The Bibliography of Soil Science, Fertilizers and General Agronomy 'was the pre-eminent bibliographic resource for the discipline', followed later by *Soils and Fertilizers*, 'to date the most comprehensive soils abstracting journal', according to Peter McDonald.[172]

Its technical communications continued '"Take-all" diseases of soils' was issued in 1942–43; the 'Spectrographic analysis of soils', the 'Design and analysis of factorial experiments' and the 'Bibliography of soil science, fertilizers and general agronomy', issued in 1948. *The Proceedings of the First Commonwealth Conference on Tropical and Sub-tropical Soils* was issued in 1949, as was 'The Practice of Soil Conservation in the British Colonial Empire'.[173]

In 1955, the Review Conference recommended the new name of the Commonwealth Bureau of Soils (rather than Soil Science, which was seen as being too narrow). The 1960 Review Conference was surprised to learn that the Bureau prepared about 6000 abstracts per year, but that only 3000 were published in *Soils and Fertilizers*. By the 1965 Review Conference the pressure of work had led the Bureau to use 'carefully edited authors' summaries that minimized delays (which the Conference thought might be emulated in other Bureaux). The Conference accepted the Director's view that the *Bibliography of Soil Science, Fertilizers and General Agronomy* should be discontinued but warmly welcomed annotated bibliographies on special subjects.

Eric Craswell was a regular user of *Soils and Fertilizers* when he worked at the Queensland Wheat Research Institute at Toowoomba and at the International Fertilizer Development Centre in Alabama in the USA, saying that the abstracts, although written in tight summary form, 'provided the whole story of the research article including its background, the quintessence of its research findings, and their implication'. Often, primary journal articles carried no author's summary or, if there was one, it was inadequate. He valued the review articles that appeared regularly in the journal and pointed to papers[174] by Dennis J Greenland on interactions between clays and organic compounds in soils in 1965 as 'citation classics' in soils science.

The Bureau developed the specialist journal *Irrigation and Drainage Abstracts*, begun in 1975.

The coverage of the Bureau overlapped with Bureaux in: Pastures, Horticulture and Forestry; and with an outside contractor covering Agricultural Engineering.

Bryan Butters, who was, according to Peter Wightman, a 'keen proponent of productivity',[175] was Director of the Soils Bureau from 1976 to 1989. According to Wightman, this led to the Bureau developing a reputation amongst other Bureaux as being 'quick and dirty'. He was also willing 'to develop new production methods' and it was during his time that the Bureau became the 'guinea pig' for new data entry methods. John Nowland was Director from 1990 to 1996.

1937 *Soils and Fertilizers* first published.

Bureau of Horticulture and Plantation Crops

The Bureau of Fruit Production was one of the original eight Bureaux established in 1929 – it was renamed Horticultural and Plantation Crops in 1938. *Horticultural Science Abstracts* was first issued in 1931; *Sugar Industry Abstracts* in 1939; and *Ornamental Abstracts* in 1975. Sir Ronald Hatton, pioneer of classification, testing and standardization of apple tree rootstocks, was its first Director.

Writing in 1953,[176] David Akenhead, then Director, described how the Bureau accommodated requests from researchers and others. The Bureau began life as the Imperial Bureau of Fruit Production in 1929. It was set up at East Malling, being 'attached to and housed by the well-known research station of that name'. Its aim was to 'discover what research was actually in progress on problems of food production in different parts of the world and to pass on the information to fruit research workers in the Empire'. As requests flowed in, it 'had also

Commonwealth Bureau of Horticulture, East Malling. ©CABI

cheerfully undertaken to pry into investigations on perennial plantation crops, vegetables and flowers; in fact, it now covered the whole field of horticulture and much more'.

He noted that every crop should be covered by the Bureau of Horticulture and Plantations Crops, the Bureau of Pastures and Field Crops or the Forestry Bureau, adding that 'only a very wise man could decide all the knotty points of demarcation between horticulture and field crop husbandry. Potatoes – relinquished this year to [the Bureau of] Field Crops – is only one of many crops thus difficult to classify'. He was pleased to be able to point out, however, that proprietary rights in knowledge of particular crops 'have not yet led to civil war between competing Bureaux and, in any event, the public gets the information from one or other of them'.

The Bureau's work involved perusing some 650 periodicals, about 2500 bulletins, 220 annual reports and numerous technical books; preparation of abstracts in a 'solid rather than snappy' periodical on a quarterly basis. It kept abreast of progress by contact with researchers through personal visits or, more often, correspondence; and responses to enquiries of 'so complex a nature as to demand the compilation for a complete memorandum either in-house or through a contracted specialist'. He gives examples that illustrate the preoccupation of researchers at the time: a request from Melbourne on the chemical composition of vegetables; from Ontario for a leaflet on the nutritive and therapeutic value of fruit and fruit juices; from Cape Town on the making of soil blocks; and one from the National Advisory Service in the UK on the prevention of abscission by the use of hormones and particular chemicals. Replies were listed in a *Quarterly Letter*.

He refers to increasing demand and says that articles of relevance to horticulture occurred in an array of journals covering agriculture, chemistry, botany, physiology, engineering and plant pathology. All this required a staff well-grounded in biology and with the command of a dozen languages or more that 'does not have much spare time'. He concluded: 'Horticulture is a slow, plodding business lending itself but little to spectacular and sudden achievement. And this holds good for the research worker in horticulture, whose useful life may be considerably less than that of some of the plants he studies. Yet even he has thrills.'[177]

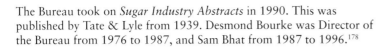

The Bureau took on *Sugar Industry Abstracts* in 1990. This was published by Tate & Lyle from 1939. Desmond Bourke was Director of the Bureau from 1976 to 1987, and Sam Bhat from 1987 to 1996.[178]

1931 *Horticultural Science Abstracts* first published.

1939 *Sugar Industry Abstracts* first published.

Bureau of Dairy Science and Technology

The Bureau of Dairy Science was founded in 1938 at the National Institute for Research in Dairying at Shinfield, near Reading in the UK, changing its name to the Bureau of Dairy Science and Technology in 1956. *Dairy Science Abstracts* was soon published monthly, covering the literature of all aspects of milk including its production and processing, becoming the first Bureau of CAB to cover patents and both production and processing. Speedy publication was considered important: printing schedules were reduced to 6 weeks and, by the early 1970s, before computerization, annual author and subject indexes were published in the December issues of the *Abstracts*.

Just after World War II the founding Director, a New Zealander named WG Sutton, recruited Ernest Mann. Mann had a 40-year career at CABI. This history of the Bureau also relies on an account by Jeremy Davis, who was appointed by Mann as Assistant Director.

> **Ernest Mann (1925–2005)**
>
> Ernest had a long association and collaboration with the library and information division of FAO while he was Director of the Commonwealth Bureaux of Dairy Science and Agriculture in Shinfield, UK. He was involved as a consultant in the development of a prototype information system for emerging dairy industries, and played a central role in the development of the FAO/IDF (International Dairy Federation) newsletters up to 2003. He was regarded as the 'father' of the International Food Information Service. In 2003 Dr Mann received the FAO/AGRIS (International System for Agricultural Science and Technology) silver medal in acknowledgement of his outstanding contribution to information services in Food and Agriculture within IFIS (International Food Information Service)–IAALD (International Association of Agricultural Information)–CABI and FAO/AGRIS, and to the FAO/IDF newsletters. Within IDF, Ernest was for many years a prime mover among a small group dedicated to promoting the interests of dairying in developing countries, and chaired the IDF Group of Experts on this topic from 1996. He was instrumental in developing proposals and soliciting support in the UK for two projects to assist the dairy industries in India and Zimbabwe.

Mann became Assistant Director in 1950 and Director in 1956. He was an active and lively leader. He soon had a full staff and embarked on a number of tours to Commonwealth countries. It was on the first of these tours, returning via the USA, that he observed that many University Dairy Departments in the USA were expanding their research reach to cover food science. This led him to champion *Food Abstracts*, which

in turn led to the establishment of the International Food Information Service (IFIS), described below. Mann retired as Director in 1986.

Abstractors had to rise to many challenges, and one unexpected one was a dairy science paper written in verse. Naturally, the abstractor felt obliged to follow suit.

Ballad: Six years' operation of a test farm for nitrogenous fertilizers in Drenthe, run by the Brink brothers at Vries. Koekoek, F. *Stikstof* 1978, 8(88), 125–136.

This little ballad, in melodious rhyme,
Tells of a farm where in quite a short time
Cows raised their yield by a thousand kg
From five zero six zero to six zero eight three.
Using more nitrogen per hectare of field
Accounted for much of this increase in yield.
On grass so much lusher and sweeter than before
The cows were in clover and ate more and more.
Because of all this effort and trouble
The farm's milk output went up almost double.
Milk fat increased, protein as well;
Within six years, results were swell,
As cash flowed in and milk flowed out
(Though '76 brought problems of drought).
All this goes to show: to keep your income rising,
Take good advice and keep on fertilizing.

Jeremy Davies was Officer in Charge of the Bureau from 1986 to 1987, and Paul Wilson from 1987 to 1994.

1939 *Dairy Science Abstracts* first published.

Bureau of Nutrition

The Bureau of Animal Nutrition (the Commonwealth Bureau of Nutrition from 1972), one of the original eight Imperial Bureaux, was based at the Rowett Research Institute in Aberdeen. From 1929 to 1944 John Boyd Orr, head of the Rowett Institute, was Consultant Director to the Bureau. Lord Boyd Orr went on to found the Nutrition Society in 1941 and become Director-General of the FAO. As indicated in Chapter 1, he was the first to hypothesize the link between ill health and under-nutrition.

A relevant Abstract is shown below.

Family Diet and Health in Pre-War Britain – a Dietary and Clinical Survey. Rowett Research Institute, 1955, 164 pp.

In 1937 Lord Boyd Orr's hypothesis, that much ill health resulted from under-nutrition consequent upon poverty, was put to the test in a dietary and clinical survey that covered 1352 families in 16 districts of England and Scotland. It was a big and courageous enterprise, which broke much

Lord Boyd Orr. ©Uni of Glasgow

new ground and gave rise to a lot of new thinking. It is a pity that almost 20 years elapsed before the report was published, and Lord Boyd Orr himself tends to dismiss it in his preface as 'mainly of historic interest'. But this is misleading, because a part-analysis and conclusions were passed to the Ministry of Food at the beginning of the War to form the basis of the country's food rationing programme and, as such, to father what remains the greatest and most successful feeding experiment of all time.

Much of the thought behind the survey and many of the important conclusions, which were based on the data in the report, have already been recorded elsewhere (e.g. Abstract. 2946, Vol. 12 and Review Article, Vol. 24, p. 1). Now that the meat has been distributed, only the skeleton remains for this report: the detail of the methods used, the tabulated results, the mathematical calculations; and Dr. D Harvey is to be congratulated on his careful preparation of this immense quantity of data after the original survey team had dispersed. It is not easily digestible without more accompanying commentary and one is made too conscious, by the large proportion of space devoted to the description of methods, of the crudity of many of the tools available at the time. But if the detail is sometimes rough, the picture is nevertheless very clear and it is sobering to look back only 18 years to see how high a proportion of people were eating less than they required, maintaining their health while living in a country with one of the highest standards of living in the world. There are a great many important lessons buried in the figures of this report, and for workers in the fields of human nutrition and sociology it will repay many hours of patient browsing. For those interested in child growth, there are the results of a large, and what must be unique, feeding experiment with children, which is not published elsewhere. 'Any investigation into modern conditions and relationships of food, health and income would have much to learn from the Carnegie Survey by profiting not only from its mistakes but also from the boldness and simplicity of the concepts on which it was based' (FE Hytten).

In the editorial of the first issue of *Nutrition Abstracts and Reviews*, Boyd Orr, JR Macleod, University of Aberdeen and Harriette Chick, Lister Institute introduced the demand for an abstracts journal in animal nutrition in this way:

" The recent extension of research in animal nutrition and of the application of its results to human and veterinary medicine and to animal husbandry has been so great, and their reports of work appear in so wide a range of journals, that it has become impossible for anyone to see the whole literature. The research worker is compelled to limit his reading to the aspect of the subject in which he is more particularly interested, although obviously advances in

knowledge in other fields may have a bearing on the problem on which he is working. On the other hand, those engaged in the application of the science of nutrition in human and veterinary medicine or in stock farming find it difficult to keep themselves informed regarding advances in fundamental research upon which improved practice is based. "

A review in 1937 by Isabella Leitch in *Nutrition Abstracts and Reviews, A and B* showed that the average British schoolboy lagged a year behind his middle-class peer in skeletal development.[179] She reported that levels of osteoporosis were much higher in the poor because of poor calcium intake. Leitch was very influential with Boyd Orr. An investigation by Boyd Orr in 1937 further confirmed the link between low income, malnutrition and underachievement in schools. In 1946, after the War, Ellen Wilkinson, Minister of Education persuaded Parliament to pass the School Milk Act. This act ordered the issue of one third of a pint of milk free to all pupils under 18 years.

Leitch was appointed Chief Operating Officer, or Deputy Director, of the Bureau in April 1940. Leitch has been seen as someone who anticipated the development of the systematic or Cochrane review, now seen as a 'gold standard' approach where all the information relevant to a subject is assessed on a rigorous comparative basis.[180] Leitch looked frail, something she attributed, ironically, to childhood malnutrition. She was a supporter of votes for women, and resembled one of Emaline Pankhurst's daughters. She made use of this by offering to lure the police away when this daughter was speaking at a meeting in London.

In 1940 Leitch responded to a request from an officer of the Somaliland Camel Corps about camel nutrition, by writing to correspondents in other countries where camels were used. By analogy with cattle nutrition, she was able to draw up plans for adequate diets that also took account of their need for salt. She says the officer reported that 'his camelmen thought it funny that advice should come from a remote armchair in a country where camels exist only in zoological gardens'.[181]

1931 *Nutrition Abstracts and Reviews (Part A, Human and Experimental and Part B, Livestock Feed and Feeding)* first published.

A journal foreword in 1943–44 notes the problems of war, but also the opportunities.

" During the war, shortage of Bureau staff, of printer's staff and of paper made it impossible to prepare annual indexes, and in the interval we planned to improve the system of indexing. Our aim has been to arrange the index so that all the information on one subject will be found under one heading or only a very few headings to which there are cross-references. "

The indexing system thus developed is in use today across CABI's databases.

The 1960 CAB Review Conference sanctioned 'on an experimental basis' work in the Bureau on classification and coding for machine retrieval and a new service of bibliographies, as a trial for other Bureaux. The Conference also considered an international service for nutrition and food technology, with two or more centres in addition to the Aberdeen-based Bureau, one in Giessen (Germany) and one in the USA. Leitch worked closely with Hans-Diedrich Cremer, Director, Institut fur Ernahrungswissenschaft der Justus Liebig-Universitat, Giessen, who Leitch credits with the initial stimulus and of creating an international awareness of the need for standards and coherence in the indexing and coding of nutritional information. The international group included the Max-Planck-Institut für Ernahrungsphysiologie and Institut für Dokumentationswesen. Cremer presented the case for a classification and coding scheme at the International Congress of Nutrition in Washington, DC in 1960.

A collaboration between the information service centre in Giessen and the Aberdeen Bureau was a step towards a functioning international information service for nutrition. The Bureau received a $15,000 grant from the Rockefeller Foundation for the work in 1964.[182] The code was devised for an 80-column Hollerith or IBM card, showing the evolution of adding metadata to digital information to facilitate retrieval (setting the scene for the modern database structure). The card system was superseded by machine-readable magnetic tapes and the standardization of data input across CABI.

The Nutrition Bureau was one of the last Bureaux to centralize – mainly because none of the existing staff chose to move to Wallingford. AA Woodham was Director from 1979 to 1984, David Fleming 1984 to 1987 and Elizabeth Dodsworth 1987 onwards, until her appointment to a more senior post in CABI Publishing in 1996.

An Abstracting Service for Food Science and Technology

Ernest Mann, the Director of the Dairy Science Bureau, championed the importance of food science and technology abstracts but found that CAB was not prepared to carry the burden alone. Allies in the US Institute of Food Technologists (US IFT) and West German Institute for Documentation Science (WGIDS) helped argue the case.

The 1965 Review Conference was satisfied that CAB could fulfil the need and cover at least meat, fish and eggs. The aim was 'to cover the literature of the product only after it had left the primary producer'. Other CAB journals already covered the primary production literature. The Conference provided £1000 for a literature survey in collaboration with the German Institute. IFIS was set up as a (unincorporated) joint venture with the US Institute of Food Technologists and the WGIDS.

The new Service shared Lane End House with the Bureau of Dairy Science and Technology. The WGIDS developed the computer processing and printing for *Food Science and Technology Abstracts*. Davis and Mann helped develop the new Bureau, which began in earnest in 1968. Davis recalls that 'the computer used was an IBM 1460 with just 8 kilobytes of memory. The computer would process the abstracts and produce the punched paper tape to cast lines of type for the printing of the Abstracts journal'. He says staff members, including two SIOs, were recruited to create a separate editorial team for the Service. There was to be significant overlap of abstracts between the dairy and food science journals, with the Bureau of Dairy Science and Technology providing most bibliographic data and abstracts, in an agreed compromise format, with IFIS generating its own unique subject indexing.

1969 The *Journal of Food Science and Technology Abstracts* was published monthly from 1969.

Centralization of CABI information services, which meant that staff from the Bureau of Dairy Science and Technology moved to Wallingford, left IFIS alone in Lane End House. This led to the formation of IFIS as a separate corporate entity, outside of CABI's structure but with CABI as a member and Dodsworth of CABI as Chair of the IFIS Board.

Bureau of Animal Breeding and Genetics

The Bureau of Animal Genetics was one of the original eight Bureaux established in 1929, and in 1938 it was retitled Animal Breeding and Genetics. It was hosted by the Institute of Animal Genetics, University of Edinburgh, whose director in 1940, Professor Francis Albert Eley Crew, was also Director of the Bureau. The chief executive of the Bureau, however, was JE Nichols, who was titled Deputy Director. In the early 1930s, Frank Fraser Darling was Director – he was later to become a well-known author, naturalist and philosopher, with a particular expertise on the breeding behaviour of deer, gulls and seals. In 1969 he gave the BBC Reith Lectures (entitled *Wilderness and Plenty*), which were an important landmark in how human impact on the environment was viewed. The Bureau moved a few hundred yards to the Animal Breeding Research Organization in 1964.

The abstract journal *Animal Breeding Abstracts* was first issued in 1933. An annual subscription cost £25 and its income grew slowly from £151 pounds in 1934 to £227 in 1940. The Institute's bibliographies included 'Biology of the Fleece' (1931), 'Fur Breeding' (1931), 'Genetics and Sex Physiology of the Rabbit' (1932), 'The works of JC Ewart' (1934) and 'Genetics of Drosophila' (1939). The Technical and Occasional Paper issued by the Bureau in 1939–40 was the landmark 'Animal breeding and genetics'; and in 1945 'Artificial insemination' was published. A further occasional paper on 'The semen of animals and its use for artificial insemination' was in press by the end of 1945.

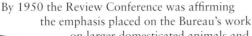

By 1950 the Review Conference was affirming the emphasis placed on the Bureau's work on larger domesticated animals and animal production, and instructing it to be more selective in the fields of genetics and endocrinology to allow emphasis on applied genetics and livestock improvement. By 1955, however, the Conference was recommending that review articles on certain aspects of genetical research on *Drosophila* and small animals should be considered of value to research workers in animal breeding.

Users liked the journals. In 1965 a survey reported high reader satisfaction with *Animal Breeding Abstracts*, the value of review articles and dependence on the Abstracts, especially where library facilities were limited as a reference source for the research worker, appreciation of the wide coverage of subjects within the field of breeding, appreciation of the Book Reviews and the need to maintain quality even if this necessitated price increases.

The 1965 Review Conference report included examples of inquiries received by the Bureau during the year that give something of the flavour of its work: from Tanganyika on the breeding cycles of indigenous cattle, the effects of early breeding on the growth and development of zebu cattle, beef production for zebu cattle, the effects of season of birth on productivity in cattle and the heritability of live weight gain in cattle; from Kenya on possible sources of Merino rams other than South Africa; from Central Africa on centres of research and information on meat quality in Britain; three inquiries from FAO on coconut milk as a semen diluent – information was limited but it has been used in Kenya, and for a bibliography on lethal defects in cattle, on reindeer; from Uganda on progress made in breeding Wiltiper sheep; and from Queensland on centres of research on Charolais cattle in France.

John Turton was Director of the Bureau from 1971 to 1992, and David Lister from 1992. Turton notes that a significant change over time was the decrease in foreign-language abstracting required – in the early 1960s, about 50% of abstracts were based on foreign-language papers, whereas by the 1990s this had fallen to 10% as scientists adopted English as the 'Esperanto' of scientific research to gain a wider readership.

1933 *Animal Breeding Abstracts* first published.

1973 *Small Animal Abstracts* first published.

1980 *Pig News and Information* first published.

Bureau of Agricultural Economics

Abstracting of agricultural economics was late to appear. In the late 1940s a service was launched jointly by the International Association of Librarians and Documentalists and the International Conference (later Association) of Agricultural Economists as an experimental venture, according to Margot Bellamy.[183] The editorial office was set up in Vienna in an Institute of the Austrian Ministry of Agriculture. The

journal was run on a shoestring and as a 'labour of love' by Sigmund von Frauendorfer, whose financial support was disappearing. The future of abstracting in agricultural economics was taken up by CAB, but not without protracted debate at the 1950 and 1960 Review Conferences.

The Interim Review Conference of 1963 recommended that CAB should accept responsibility for WAERSA and that the 1965 Review Conference should consider whether a Bureau of Agricultural Economics should be established. The move from Vienna was completed at the end of 1964. After some consideration of locating the Bureau in India, the move to Oxford was confirmed in 1966. The Bureau was housed in the Oxford University Agricultural Economics Institute. Access to core literature was facilitated by 'close connections with excellent libraries and by donations from private individuals, institutions and publishers'. WAERSA steadily grew in scope, extending from farm economics to wider issues of supply and trade, regional development, conflicts over land use, surpluses and common markets. By the 1980s WAERSA included food policy, food industry, the policy, social and ethical aspects of biotechnology, and the funding and organization of agricultural research.

1959 *World Agricultural Economics and Rural Society (Sociology) Abstracts (WAERSA)* first published.

1978 *Rural Extension, Education and Training Abstracts*, *Rural Development Abstracts* and *Leisure, Recreation and Tourism Abstracts* first published.

The Bureau of Agricultural Economics, in spite of reservations about cutting its links with centres of academic excellence, moved to Wallingford in June 1987. JO Jones was Director of the Bureau from 1966 to 1981, Paul Stonham from 1981 to 1984 and Margot Bellamy from 1984.

Forestry Bureau

The work of the Imperial Bureau of Forestry began in 1938. It was attached to the Imperial Forestry Institute in Oxford, whose library was the principal source of material for the Bureau. NJ Oliphant, Director of the Forestry Institute was also Director of the Forestry Bureau; L Chalk acted as Director for a year and was replaced by Professor HG Champion in June 1940. JWB Sisam of the Dominion Forestry Service of Canada was appointed Deputy Director, or Chief Operating Officer, of the Bureau in June 1939 and served until 1945, when he was replaced by CFC Beeson of CIE and formerly Forest entomologist at the Forestry Research Institute, Dehra Dun, India. By 1948 FC Ford Robertson was Director – he received an OBE for his work in 1959.

1921: Early Record on the Origins, Aetiology and Spread of Dutch Elm Disease

An unknown disease of Elms. Spierenburg, D (1921) *Tijdschrift over Plantenziekten*, 27(5), 53–60.

The disease here described is believed to be entirely new to the Netherlands, and was first brought to the notice of the Phytopathological Service in the autumn of 1919. During 1920, further complaints were received from all parts of the country, so that it appears to be already widely distributed. The examination of the diseased wood indicated that in a few cases the attack began in 1917, but, as a rule, the symptoms were confined to the annual rings of 1918, 1919, and 1920.

In the tops of trees in leaf are dry and withered masses of dead leaves and branches in the midst of the living foliage. The branches are dry, wrinkled, and have a singed appearance, the smaller ones being bent at the tip. The buds for the next year's shoots are mostly small and dried up, and the remaining living foliage dry and brittle. Often the green leaves have dry brown edges. Sections through the wood of the branches and trunks reveal a circle of small brown specks occupying one or more of the outermost annual rings. In the thinner twigs the whole thickness of the wood may be marked by these brown specks, which extend to the tip of the twig. Sometimes large areas of the inner wood of thick branches are dis-coloured [sic] by an infiltration issuing from the brown specks of the outer annual rings. The roots, occasionally the trunk, the dis-coloured [sic] rings, and sometimes the pith of diseased trees may also be marked by large brown spots, darker in colour than the specks in the rings. The walls of the wood vessels and of the parenchyma and medullary ray cells are colored brown. Of the two varieties of elm principally used for street-planting and other ornamental purposes, *Ulmus monumentalis* and *U. campestris latifolia*, the former is the more susceptible to the disease.

The beetle *Eccoptogaster scolytus* (*Scolytus scolytus*) F. was found in many of the diseased trees, except at Oud-Beierland, but the writer thinks that it follows the disease and has nothing to do with the causation of the latter; nor has the cicada, *Typhlociba*, which was found on the leaves and branches. A number of fungi were also isolated from the diseased material, including *Graphium penicillioides*, *Cephalo-sporium acremonium*, and species of *Fusarium*, *Phoma*, *Botrytis*, *Didymochaeta*, *Verticillium*, and *Pestalozzia*. Inoculations were undertaken with the first two of these fungi, hitherto with negative results. The writer is, indeed, by no means satisfied that the disease is caused by a parasite, being inclined rather to attribute it to physiological disturbances due to excessive drought, severe frost, or defective soil conditions.

Cases of one-year-old trees attacked by the disease are reported from nurseries at Oudenbosch, while an average annual loss of 20 per cent. is estimated in nurseries in another locality, but it is not certain that all these cases can be attributed to the disease in question.

Results of Dutch elm disease. ©iStockphoto

The only instructions for treatment, which can be given at present, are to cut away the dead branches, applying carbolineum or tar to the wounds, and to refrain from pruning. Trees attacked by beetles should be painted with 30 per cent carbolineum in May.

Forestry Abstracts was published quarterly from May 1939.[184] Even in 1939–40 it was 'dealing with approximately 260 periodical or series publications representing 39 countries and 15 languages'. Its first technical communication being prepared in 1940 dealt with literature on Forest Fire Hazard Research. A project to distribute a News Bulletin for 247 forest officers within the Empire at an annual charge of two shillings and six pence – producing a deficit of £24 – was judged as 'very successful'. A wartime Technical Communication in 1941–42 was entitled 'Gas Producers for Motor Vehicles' and their operation with Forest Fuels – another 'Wood Waste Utilization'. In 1944–45 Technical Communications included: 'The Application of Meteorology To Forest Fire Prevention' and one on 'Forestry Credit'. In 1946 *Forest Products and Utilization* appeared separately as a quarterly publication, dealing with 'the whole subject of forest utilization and forest technology' and was expected to be of interest to the forest trade and industry.[185] A Technical Communication issued in 1947–48 reflecting changing agricultural practice was entitled 'The Use of Aerial Survey in Forestry and Agriculture' and, in 1948–49, 'The Establishment of Vegetation on Industrial Waste' was published.

Coverage of foreign journals was a key feature of CAB Abstracts. One striking example of the importance of foreign journals was an article on the relascope, which had been published in the German language and might have been missed without the diligent attention of the Forestry Bureau. As shown by the abstracts included below, this invention was to become a major component of forestry research in future years, but might have lain neglected for some time without CAB Abstracts.

1949: Foreign Journals and the Relascope Story

The 'relascope'. Bitterlich, W (1949) *Allg. Forst-u. Holzw. Ztg.*, 60(5/6), 41–42.

This name is given by Bitterlich to an instrument head which he has designed (but which is not yet in production); when fitted on to a suitable stick, it forms a multi-purpose instrument for: (a) Winkelzahl observations, with automatic correction for slope (cf. *For. Abstr.* 10 (Nos. 2314–2316)); (b) finding Pressler's 'Richthohe' (distance from b.h. to the diam. which is 1/2 d.b.h.); and (c) form height and form coefficient. The essential features of the device (which is illustrated) are as follows: A plummet carries at its fulcrum a cog engaging at right angles with a second, similar, horizontal cog. The latter carries two vertical split pins, which pass through holes in a horizontal, detachable frame forming two opposite quadrants, on the arcs of which are graduated scales reading off against a pointer on the fixed head. Into the split pins the Winkelzahl measuring blade fits; this serves to hold the quadrant frame flat against the horizontal cog, and is itself held in position by two round-nosed set screws in the split-pin arms that click into suitable holes in the blade. The blade is readily removed when it is necessary to detach the quadrant frame and change from one scale to the other. Both scales could be fitted to a single quadrant, but the balance would then be impaired. Now: (a) For checking the trees that satisfy a required Winkelzahl, the instrument is manipulated like the stick hitherto used, with the advantage that on a slope the pendulum twists the measuring blade obliquely to the line of sight, so that its apparent length is reduced by the cosine of the vertical angle of observation, i.e. an automatic correction is made for the increase due to gradient in the distance between observer and tree. The stick used is 70 cm long, giving a distance of 70.7 cm from the observer's eye to the axis of rotation of the quadrants and measuring blade. The blade has a width of 20 mm, with two square projections giving spans of 14.1 and 10 mm respectively between their outer and inner corners. Using these 3 scale lengths, the corresponding multipliers for obtaining basal area per hectareare: 2, 1 and 1/2. (b) To find the point where diam. = 1/2 d.b.h., the observer stands at such a distance that the 20 mm scale exactly matches d.b.h., and follows the stem upwards until its apparent diam. exactly matches the 10 mm scale.(c) The quadrants form a special kind of hypsometer using the same similar triangles as Faustmann's mirror hypsometer, but giving modified readings on the arc scales. Distance from the tree is fixed optically by the observer's standing as in (b), when the distance is d.b.h. X 35/35. Tree volume as given by Pressler's Richthohe (R) is 2/3 g (R+m/2), where g = basal area and m = breast height. Now 2/3(R + m/2) corresponds to the form height h.f. and h.f./d is obtainable, using a suitable scale on one of the quadrant arcs, as the difference between l(sub(1)>-the reading to the point where diam. = 1/2 d.b.h. and l2)- the reading to the (estimated) point m/2. Multiply by d then gives form height. The second quadrant scale is graduated to give values multiplied by pi/4, so that the form coefficient K = pi/4.h.f./d (cf. For. Abstr. 10 (No. 2333)) is obtained directly as L(sub(1-l2, and has only to be multiplied by d3 to get the stem volume. Such measurements of form height and form coefficient should be especially useful in the mountains, where large errors arise when using ordinary volume tables, owing to wide variation in stem form. Final appraisal of the practical utility of the instrument must wait until it has been manufactured and fairly widely used.

The relascope: Bitterlich's Spiegel Relaskop (1965). Finlayson, W. Feinmechanische-optische Betriebsgesellschaft m.b.H., Edinburgh & Salzburg, UK & Austria.

A practical guide, describing both the standard and the wide-scale model and how to use them for various mensuration tasks, including recent developments (cf. F.A. 30 Nos. 6178–6179). A table of reciprocal values for mean b.a. (required for the determination of stem numbers) is appended.

The 1955 Review Conference stated that 'an expansion of the Bureau is very desirable so that it can cope more adequately with its wide field and the rapid increase in the literature to be dealt with'. However, *Forest Products and Utilization Abstracts* had been discontinued, although it reappeared in 1978 as *Forest Products Abstracts*. Growth continued into the 1960 Review Conference as, for example, the Centralized Title Service, which had started experimentally in 1951, proved to be a self-paying proposition and was endorsed to continue, with provision for a scientific assistant having been agreed 'to permit time for the Director and Assistant Director to deal with the more difficult abstracting'. The Bureau

had high quality standards and, by 1965, it was being told by the Review Conference to consider whether less exacting standards and more use of outside abstractors might enable 'better coverage and quicker publication'.

1939 *Forestry Abstracts* first published.

1978 *Forest Product Abstracts* first published.

An account of work at the Bureau[186] by William Finlayson, Director (1976–86) gives a flavour of changing times. When he began, the Bureau 'didn't even have electric typewriters' and that when he left 'everything was thoroughly computerized, and the age of the Internet had arrived'. There was 'a major reform in the typing room. As seemed quite natural and normal in those days, the abstractors did their work in manuscript, and everything was then typed before being sent to CAB headquarters for printing'. The Forestry Bureau 'had about half a dozen highly skilled typists [who were] still working with manual typewriters (but also) did not have proper typists' desks.' After a discussion with CAB headquarters this was put to rights.

Finlayson says he 'did not at any time have much to do with CAB's other arms'. Forestry, according to Finlayson, 'was concerned solely with the collection, recording and dissemination of information'. It was a 'sort of lodger in the Commonwealth Forestry Institute, itself attached to Oxford University [but] it had a very effective symbiotic relationship with the Institute's library'.

Finlayson described the abstractor's routine, which 'began when the latest issues of one of the journals that had been allocated to you landed on your desk and you looked through it to see which of the articles ought to be recorded in *Forestry Abstracts*. The answer could be all of them, none or anything in between. [This] depended on a great deal of special knowledge and intelligence'. In Finlayson's view 'these preliminary aspects of selecting what was worth recording, and generally rejecting and replacing [any] misleading [authors'] summaries [was crucial]'. Finlayson felt that 'ideally, the abstractor would know any precursors to the article being abstracted and perhaps direct plagiarism [and of] simple repetition'.

Early abstracting. ©CABI

Finlayson decided to drop the Oxford Decimal Classification for Forestry, a pre-occupation of his predecessor Percy Beak (see box, below) because 'the allocation of a series of numbers to every abstract employed two people full time when only a little logic was needed to see that the numbers had become unnecessary when the database could be searched by keywords, especially when these were made available in what was then the new CAB Thesaurus'.

The Bureau was later headed by Cliff Elbourne and Ken Becker.

Percy Beak: Director of the Commonwealth Forestry Bureau from 1970 to 1976

By William Finlayson

Percy Beak was a remarkable man, a village lad from West Oxfordshire who had started his working life as a 'laboratory boy' in the Botany Department of the university, but who, largely on the strength of a talent for learning languages and a capacious memory, had climbed the ladder, step by step, until he was recognized both as a truly great technical editor and as an authority on all the scientific literature that touched on forestry, particularly in English, Russian, German and French – in something like that order: his first wife had been Russian. I remember having once asked Professor Anderson at Edinburgh about how he dealt with his information needs, when he replied: 'I never even try to look things up, I just ask Percy Beak'. Beak was Assistant Director of the Bureau by 1948.

I had no hope of emulating Percy, but I would have been less concerned by that thought if I had been able to look into the near future. I might have realized that the great need was going to be not so much for his traditional, if almost superhuman, scholarship, as it would be for a willingness to adopt the new technology that was soon flooding in. He had in fact spent a vast amount of energy, and invested a lifetime's worth of intellectual capital, on a dead end, his 'Oxford Decimal Classification for Forestry', which gave numerical values to a great many mental concepts, as an extension of the Dewey system. It was largely to be swept aside, for our purposes, by the computer's ability to deal in words, not just numbers, which – it is now hard to recall – was something that very few people had foreseen.

Bureau of Plant Breeding and Genetics

This Bureau, one of the original Bureaux established as the Imperial Bureau of Plant Genetics (for Crops other than Herbage) in 1929, was attached to the then Plant Breeding Institute in Cambridge. *Plant Breeding Abstracts* began in 1930. It was renamed the Bureau of Plant Breeding and Genetics in 1938. RO Whyte noted that it was only through the work of the Bureau that key publications on vernalization from the Soviet Union became known to an English-speaking audience.[187] The Bureau helped organize collecting expeditions, such as the British Empire Potato Collecting Expedition to the Andes in 1938, to supply plant breeders with genetic material to assess for disease and pest resistance. Jack G Hawkes went on the trip, and continued to work at the Bureau until 1948. Starting

in Lima, the expedition travelled 9000 miles through Peru, Bolivia, Argentina, Ecuador and Colombia, finishing 8 months later in Panama. It collected many samples of seeds and plants, as well as 1164 potato 'accessions' (samples). At Machu Picchu, the collectors were overawed by the archaeology and missed discovering a rare species of potato growing next to their hotel (it was found a few years later by local professors, who named it *Solanum hawksii*, in honour of Hawkes).[188]

In 1945–46 the Bureau issued a Technical Communication entitled 'The new genetics in the Soviet Union', reviewing a controversial issue of the previous decade: the 'new genetics' of Trofim Lysenko and his school, which had repudiated Mendelism, and in its place established a new genetics, founded on the authority of Darwin and Michurin, and elaborated from his own experiments. He condemned the work of Mendel, Bateson and Morgan as clerical, bourgeois-capitalistic and fascist. Written by the Director, PS Hudson and RH Richens, it was, no doubt, a timely review. An example below from 1950 indicates how some authors used political rhetoric in scientific papers.

The government soil map of the U.S.S.R. and present-day problems of Soviet soil mapping. Gerasimov, IP (1950) *Pochvovedenie*, pp. 195–206.

A soil map of the USSR is being prepared on a scale of 1:1000, 000 by reducing regional maps on scales of 1:50,000 to 1:200,000 or detailed kolkhoz maps on a scale of 1:25,000. It will serve as the basis for national agricultural planning. It will be constructed on the principle that the soil is a dynamic, evolving organism and to show how its biological evolution can best be controlled in the interests of mankind. All traces of reactionary bourgeois influence which regards soil as a static geological deposit incapable of change by man and which is inextricably associated with inhuman fascist-racial theories and imperialist exploitation will be eliminated from the map.

Hudson's role included visiting agricultural scientists in the Soviet Union, and in 1954 he told *The Times* that a particular trip 'struck me as exactly like a Chekov play,[189] with much vodka and nothing happening when it was meant to happen. He noted that Russian scientists felt very isolated from their counterparts in other countries.

MS Swaminathan FRS. ©CABI

Delivering the keynote address at the 1990 Review Conference, MS Swaminathan said that he 'first came into contact with the Commonwealth Agricultural Bureaux in 1950' when he commenced his studies for a PhD degree. The Bureau of Plant Breeding and Genetics was 'a mine of valuable information' and *Plant Breeding Abstracts* was the only source of information on the 'extensive research carried out in the USSR on potato'.

Richard (Dick) Hook Richens (1919–84) was Director from 1964 to 1979. He also chaired CABI's Mechanization Committee, which recommended computerization. Richens was a world elm expert, and wrote to *The Times* to comment on 'a magnificent row of hedgerow elms, immediately recognizable as to species and variety' (*Ulmus minor var. vulgaris* (= *U. procera*)) present in George Stubbs' 1783 painting 'Reapers' in the Tate Gallery, London, but removed from a 1785 version of the painting.[190] He noted that such 'elm cliffs' were likely to pass into history through Dutch elm disease, and needed to be celebrated. He was also an authority on machine translation of languages. He emphasized the importance of achieving the right balance of effort between man and machine, which he called 'companionability'. He developed the concept of breaking language down to its basic elements, which he called 'nude syntax', as celebrated in a paper: 'R.H. Richens, translation in the nude'.[191]

Olga Holbek had joined CAB in 1955 and was appointed Director in 1980. She was widely feared among the SIO cadre in the Bureau as a stickler for accuracy. Ray Watkins was Bureau Director from 1987, followed by Shaun Hobbs.

1930 *Plant Breeding Abstracts* first published.

1983 *Wheat Barley and Triticale Abstracts* and *Maize Abstracts* first published.

1989 *AgBiotech News and Information* first published.

1991 *Plant Genetic Resources Abstracts* first published.

The early 1990s also saw the introduction of database subsets on the Spectrum series of CD-ROMs, and the Bureau produced PlantGeneCD, which contained database records on plant breeding, genetics and plant genetic resources.

AgBiotechNet, launched in 1989, was the first of the many CABI Internet resources.

Improvements in communications in the 1970s

From their establishment, the Bureaux were isolated from each other and identified as much with their parent institutes as with CAB, a point reinforced by Finlayson and Wightman. Literature was acquired through the host institution. Many SIOs thought of themselves as a part of the research or academic system and enjoyed mixing with the subject experts, and thereby developed an awareness of the research process and the latest techniques in the field. In the words of one, 'The subjects you covered came alive when you knew some of the leading workers'. Some minor conflicts arose with the hosts when a Bureau was struggling with a backlog and parent institute staff wanted quick circulation of journals, but generally the co-location served the host institution well and ensured that CAB's staff were kept close to their subject field.

There were, however, inefficiencies. Abstracting, indexing and journal production processes were all individual to units with few standard practices and significant duplication of effort. Scrivenor records this

point in his history, *CAB, the First 50 Years*, without elaborating on its implications for efficiency. The Append System enabled copies of records of interest to be sent from one unit to another but, apart from this, cooperation between the Bureaux was limited. Bureaux defended the coverage of their subjects vigorously, but also resented suggestions that only certain SIOs could handle centralized screening, as shown in an 'abstract' of a note from Ernest Mann's 1972 letter on the subject that circulated around the Forestry Bureau:

" Come, pad out your pages and lower your sights!
Mix metaphors freely with other delights!
For centralized scanning, as everyone knows,
Can only be done by the best SIOs
The whole Sub-Committee have taken the view
That the pearls they are casting are not for the few. "

Improvements in communications in the 1970s arose from the formation in 1973 of a CAB Branch of the trade union, the Institution of Professional Civil Servants (IPCS, later IPMS and then Prospect). It did much to improve communication between all staff, with its regular branch meetings and an annual general meeting attended by representatives from all units. It established direct communication between staff and senior management through a Joint Consultative Committee. There were also three staff conferences in the 1970s, enabling information scientists and clerical staff from all Bureaux to meet en masse. Whilst these meetings, which reportedly focused as much on professional as industrial matters, had little direct impact on working practices, they did highlight differences in processes between units and perhaps began the stirrings of 'One CABI'.

Bureau of Hygiene and Tropical Diseases

In 1993, CABI agreed to take over the Bureau of Hygiene and Tropical Diseases, which had been founded in 1908 in London. Its journals included the *Tropical Diseases Bulletin*, first published in 1912, and *Abstracts on Hygiene and Communicable Diseases*, first published in 1926. The arrangement included the Public Health and Tropical Medicine (PHTM) database, and led to the CAB HEALTH bibliographic database, later renamed Global Health, covering all major aspects of human health and disease. CABI had been processing the records produced by the Bureau on a contract basis before the transfer.

Crop Protection Bureau

The transfer of the scientific institutes' information work to Wallingford in 1987 (described in more depth in the next chapter) created the Crop Protection Bureau, which combined entomology, mycology, nematology and weed science (following the transfer of *Weed Abstracts* from the Weed Research Organisation), with Peter Scott as Managing Editor. At the same time, staff working on animal and human entomology, mycology and helminthology joined the Animal Health Bureau at Wallingford.

CAB ABSTRACTS

CAB Abstracts, available on the CAB Direct platform, can reasonably claim to be the world's leading database covering agriculture and the environment, and its scope extends considerably beyond that. The creation of a unified database from the diverse inputs from geographically separated Bureaux was a huge challenge, but enabled the creation of a powerful resource that was much more than the sum of its parts.

1969: CABI looks to computerization

In 1969 a CABI Mechanization Committee suggested that, despite the risk of 'the computer mystique distorting the real usefulness of computers to CAB', that there was a 'prima facie case for considering a plan for computerizing CAB's activities'. At that point, CABI's journals were produced by its separate Bureaux sending manuscripts, often hand-written, to the printers. A report[192] for the committee suggested CABI would benefit by being able to offer more services (such as current awareness, specialist searches, sales of magnetic tapes of data), and that such development was 'essential to the future of the Bureaux'. Reflecting the status of computing at the time, it argued that CABI would not need 'to use a computer full-time.' It also noted that 'the possibility of some centralization of abstracting, though consistently rejected by a large number of CAB staff, is worthy of serious attention'. They quoted from an earlier report by the chillingly named Committee of Council of Indefensible Variations (1965) that suggested this would give more uniformity of input. The Mechanization Committee's recommendations were supported.

1973: Journal production is computerized

Journal production was computerized and, from 1973, a single CAB database was made available in both printed form and machine-readable magnetic tapes: a revolutionary change. According to Wightman, 'CABI developed or adopted a very good structure for its database records. Fields were well defined with good validation of their contents and good validation of field combinations for different record types'. This meant that certain kinds of errors could be detected automatically.

Thus it was that the 'computer system was specially designed to produce CAB Abstracts journals, and to make CAB abstracts available in machine-readable form'. Under the system, each Abstracting Unit sent its abstracts, with bibliographic and indexing details, to the Production Unit, on a standard form. The material on these forms was converted into computer-readable form, read into an IBM 370 series computer, checked and corrected. The system then automatically organized the abstracts into sequence for several Journals according to the all-important subject codes assigned by SIOs. The computer also compiled subject and author indices, on the basis of indexing written for each abstract by the SIOs. Finally, it produced a magnetic tape to control an automatic typesetting machine, which made masters from which the journals were printed.

All references were stored on the magnetic tapes, creating a machine-readable archive and providing the basis for an online retrieval service. Input forms were sent, weekly, by the Abstracting Units or Bureaux to the Production Unit, which then sent these to a 'data conversion contractor'. The contractor created magnetic tapes and returned these to the Production Unit, which dispatched magnetic and paper tapes twice weekly to the 'Computer Bureau'. This Bureau in turn sent the tapes and printouts twice weekly back to the Production Unit for proofreading by 'outside proofreaders.'[193]

The whole process could take up to 56 days. Some 70% of abstracts required no correction, around 25% required one correction and 5% required two or more. And there was a further cycle for printing of the journals from the abstracts computer records, adding a further week to the timetable. To speed things up the final edits were scratched into the Ozalid copies to form the basis of the printed journals. The 'Computer Bureau' in the early days was in the former Mars chocolate factory near to CAB's headquarters at Farnham House.

1974: A civil service study examines cost reduction and production efficiency

According to Wightman, a Civil Service Department Study of 1974 had a bigger impact on the everyday work in the Bureaux than computer-assisted journal production. Commissioned to examine cost reduction and production efficiency, 'the recommendations threatened their working practices, job satisfaction, status and career prospects. Coupled with a new Executive Director (EA Runacres, whose qualities were not always appreciated by staff) this report, in Wightman's judgment, 'marked the beginning of the end for the old Bureaux and the start of the modern CABI. Little happened initially. Bureaux Directors were reputed to have secured their positions at the 1975 Review Conference, making sudden change unlikely but the seeds were sown'. As we shall see, however, this was a temporary reprieve as pressures for efficiency and self-sufficiency mounted.

1977: The Bureaux take the lead in an online search service, database thesauri and CD-ROMs

CAB began an online search service, for researchers. DIALOG, an offshoot of the Lockheed Corporation, hosted the database. People dialled in to an early version of online. It was capable of handling 30 characters a second through an 'old grey terminal and old-fashioned telephone with an acoustic coupler'. CAB ran searches on demand – it took about 6 weeks.

The new online service was launched at the Royal Society, London on 2 February 1977.

Early online DIALOG search. ©CABI

DIALOG was an interactive information retrieval computer language developed at the Lockheed Research Laboratory at Palo Alto, California. In introducing the new service at its launch, John Turton from CAB's Bureau of Animal Breeding and Genetics explained that 'interactive' meant that the user put a series of commands or requests to the computer via a keyboard and obtained a real-time response in the form of hard copy or display on screen.

1979: CABI scores highly in a comparative study of databases

A comparative user study[194] of the performance of CAB Abstracts and AGRICOLA, a database produced by the US National Agricultural Library, conducted in 1979 reported an overwhelming preference (70%) for CAB Abstracts. This arose from CAB Abstracts producing a greater number of hits (that is, references per search), having a policy of covering (only) articles of sufficient scientific repute, together with the presence of abstracts. The analysis also showed, however, that the cost of processing CAB Abstracts was double that of AGRICOLA. The high cost was a recurring theme in the organization's history that drove many of the changes in charging regimes and in cost reduction that feature from the 1950s.

1978–82: The CAB Thesaurus: a key to indexing and search

As Neave, one of CABI's founders, argued in 1919, inconsistency in language usage and scientific terminology is a barrier to exchange of information in the biological sciences. It is also a barrier to effective indexing and literature search.

The starting point for the CAB Thesaurus was the CAB Abstracts Word List (1978), which was a register of the frequency of occurrence of the 25,000 terms used in the subject index phrases of the CAB abstract journals and in the descriptor field of the CAB database. In order to construct hierarchies and to maximize harmonization with other thesauri, particularly FAO's AGROVOC and CEC (Commission of the European Communities)'s thesauri on veterinary science and agricultural economics, many additional terms were needed and many synonyms had to be eliminated. It was originally planned that the CAB Thesaurus and AGROVOC should be developed in parallel, but as the CAB Thesaurus contained some 48,000 terms, it required a longer time scale. Nevertheless, all these thesauri are to a great extent compatible.

The first edition of the Thesaurus was published in 1983, providing for the first time a list of terms, and their relationships with other terms, used for indexing the CAB database. It was published in conventional printed form, in microfiche, on tape and online.

1980: Review Conferences look to self-sufficiency in information services

In the 1970s serious attention was given to the cost-effectiveness of the service. A special Interim Review Conference in May 1973 examined membership contributions and developments in CAB, particularly its information and abstracting services. The Conference made specific recommendations on journal prices and maximizing revenues. A review of CAB's management was commissioned,[195] which recommended the adoption by CAB of 'a rigorous business approach'.

The 1980 Review Conference[196] 'recommended that the Information Service should operate on a self-sufficiency basis, including provision for capital requirements'. Member countries appeared particularly keen to ensure that CAB maximized revenue from sales to non-member countries.

Leading to fundamental changes

This represented a fundamental change for the Information Services: from member country funding, to a cost-effective and self-supporting service, generating surpluses to fund new technology and infrastructure. With reductions in membership income, Information and Publishing Services were also expected to generate increased income to support the whole of the organization.

One approach was to increase prices. Norman Jones, who was Secretary or Executive Director of CAB from 1977 to 1984, recalled that it was clear prices for journals had to be raised 'to take the financial load off member countries,' but noted the apprehension held about such increases and 'the interesting challenge of thinking of a price.' In the end, a judgment was reached based on responses to earlier price increases – the Americans and Russians 'kept on purchasing' – that demand was inelastic because of the uniqueness of the products and the outstanding reputations of the abstract authors. It was agreed that prices would be increased until such time as there was a serious reaction against such increases. Jones observed that whilst there was some drop in orders there were no dramatic reductions in volumes of sales.

In 1981, CAB database processes were updated through the installation of computer terminals, mini-computers and printers at each CAB unit, thus enabling edited abstracts to be entered directly into the database.

CAB Abstracts on CD. ©CABI

Don Mentz. ©CABI

The new data entry system linked 15 input centres to a central computer at headquarters, designed to speed up input and eliminate contractor keyboarding and put quality control in the hands of the originating Bureau. It provided the scope, at least in theory, for greater flexibility in types of data, to facilitate corrections and to allow for semi-automatic production of repackaged journals.

In 1984 CABI introduced database management, using Pergamon and Langtons typesetting, and then finally bringing it all in-house using VAXes and BASIS data management software. CABI went on to make the first CD-ROM (prototype, possibly with Pergamon), then with Silver Platter and Compact Cambridge. CABI subsequently introduced its own in-house typesetting software, mostly for journals but also for some books and other publications, e.g. *The Dictionary of Fungi*, *Pesticide Manual*, *List of Research Workers*, *AMREF* and *UK Pesticide Guide*, some of which were for external customers.

1987: Centralization

Centralization of the dispersed Bureaux to a single location was amongst the most dramatic changes in CABI's history. It was disruptive to staff, many of whom lived significant distances from Wallingford, the site chosen, and CABI lost a lot of good information scientists in the process. It resulted in some cases in compulsory and expensive redundancies, and may have contributed to a crisis in the mid-1980s in the organization's Pension Scheme. It also ruptured the links that the Bureaux had with their hosts' research institutions and with the four CAB Institutes, making it harder to ensure that abstractors stayed closely in touch with the scientific field concerned.

It may have reduced critical mass at the CABI Institutes where, in some cases, abstractors doubled as taxonomists, but it also freed up space for laboratories. With the income-generating Information Services separated off, the Identification Services came under increasing pressure to generate a substantial part of their funding. Identification charges were first introduced for non-member countries and for commercial organizations – and eventually for member countries. All this had implications for the Institutes before and after their merger as CABI Bioscience in 1998.

And yet the process of centralization and their merger into an Information Division went, according to most of those who stayed with CABI, remarkably smoothly. Credit must go not only to Don Mentz, the Director-General at the time and his support staff, but also to the strong attachment felt by many staff to CABI and to the generally constructive attitude of the trade union. Indeed, one union leader at the time of centralization said that she had worked very closely with the Director-General, even though the Bureau to which she belonged had fiercely resisted centralization.

There were also positives. The separate locations had led, initially at least, to different and inconsistent abstracting methods evolving across the Bureaux; computerization and then co-location helped address this concern. Co-location enhanced the cohesion amongst the Bureaux and introduced scope for further integration, rationalization and cost reduction, and a more consistent approach to database production.

'Think Pieces' identify standard procedures and indexing and point to 'One CABI'

In 1989 Mentz commissioned 'Think Pieces' to identify standard procedures and indexing across the database (the focus on 'database' instead of 'abstract journals' would still take some time to be accepted in the language of the editorial processes). There were four think pieces, each led by a member of staff: Backlogs (led by Chris Gordon), Procedures (Elizabeth Dodsworth, who prepared this section), Indexing (Stella Dextre-Clarke) and New Products (Christina Cunliffe).

The 'Backlog' was a new concept within the Information Service. With centralization each Bureau's workload and rate could be seen by all, but also by the centralized Accessions system, managed by the newly appointed Sue Smith, who was highly efficient. CABI now had a tracking system to show how long it was taking for journals to be processed. Timeliness became the mantra!

Operational Procedures recommendations reflected an era where it was not yet the norm for everyone to have a computer on their desk. For example, one recommendation was that SIOs should 'have the choice of keyboarding and/or correcting their own records' and 'full word-processing facilities'.

The Indexing Think Piece recognized, with the greater importance of the CAB Abstracts database as a whole, the increasing importance of using standardized metadata, and focusing on the quality of the metadata and not just of the quality of the abstract and accuracy in documenting other bibliographic information. One opportunity for change was identified that lies at the heart of the modern CABI: 'With our emphasis on developing countries as a main customer base, we have given relatively low importance to our machine-readable products. Now that CD-ROM promises to bring database searches to remote places, the time for improving this means of subject access is ripe.'

Even now, many users of CAB Abstracts in developing countries want CD access, because there are barriers to accessing the Internet: cost, connectivity, reliability of service and high cost of investment in hardware (PCs, printers, service agreements and security).

The Coordination of New Products Think Piece highlighted the existing 'silos' based on the Bureaux structure and recommendations included streamlining the decision-making process within the Information Services, but also highlighted the need to think across the whole of CABI elements of 'One CABI'. It said that senior management, through the Director-General, should establish a policy that new products and services are a necessary part of CABI's development; and because different parts of CABI have complementary skills and resources, a unified CABI approach to new initiatives is appropriate.

Interestingly, new products under consideration, but identified as 'low priority' were: *Climate Abstracts*, along with *Directory of Agricultural Software*, *Acridological Alert* and *Farming Systems Alert*. Those identified as 'high priority' were: *Plant Genetic Resources Abstracts* (PGRA), *Research Trends and Database Coverage*, *Crop Protection Market* and *CAB Abstracts in CDS/ISIS format*. PGRA is still published, while *Conservation Abstracts* was rejected and *Meat Technology* went forward in partnership with IFIS as *Meat Focus International*. This hybrid 'news, views and abstracts' journal was subsequently shed from IFIS's and CABI's portfolios and, after around 15 years, ceased publication.

After the Think Pieces and the 1990 Review Conference, further changes were put in place.

Firstly, five broad divisions replaced the Bureaux structure:

- Crop Protection and Plant Breeding, headed by Peter Scott;
- Plant Sciences – Peter Wightman;
- Natural Resources, Forestry and Economics – Margot Bellamy;
- Animal Sciences – John Turton (to 1993), David Lister; and
- Veterinary Sciences – George Philips.

Then, in 1996, this structure was briefly replaced by the Information Institute – with Scott as its Director and the editorial teams now in two divisions: Plant Sciences and Natural Resources, under a Director, Shuan Hobbs; and Human and Animal Sciences also under a Director, Elizabeth Dodsworth. The Information Institute ceased to exist within 3 years, around the same time that the Bioscience Institutes were merged into CABI Bioscience. The two divisions, however, more or less continued to 2004. After this the Compendium Team became a separately managed editorial unit under Scott, reporting to the Director-General until around 2002, when it was absorbed back into the Publishing Division. At the same time, an overall Operations Group managed all Database Production processes and this group contained, as well as the Editorial Directors, two Quality Managers – Mike Hails and Wightman, and Smith in charge of Accessions. The process of streamlining management in information services continued in 2004 with the management of all editorial and database production placed under one Content Director, Hobbs.

These actions provided the basis for a new, more integrated and commercial organization – transforming CABI's information services into a 'publishing business' – the idea of a modern CABI was beginning to take hold.

The Migration from Print to Online and the Impact that Technological Developments had on CABI's Publishing Programme[197]

Abstract journals

Since CABI's first abstracting journal, the *Review of Applied Entomology* appeared in 1913, abstracting journals and other reviews appeared progressively over the following decades. CABI still publishes 44 individual titles covering very broad subject areas (e.g. *Forestry Abstracts* and *Horticultural Abstracts*), as well as single-crop titles such as *Potato Abstracts* or specialist titles such as *Rural Development Abstracts*. Now all 44 are available as searchable online databases as well, but there is still demand for the printed works. Each abstract journal is a defined subset extracted from either CAB Abstracts or Global Health: the principal sources of publishing revenue and the core products in the overall portfolio.

The emergence of online databases

Computerization meant that CABI's raw data could, for the first time, be delivered to third parties on magnetic tape and loaded into huge databanks alongside similar databases from other producers. DIALOG offered the first publicly available online research service in 1977. Information professionals could now interrogate data stores remotely and download records for further manipulation and processing. As each online system had its own syntax and language for searching its set of databases, and as charging was done by the minute, the task was left to information professionals to minimize costly mistakes in the search string. CAB Abstracts database was put onto the DIALOG platform in the mid-1970s, making CABI one of the earliest online publishers.

Controlled vocabularies

Online databases did not need printed indices, but they did need controlled vocabularies so that the user could guarantee the accuracy of their search results. CABI responded to this need by creating the CAB Thesaurus – a large, controlled vocabulary (now containing over 100,000 terms). Standard procedures and indexing across the database introduced after centralization also proved critical. In 2008 the entire CAB Abstracts database to date was re-indexed using the 2007 edition of the Thesaurus. In today's digital world, resources such as the CAB Thesaurus and standardized procedures are as valuable as ever as a means of sifting and sorting vast amounts of online information.

Personal computers and transfer of datasets

In the late 1980s access to online information remained the preserve of the few, given the expense and need for specialist information retrieval skills. However, personal computers with floppy disk drives and, subsequently, CD-ROM drives, allowed transfer of reasonably large datasets (either with or without associated search tools) from machine to machine. This meant that users could access large databases without having to go online, and anyone with a PC could learn how to become 'information literate'. In the late 1980s CABI launched the first 'CABCD' – the CAB Abstracts database on CD-ROM, produced in partnership with SilverPlatter. Each disk held around 450,000 abstracts, so that the whole database dating back to 1973 could be fitted on to just a few disks. This development revolutionized CABI's online publishing programme, and also meant that top-quality research information could be delivered to libraries in developing countries, where online access had never been a reality. CABI's longstanding training courses in information management offered to librarians from developing countries then explained how to set up a PC with a CD-ROM drive, carry out basic computer maintenance and search for information with the SilverPlatter software, SPIRS.

John Allen with the entire collection of *The Review of Applied Entomology*, CABI's first abstract journal, which fitted onto a single CD ROM. ©CABI

Gradually, library customers shifted away from the pay-as-you-go business model offered by DIALOG and its peers, and towards the fixed-price CD-ROM subscriptions offered by companies like SilverPlatter. CABI added specialist CDs, including the snappily named TREECD, which contained every record ever published in CABI's forestry journals since 1939.

The Internet and the World Wide Web

The arrival of the Internet and the World Wide Web in the late 1990s led to the next paradigm shift in CABI's publishing business. Internet and interoperable databases did away with the need to press quarterly CD-ROMs and ship them around the world. Information could be held centrally and access could be controlled by usernames and passwords, or by IP address recognition. Bibliographic citations could be linked seamlessly to the original journal article on the web, removing the need for CABI to offer a document delivery service. Individuals who did not have an information science background could search scientific databases. These information consumers were, by now, using the Internet in their everyday lives to purchase books or to plan their holidays. Expectations were on the rise! As a result the entire printed backfile of abstract journals were digitized from 1972 back to 1913.

From 2000 all of CABI's primary and review journals were hosted within the Ingenta journals system, alongside other major science publishers such as Elsevier Science, John Wiley and Blackwell Science. Linkage between full-text journals and the bibliographic databases hosted by Ingenta was a key element of this new relationship.

CAB Direct

Whilst CABI still makes use of platforms such as Ingenta, in the late 1990s it took the strategic decision to develop its own online delivery platform, CAB Direct, so that it could offer more flexible access to its databases than that provided by such third-party vendors. This first-generation platform, developed in partnership with Ingenta, was seen as a trailblazer in the industry; very few publishers were then prepared to invest in their own platforms. The third version of CAB Direct, launched in collaboration with Semantico in 2009, has embraced many of today's web technologies, such as user-tagging, RSS data feeds and the inclusion of an application programming interface that enables third parties to embed CAB Direct in their own applications.

Back to the future

At its heart, CAB Direct seeks to do, for today's market, what CABI's abstract journals did for the research scientists of the early 20th century: to deliver a comprehensive and up-to-date database on global agricultural research in a consistent and efficient manner. In parallel with the evolution of CABI's secondary databases has been the development of e-books and reference works, including the Compendium series (see Chapter 11) as a database on crop protection. Whilst CABI has embraced the digital age, in both its back-office production processes and its delivery systems, the only certainty about the future is that change in the publication environment will continue!

CABI AND ITS MEMBER COUNTRIES

Origins of membership

Initially, CABI's first progenitor – the IERC – was an initiative of the Colonial Office, which canvassed the Colonies and the Dominions for their views. Letters from 1909 ask Governors of the Colonies whether they would fund the scheme (annually between about £50 for colonies such as Barbados, Newfoundland and Zanzibar, £100 for Hong Kong and £500 for Northern Nigeria) provided the British Treasury granted £1000 a year. The Office, and then the Committee, were keen to keep the Colonies informed on progress. This attitude, the broad Empire representation on the Committee and reviews by Imperial Conferences formed the basis of CABI's governance, financing and operations.

A unique beneficial intergovernmental form

CABI represented a new form of intergovernmental body based on the view that the UK, and its Dominions and Colonies, might cooperate to deliver scientific and information services. By doing so, it was hoped scientific discoveries to overcome pests and diseases of crops, animals and humans would boost economic development in the Empire. It evolved from Empire to Commonwealth and beyond to become truly international. Its hybrid funding by both fees and membership subscription for services remains unique amongst intergovernmental organizations, as do its governance arrangements of Review Conferences, an Executive Council of member countries and an independent Board.

CABI's unique intergovernmental status has allowed it to build particular relationships of trust with its members and with other international agencies. It has also enabled it to bring its linkages and relationships into its project proposals that complement its technical competencies.

Although it has not always be seen as a benefit by the organization, the decision right at the beginning to divide funding between a common fund (or provide core funding, as it might be known today) and revenues from paid-for services, including the encouragement from its member countries that it should 'maximize its income and reduce its reliance on membership contributions',[198] endowed the organization with a spirit of enterprise that serves it well today in a market-driven environment.

Reliance on membership fees had fallen, by the year 2000, to less than 5% of total income as the absolute level of the fees decreased and as other incomes grew, especially with increased sales of information services to non-members. The low level of untied funding made it difficult for CABI to deliver public goods without charge to member countries and to invest in growth.

Nevertheless, the base level of member country fees has enabled CABI to deliver a basic level of services to least-developed member countries and provide a minimum underpinning to its finances. At least once during its history, supplementary funding from member countries has rescued CABI from financial difficulties: in 1985 special contributions of £500,000 were levied on member countries over the years 1984–85, 1985–86 and 1986–87 to meet a crisis in funding of the superannuation scheme.

These considerations suggest that CABI's membership structure, as it has evolved over 100 years, remains relevant for the 21st century.

Growth in member country numbers

When the Executive Council was established on 1 April 1929, there were 11 member governments or 'territories' represented: Scotland, Australia, England and Wales, Northern Ireland, Canada, South Africa, New Zealand, the Irish Free State, India, Southern Rhodesia and all Colonies, and Protectorates and Mandated Territories (represented by an official of the Colonial Office).

By 1980, after many of the colonies had gained independence, 26 member governments plus the Dependent Territories were represented on the Executive Council: Australia, the Bahamas, Bangladesh, Botswana, Canada, Cyprus, Fiji, The Gambia, Ghana, Guyana, India, Jamaica, Kenya, Malawi, Malaysia, Mauritius, New Zealand, Nigeria, Papua New Guinea, Sierra Leone, Sri Lanka, Tanzania, Trinidad and Tobago, Uganda, the UK and Zambia.

In 1981 a Memorandum of Understanding meant that the UK could recognize the international status of the Commonwealth Agricultural Bureaux for the purpose of a Headquarters Agreement. On 8 July 1986 CAB was reconstituted as CAB International, and the Agreement was signed by the UK Government and CAB International. Thirty member countries signed the Agreement, including six new ones: Brunei Darussalam, Solomon Islands, Zimbabwe and the Dependent Territories of the UK. Of the member countries, Fiji and New Zealand subsequently withdrew. Belize, Hungary, Indonesia, Morocco and the Sultanate of Oman later joined but withdrew.

Since 1986, Anguilla, Bermuda, British Virgin Islands, Chile, China, Côte d'Ivoire, Grenada (in 2010), DPR Korea (in 2009), Montserrat, Myanmar, Pakistan, the Philippines, South Africa, St Helena, Switzerland and Vietnam have joined.

As a consequence, CABI currently has 45 member countries (plus two in the process of joining).

Liaison with member countries

CABI believes that its liaison with member countries has enabled it to keep in touch with international development priorities and to hone its appreciation of national needs. Its main points of contact with its members are through in-country-based Liaison Officers and Executive Council members in London. CABI encourages 'regular communication between Liaison Officers and its regional centres; and it welcomes Liaison Officer contribution to the development of CABI's strategy and activities'.

To enhance relationships with existing and new member countries, regional offices in the Caribbean, Latin America and Eastern Africa were created as adjuncts of the Research Stations of the Institute of Biological Control, and later as semi-independent CABI Centres. A regional office had already been set up in Malaysia, again on the back of a former Research Station.

With a similar objective, in 2007 and 2008 CABI held Regional Consultations for its members in Asia–Pacific, Africa, the Caribbean and Latin America. In addition, CABI established a series of direct dialogues with member countries in each region of operation. These consultations aimed to strengthen understanding of CABI's activities and capabilities in support of international development, and to engage with the regional priorities of member countries. These priorities help to shape CABI's strategic programmes and to establish the particular forms of mutual commitment and financial resourcing required to deliver its mission. The outcomes of the meetings identify regional needs and priorities of work where CABI has relevant expertise, skills and comparative advantage, which CABI addressed and reported back on at the 2009 Review Conference. The seven priorities of focus for members were:

- trade development and good agricultural practices for market access;

- institutional capacity strengthening and knowledge management;

- pests, diseases and invasiveness of biofuel crops;

- monitoring of and adaptation to climate change;

- microbial collections: use and management;

- integrated pest management in relation to high-value crops; and

- technology transfer and exchange between member countries.

At the 2009 Review Conference members were also presented with CABI's forward vision of the Global Plant Health Centre – Plantwise – a global database of plant pests and diseases with the potential to become CABI's long-term strategic focus, defining and shaping all CABI's activities. It would also respond directly to several of the priorities identified through the Regional Consultation process.

Membership benefits and fees

The current basis of membership fees was set by the 1990 Review Conference (RC 1990), and has remained largely unchanged since. In the 1970s, member country contributions were as high as 50% of CABI's operating costs but, by the end of the 1980s, had reduced to approximately 15%. RC 1990 agreed to reduce the total member country contributions to the level of 3% of CABI's operating costs by 1995. The Review Conference of 1999 removed the product discounts and free services that CABI had historically provided to its members. It also set a minimum contribution level of £3000 per annum.

At the 2009 Review Conference members were presented with a paper with an updated structure of membership benefits and fees, enabling CABI to deliver greater simplicity and transparency in the calculation of individual member country fee levels; provide CABI with a financial incentive to expand the base of member countries; establish a tangible and financially quantifiable set of membership benefits; and generate a basis for addressing the significant arrears of membership fees from some countries.

In 2009 a new, simple banding structure (linked to the UN Index Number) was adopted and the minimum contribution level increased – the first increase in membership rates since 2000. The Review Conference agreed to the elimination of the 3% cap on total membership contributions, to allow CABI to benefit from attracting new members and operating more cost effectively. Equally, CABI funding from member countries would decrease if membership fell, rather than the gap being made up by increased contributions from the remaining members.

The Review Conference of 2009 also agreed to the adoption of a clear statement of member benefits, free-of-charge products and services and additional discount packages to help the least-developed member countries and post-conflict states. The benefits included free identification of microbial samples, discounts on printed books and access to CAB Abstracts, Global Health, CAB eBooks and CABI Compendia; and free consultancy days, networking and linking opportunities and a chance to help shape CABI's priorities and focus

2009 CABI Review Conference. ©CABI

with input to Review Conference meetings every 1–2 years. Members also have a dedicated website.

The following sections provide some more background on CABI's centres in member countries (their origins are described in earlier chapters, where relevant).

CABI in Africa

Africa has been a focus of CABI's work, virtually from the beginning. African Colonies were the first to be consulted on the concept of cooperation in entomology, and the first entomological expeditions were mounted to East and West Africa around 1909. The CIBC in Uganda has been described earlier. Activities in Kenya up to 1998 are described in Chapter 6.

CABI-ARC developed a strategic plan for the period 1998–2002, and also started promoting and marketing its project development, implementation and coordination expertise, coupled with the production of publicity materials, posters and newsletters.

Empowered by the perception that they were now driving their own agenda, in direct response to on-the-ground demand in Africa, staff at CABI-ARC worked tirelessly to grow the project portfolio and, soon, new and even bigger projects from a more diverse funding base followed. These included projects funded by DFID/NRI: for example, management of maize grey leaf spot, microbial control of termites in Africa, development of mycoinsecticides for cocoa mirids and management of banana weevil, as well as a continuation of projects funded under the initial tranche of NRI RNRRS funding. New donor-funded projects included: a CIDA-funded project on the production and use of the *Metarhizium* mycoinsecticide for locust and grasshopper in Africa; a consortium-funded LUBILOSA Phase IV and an FRP (Forestry Research Programme)-funded initiative on Agroforestry Pests Programme development. From an information for development perspective, projects included: quantitative evaluation of information pathways; selective dissemination of information (SDI) service – an impact study; Tanzania information training workshop; low-cost book publishing; and uptake and adoption factors in peri-urban vegetable systems in Kenya.

These relatively small initiatives were followed by the securing of much larger regional initiatives – multi-million dollar, multi-country initiatives – specifically on smallholder coffee production, including the CFC-funded projects on coffee wilt and coffee stem borer, together with the EU-funded project on the Coffee Research Network of East and Southern Africa (CORNET). Finally, CABI-ARC secured a GEF-funded project valued at US$2 million entitled, 'Removing the barriers to invasive plant management in Africa'.

In 1995 under the regional Africa forestry IPM programme, the first release of a BCA against the eucalyptus borers *Phoracantha semipunctata* and *Phoracantha recurva* was carried out in Zambia. An egg parasitoid, *Aventianella longoi* was used which, although originally from Australia, had successfully been introduced into South Africa. The Plant Protection Research Institute provided parasitoids that rapidly became established in the field, and within 10 months had dispersed

Studying cocoa mirids, Kenya. ©CABI

Improving productivity and quality of coffee in Angola. ©CABI

approximately 70 km from the release site. IIBC and the Zambia National Programme ran a training course for national scientists.

From 1991 to 1999 CABI implemented a CIDA-funded project on forest aphids and other forest pests, with the aim of permanently biologically controlling the cypress aphid (*Cinara cupressi*), pine woolly aphid (*Pineus* sp.) and pine needle aphid (*Eulachnus rileyi*) in nine countries. BCAs for cypress aphid were established in Malawi, Kenya and Uganda; for woolly aphid in Uganda and Zambia; for leucaena psyllid in Tanzania, Kenya and Zambia; and for eucalyptus borer in Zambia. The project was a huge success: the cypress aphid pest no longer causes economic damage thanks to the introduced natural enemy – the *Pauesia* wasp.

2000–10: Such was the expansion of CABI in Africa that, by 2006, just a decade after the initial changes had been implemented, CABI's project portfolio had increased from 5 to 35; financial turnover at CABI-ARC had increased from £300,000 to nearly £3,000,000 and the 'bottom line' had improved from an overall deficit of £150,000 to an overall profit of £250,000. More importantly, CABI's graduate staff complement and diversity (nationality) had risen from 6 to 36 and from 2 to 12, respectively; and the number of countries in which CABI was working had trebled, as had CABI-ARC's funding base.

In 2006 Dennis Rangi was made Executive Director, International Development. Shortly after, Sarah Simons became Global Director, Invasive Species and Roger Day, previously one of the coordinators at CABI-ARC, assumed the post of Director, CABI-Africa. George Oduor, one of the coordinators at CABI-ARC, left for Angola to manage a multi-million-pound project (funded by CFC (the Common Fund for Commodities) and the Angolan government) to rehabilitate coffee in Angola following decades of neglect due to war. At the beginning of 2009 Morris Akiri, previously Finance Manager for International Development, became Regional Director.

The first Africa Member Governments Meeting was held in Nairobi in 2000 at the CABI Africa Regional Centre following the 1999 London Review Conference, during which African delegates expressed the need for regular consultative meetings. At the Nairobi meeting, 10 of the 13 African Member Governments discussed ways of increasing understanding and ownership of CABI, and developing a new vision for CABI's role in Africa. In 2001 Burundi became the 14th African country to join CABI and the first Francophone member country. The Ivory Coast followed in 1994, and Morocco in 2006.

The Secretariat of the Global Invasive Species Programme (GISP) relocated to CABI Africa offices in 2007, after being hosted by the South African National Biodiversity Institute (SANBI) in Cape Town for 4 years. The decision was reached in an effort to consolidate the Programme's sustainability, in view of its evolution from a mainly voluntary programme to a registered not-for-profit organization with four founding members, namely CABI, the World Conservation Union (IUCN), The Nature Conservancy (TNC) and SANBI.

The second Africa Member Governments Meeting was held in Nairobi in 2007, with 11 member governments represented, to identify regional priorities that would form the basis of CABI's strategic programmes. In 2009 the CABI Governing Board meeting was, for the first time, held in Africa.

The Projects from 2005 onwards included:

- improvement of coffee production in Africa by the control of coffee wilt disease (Tracheomycosis) (2000–07), with CFC, EU and DFID funding;

- Removing Barriers to Invasive Plant Management in Africa (2005–10), with funding from the Global Environment Facility (GEF);

- entomopathogenic fungi: a component of integrated tick management (2007–10), with funding from Biosciences Eastern and Central Africa;

- Community-based Armyworm Forecasting (CBAF) for improved cereal productivity and profitability in Malawi, Tanzania and Zimbabwe (2007–10), with funding from the EU;

- Good Seed Initiative: Scaling out in Africa and South Asia (2008–11), with funding from SDC (Swiss Agency for Cooperation and Development);

- improving cotton production efficiency in small-scale farming systems in East Africa (Kenya and Mozambique) through better vertical integration of the supply chain (2009–13), with funding from the EU;

- Transfer and Dissemination of Emerging Agricultural Technologies of New Rice for Africa (NERICA); Improving Access to Quality Seed through public–private partnership in Uganda (2010–11), with funding from DFID; and

- a sustainable credit guarantee scheme to promote scaling-up/-out enhanced coffee-processing practices in Ethiopia and Rwanda (Coffee Quality II), with funding from CFC (2010–13).

Armyworm forecasting in sub-Saharan Africa. ©CABI

Opposite: training for maize farmers on best storage practice, Africa. ©CABI

Global Invasive Species Programme: The First Decade

Phase I of GISP (1997–2000)

The Global Invasive Species Programme (GISP) was established in 1997 in response to the first international meeting on invasive species, convened by the UN and the Government of Norway, and held in Trondheim, Norway, in 1996. It was launched as a small, voluntary association between three international, not-for-profit organizations, namely CABI, IUCN (formerly the World Conservation Union) and SCOPE (the Scientific Committee on Problems of the Environment of the International Council for Science). GISP's aims were to publicize and address the global threats of invasive species and to provide support to the implementation of Article 8(h) of the Convention on Biological Diversity (CBD).

GISP was coordinated initially from Stanford University, USA, with an international team of invasive species experts including scientists, lawyers and policy makers, focusing on consolidating existing information to provide tools for the understanding and management of invasive species. This led to *Global Strategy on Invasive Alien Species* (2001) and a range of products including Invasive Alien Species: A Toolkit of Best Prevention and Management Practices (2001).

Phase II of GISP (2001–04)

Phase II was launched in 2001, with the primary focus of implementing elements of the Global Strategy, notably networking, training and capacity building. Its achievements included five high-profile regional workshops and associated reports; CBD experts' consultations on invasive species in inland waters and island ecosystems; and a study of invasive species and development assistance in South-east Asia. The Board decided to relocate the Secretariat (Sec) to South Africa, to reflect a focus on developing countries and improve opportunities to secure multi-lateral funding.

Phase III of GISP (2005–07)

Phase III was launched in 2005, when GISP became a legal entity with four founding partners, namely CABI, IUCN, SANBI and TNC. The GISP Sec focused on securing donor-funded projects in an attempt to ensure financial sustainability beyond the start-up funding, gained preliminary funding for a global project on invasive species and established GISP as a key partner in the 2010 Biological Indicators Partnership (BIP) project.

Phase IV of GISP (2008–present)

The current phase of GISP (Phase IV) was launched in March 2008, and is coordinated from a modest Sec hosted by CABI in Nairobi. The GISP Sec is headed by an Executive Director (currently Sarah Simons,

on secondment from CABI). GISP is now described as an international partnership dedicated to addressing the global threats of invasive species through policy development, awareness raising and information exchange.

Jeff Waage, former Managing Director CABI Bioscience was Chairman of the GISP Board between 2000 and 2002, and Dennis Rangi, CABI's Executive Director, International Development was Chairman between 2006 and 2009. The current Chairman is William Jackson, Deputy Director-General IUCN.

Common mynah. ©iStockphoto

Opposite: lionfish. ©iStockphoto

CABI Europe – Switzerland

Established in 1948, CABI Europe-Switzerland (E-CH) focuses on the management of invasive weeds and insect pests through the promotion of safe biological control and the use of natural enemies (parasitoids, predators and diseases) to control pests and weeds. Staff play an active role in CABI's contribution to aspects of biological control policy, linking with organizations such as FAO, OECD (Organization for Economic Co-operation and Development), EPPO (European and Mediterranean Plant Protection Organization), IOBC (International Organization for Biological Control) and national authorities, to provide inputs to protocols and guidance documents required for regulation, as well as research, on the development of methods to assess risks associated with potential BCAs.

The Centre's research also contributes to methods of assessing the risks and impacts of invasive alien insects, through the development of inventories, and to establishing a black list of species that require particular attention and regulation, because of their current or potential environmental impact. By doing this, the Centre contributes in the development of regional and national strategies on prevention and management of invasive species in Europe.

To assist biodiversity conservation, the Centre's research assesses multitrophic interactions (between different levels in the food chain) below and above ground, as well as nutrient cycling in the context of biological invasions, land-use change and climate change. It is currently studying interactions between global warming and biological invasions, and assessing the possible impacts of climate change on agricultural production and ecosystems through their effect on pests and insect–plant interactions.

The Centre's integrated crop management (ICM) team provides technical support and facilitates activities that improve agricultural practices. For example, it promotes appropriate use of natural resources and supports the implementation of IPM in order to reduce unnecessary use of pesticides.

CABI E-CH annually hosts international student placements whereby biology and agriculture students receive hands-on training in practical aspects of applied biological control research, working in project teams with high-impact outcomes. There is also a graduate student programme, with links to universities around the world. As a result, this is a truly international centre, normally with staff and students from more than a dozen countries working together each summer.

Swiss links

Since its inception in 1948, the CABI Centre in Switzerland has maintained close relationships with the Swiss federal research stations and universities, the Swiss Agency for Development and Cooperation (SDC), Intercooperation (IC) and the plant protection industry. These links have strengthened since Switzerland became a member of CABI in 2000; for example, it is currently collaborating with several Swiss universities, including Berne, Fribourg and Neuchâtel, on joint projects.

Contribution to development activities

The Centre supports CABI's mission in the developing world, providing expertise in biological control and IPM in temperate agroecosystems in support of CABI's Centres in developing countries. Since 2003, Feng Zhang has been seconded from CABI E-CH to CABI Southeast & East Asia, in Beijing, to help develop new CABI activities in partnership with this important member country. Recent examples of the Centre's contribution to CABI's development agenda include the ongoing SDC-funded programme for pest management in the Democratic People's Republic of Korea, and the training of farmers in integrated production (IP) in Kosovo and Albania.

Western corn rootworm[199]

In 2005 an article in *Nature*[200] described a phenomenon that not only might potentially control Western corn rootworm (WCR) beetle, but is also a scientific 'first'. It was a collaboration between researchers at the University of Neuchâtel, Switzerland, the Max-Planck Institute for Chemical Ecology, Jena, Germany and Ulli Kuhlmann and Stefan Toepfer from the CABI-Switzerland Centre.

Produced by maize roots in response to feeding by the WCR, the sesquiterpene (E)- caryophyllene strongly attracted the pest-eating nematode *Heterorhabditis megidis*. While plant leaves often release volatile chemicals when attacked by pests, attracting the pest's natural enemies, it was unknown in plant roots. Olfactometers showed the attractivity of WCR-damaged maize roots to the nematodes, and identified the released chemical. (E)-caryophyllene could diffuse rapidly through moist sand, and was thus an effective underground signal.

Field experiments in Hungary (where WCR is an established pest) backed up the laboratory results. Nematodes infected many more WCR larvae near a maize variety that produced the signal than near a 'non-producing' variety. The number of adult WCR beetles emerging near non-producing plants that had been 'spiked' with the signal was less than half that for plants without the chemical, suggesting that addition of the chemical could control the pest.

Maize varieties differ in their ability to produce the signal; most varieties used in North America no longer emit the signal but, in contrast, European lines emit varying but significant amounts of it. It seems that the ability to produce this compound has been lost during breeding in North America but retained, by chance, in Europe: the first finding of the loss of an indirect plant defence signal through breeding. This may be why attempts to control WCR with nematodes in North America have met with mixed success, and suggests that planting varieties which do emit the signal would attract more nematodes, boosting natural control of WCR. Maize breeders might achieve better WCR resistance by ensuring that plants express the signal.

Opposite: Western corn rootworm (WCR) surrounded by ants. ©CABI

China

As the most populous member country of CABI and one of the fastest growing economies in the world, China is of strategic importance and has a large professional and technical workforce involved in agricultural research, education and extension, with extensive information support services. Science policy in China has changed dramatically over the last 5 years, with research institutes and academies re-engineering their activities and businesses to address demand-led programmes. These institutions and their researchers are looking for international collaborators.

CABI's links with China began in 1980 when the Agricultural Information Institute (AII) of the Chinese Academy of Agricultural Sciences (CAAS) invited a CABI delegation to China. Out of this came a long-term programme through which abstracts of Chinese agricultural literature are supplied to CABI by AII for input to CAB Abstracts, in exchange for CABI information products and services. The relationship reached a milestone with an agreement to collaborate on a national agricultural research information project for China, funded by the Asian Development Bank.

China becomes a member of CABI

In 1995 China became a member country of CABI. This gave Chinese organizations the opportunity to purchase CABI's publications at discounted prices; and it was a major boost to the full internationalization of CABI, being well beyond the Commonwealth. It led to a considerable expansion of CABI's interests and activities throughout Asia.

Joint China–CABI Office

In 2002 at the invitation of the Chinese Academy of Agricultural Sciences, CABI opened a joint China–CABI Office within CAAS International Centre in Beijing, alongside the offices of several CGIAR centres (e.g. IRRI, IPGRI (Biodiversity International), CIMMYT and CIP). The office facilitates collaboration, particularly with national programmes aimed at the sustainable development of Chinese agriculture and related sciences. Key publishing/information initiatives are under way, with strong scientific research partnerships around the Chinese Agriculture Invasive Species Programme and Microbial Agriculture Programme.

2004 Review Conference in Beijing

CABI's 15th Review Conference was held in Beijing in 2004, the first outside the UK in the organization's history.

IPM and Bt cotton and other crops

As one of the world's leading producers of cotton, China suffers from heavy and often unnecessary use of pesticides in cotton production. CABI has helped to reduce this reliance by developing and implementing IPM methods for cotton in China. Through field trials and farmer participatory training, pesticide inputs were reduced and net profits for smallholder farmers increased. Bt cotton (genetically modified (GM) to confer resistance against some key pests) was one of the first GM crops to be developed, and is a potentially valuable component of an IPM programme, helping farmers to get off the insecticide treadmill. Although it has been planted widely in a number of countries, debate has continued about its efficacy, sustainability, environmental impact and economic viability. CABI, working with several international and Chinese partners, was involved in an EU project to assess the environmental and agronomic suitability of GM cotton plants for control of caterpillars in smallholder IPM farming systems in China. This focused on tools to enable farmers to make appropriate decisions on the use and management of Bt transgenic cotton.

Following a visit of the UK Government Chief Scientific Advisor to China in March 2009, and in response to the UK–China Food Security Action Plan, CABI, the British Embassy together with IPP (Institute of Plant Protection)-CAAS developed a project entitled 'Benefits and Risks of Genetically Modified Crops: Implications for Agricultural Research Cooperation, Frontier Science, Public Engagement and Policy'. The project was supported by the UK Department for Business, Innovation and Skills (BIS), as well as by CABI and IPP-CAAS. It involved two workshops and associated visits in January and April 2010 (in the UK and China, respectively) focused on developing a research proposal to apply for international research funds. A proposal entitled 'Balancing Ecosystem Services and Economic Potential of Genetically Modified Crops in Poor Rural Areas of China' was submitted to DFID, and a consortium of partners from China, the UK and international organizations was formed.

Opening of the CAAS–CABI project office in Beijing. ©CABI

Cotton boll. ©CABI

White Agriculture

The Chinese White Agriculture (Microbial Agriculture) Programme is concerned with the use of microorganisms to help meet the multiple challenges of significantly increasing food production in China whilst protecting the environment and improving rural livelihoods. In 1999 and 2004, CABI co-hosted the First and Second International White Agriculture Workshops, respectively, in Beijing. Since then the White Agriculture concept has gained momentum in China, with some 12 laboratories and institutions throughout the country now embracing the concept and common objectives. In particular, CABI is helping to strengthen China's beef production by training scientists in the development of technologies that convert waste straw into nutritious silage.

Alien invasive species

In China, the invasive weeds mile-a-minute, water hyacinth and privet cause serious economic losses and threaten native biodiversity. CABI has been working with Chinese partners to assess the potential for biological control programmes for each of these weeds. CABI has also been able to survey, collect and study potential weed BCAs in China that could be used against several important weeds of Chinese origin in other parts of the world. In addition, CABI has provided technical backstopping to FFS programmes for a number of vegetable crops in China and other Asian countries. This included developing curricula and teaching resources to train agricultural extension workers and farmers, training in parasite rearing/production for biological control and supplying new BCAs. More recently, CABI has helped develop the China national Invasive Alien Species strategy; co-organized the Workshop on the Prevention and Management of Invasive Alien Species, held in November 2004, and an APEC Invasive Alien Species Workshop held in September 2005; assisted in the development of a joint project proposal with the Centre for Management of Invasive Alien Species, CAAS/MOA (Ministry of Agriculture) and CABI, which has received funding approval from the Chinese Ministry of Science and Technology. The project is aimed at the development of a sustainable management strategy and control technology for the invasive alien weed, *Eupatorium adenophorum* or sticky snakeroot, in China.

In response to the global challenge of invasive alien species (IAS) and in conjunction with the International Day for Biological Diversity – IAS in 2009, as well as International Year of Biodiversity for 2010 – an International Congress on Biological Invasions was strategically planned, fully supported and jointly sponsored by the Chinese Academy of Agricultural Sciences and CABI; and organized by the Fujian Agriculture and Forestry University and Fujian Academy of Agriculture Sciences, in collaboration with AAFC, CSIRO, Kansas State University, USDA-APHIS (United States Department of Agriculture, Animal and Plant Health Inspection Service), FAO/IAEA (International Agricultural Exchange Association), IPP, the Chinese Society of Plant Protection and GISP, with supplementary financial support provided by The Crawford Fund and AusAID (Australian Government Overseas Aid Program). It concluded with unanimous support for a 'Fuzhou Declaration'.

IPM in the Democratic People's Republic of Korea

A four-way collaboration in a Democratic People's Republic of Korea (DPRK) Maize IPM Project, involving China, has been carried out by CABI, the DPRK Academy of Agriculture, CAAS and the Hebei Hengshui Tianyi Biocontrol Company. The project has also included an intensive training programme of North Korean scientists in China. This has led to a number of DPRK IPM projects involving Chinese technology transfer and capacity building.

Agricultural research information

A major constraint preventing scientists in developing countries from accessing international information resources is inadequate library budgets. CABI and China have been trying to overcome this problem through sponsorship, organized consortia and licensing arrangements. At the invitation of the CAAS, CABI has been involved in a Chinese initiative to develop a nationwide agricultural research information system (ARIS) to access global information and services. Through funding from the ADB and other donors, more than 40 major Chinese agricultural and forestry research and training institutions were provided with agricultural databases – together with training in their use. Continuing access to new information tools is made possible through organized consortia of bulk purchase set up by CAAS, CAU (China Agricultural University) and CABI. In addition, CABI has also allowed 30 agricultural journals to be reprinted in China and sold at prices affordable to the Chinese user community. These measures have had a great impact on the development of Chinese agricultural information systems and services, and on agricultural research and education in that country. CABI assesses the information needs of Chinese users through regular consultations with its Chinese Library Advisory Board (CLAB), attendance at national conferences and visits to institutions in China.

Many useful research results generated by scientists in developing countries fail to be disseminated internationally. CABI co-published with the CSAB (the Chinese Society of Agricultural Biotechnology) and CAU the *Chinese Journal of Agricultural Biotechnology*, aiming at bringing cutting-edge Chinese research to an international audience. The journal takes the best papers published in Chinese in the *Journal of Agricultural Biotechnology*, translates them and makes them available to the international community.

Many developing countries have difficulties in accessing scientific information because of inadequate infrastructure for information and communication technologies, particularly in the agricultural sector. To address this problem, CABI co-organized an international conference in Beijing to examine the new challenges and opportunities facing agricultural information management, technology and markets in the 21st century. As a result, dozens of information and library centres worldwide have agreed to cooperate in developing strategies for tackling such knowledge transfer problems.

Training of Chinese scientists at CABI Centres

At its centres around the world, CABI provides both information management and scientific research training and work/study placement opportunities. In recent years, several Chinese delegations, study tour groups and individuals have visited and been trained at CABI Centres in subjects ranging from agricultural information technology and use of the Crop Protection Compendium to biocontrol of western corn rootworm and hoary cress.

Malaysia

History

The origins of the Malaysian office are mentioned in Chapter 6. In June 1988, the CABI Asia Regional Office (CABI-ARO) was established in Kuala Lumpur, Malaysia followed by CABI's Regional Station for Biological Control located at MARDI in 1992. Y Bhg Dato' Khairi, after serving CABI-ARO for 6 years, was replaced by A Zamzam Mohamed, former Director of Strategic Research of MARDI as the 3rd Regional Representative in 1995. During his tenure the ARO office was moved from Kuala Lumpur to SHL Business Centre, in Serdang Raya, for about 1 year before moving to the MARDI Complex in 1997.

Later in 1997 the CABI Southeast Asia Regional Centre (CABI-SEARC) was formed when CABI-ARO became fully integrated with the Malaysian Centre of CABI Bioscience (formally CABI-IIBC Regional Station), located within the campus of MARDI in Serdang, Selangor. In October 1998 Loke Wai Hong became the 4th Regional Director.

In 2006 CABI–SEARC was again reorganized, by the merger of CABI Malaysia and China offices, as CABI Southeast & East Asia (CABI-SEA).

CABI-SEA (Malaysia)'s main areas are training activities (for scientists, extension workers, farmers and SPS (Sanitary and Phytosanitary/Plant) health officers); on-farm applied research and technical backstopping studies; introduction, establishment and impact evaluation of useful insect BCAs; and information support and services. Biological control and IPM/ICM development and implementation at farmer level are a particular focus, including training for national institutions. CABI-SEA has close linkages with relevant local institutions in South-east Asia, and is close to a large number of key national and international institutions, with which it has collaborated closely.

CABI-SEA's scientific experience includes the following:

1. Assessing the need to introduce exotic natural enemies

The unit's work facilitates the introduction, rearing, establishment and impact assessment of suitable BCAs. A number of newly emerging pests in the area have become very important on vegetables, such as leafminers, *Spodoptera exigua* and a new cabbage root worm (still unidentified).

2. Assisting in production of quality BCAs

The unit has supported field releases and provided on-site training, advice and development of rearing facilities and technical information. CABI-SEA supported the introduction of the parasitoids *Diadegma semiclausum* and *Diadromus collaris* to provide effective control of diamondback moth that was attacking highland vegetables in Dalat (Vietnam), and arranged for training.

3. Development of training curricula specific to a particular crops and locations

CABI-SEA has developed training of trainers (TOT) and FFS participatory activities related to specific crops and locations. CABI-SEA has experience through the ACIAR-funded projects on cocoa in PNG and on coffee in PNG and Indonesia; by assisting FAO and the ADB in these activities in Laos, Vietnam, Philippines and India in various crop ecosystems.

4. Organizing short training workshops

Training workshops have covered pest and natural enemy identification and exercises for use in farmer participatory training and research, etc. CABI-SEA has carried out many of these, not only in Malaysia but also in other ASEAN (Association of Southeast Asian Nations) countries, through the AusAID-funded project, SPS Capacity Building Programme.

Backstopping and other technical support

CABI-SEA can assist because of its access to screen-houses and field facilities.

Examples of projects implemented and completed by CABI-SEA:

- Biocontrol of *Mikania micrantha* in Malaysia (funded by MOPGC (Malaysian Oil Palm Growers' Council));

- Vegetable IPM Project in India, Indonesia, the Philippines and Vietnam (funded by UNDP through FAO);

- Cotton IPM Project in China, India and Pakistan (funded by ADB);

- Biodegradation of Crop Residues in Indonesia (CABI-PF, co-funded with IMI);

- CSA (Community Supported Agriculture) Regional Vegetable IPM Project in SE Asia (Bangladesh, Laos, the Philippines and Vietnam; funded by FAO);

- Leafminer Control in Asia (Indonesia, Malaysia and Vietnam; funded by CABI-PF);

- Use of *Melia excelsa* in Pest Control (funded by IRPA (International Radiation Protection Association) through FRIM (Forest Research Institute Malaysia));

- Bt Resistance Management (funded by IRPA through MARDI);

- Management of Leafminers on Chrysanthemums (funded by IRPA through MARDI);

- ASEANET (ASEAN Network on biosystematics of insects, nematodes and fungi; funded by BioNET Tech. Sec.); and

- Training component of the IPM of vegetables in DPR Korea (funded by SDC).

Since 2005, by working with the Department of Agriculture, Malaysia, CABI-SEA has successfully applied for APEC (Asia-Pacific Economic Cooperation) support for the following:

- Building Biosecurity Planning and Surveillance Capacity for APEC Member Economies (2005);

- Capacity Building in Surveillance and Diagnosis for Leafminer, Whitefly, Thrips;

Opposite: cabbage farmers in DPRK. ©CABI

- Mealybugs in Developing APEC Economies for Improved Market Access (2006 and 2007);

- Understanding and Developing Risk Management Options for Market Access (implemented in October 2008);

- Malaysian Tropical Fruits Information System (MTFIS) – in collaboration with MARDI and the International Tropical Fruits Network (TFNet) – secured Malaysian Ringgit 1.7 million from the Malaysian Government to develop a bilingual tropical fruits portal;

- CABI-SEA also gained funding from IDRC to implement the project 'Knowledge Networks and Systems of Innovation to support Implementation of Sanitary and Phytosanitary Standards in the Developing Countries of Southeast Asia' in 2007–08;

- CABI-SEA projects in Negara Brunei Darussalam include engaging consultants in the development of viral disease identification and management on agricultural crops and ornamentals, and in developing and producing a manual on IPM for citrus;

- CABI-SEA secured two ACIAR-funded projects on 'Managing Cocoa Pod Borer (CPB) in PNG Through Improved Risk Incursion Management Capabilities, IPM Strategies and Stakeholder Participatory Training' (for 3 years, starting in 2008); and 'Incursion Prevention and Management of Coffee Berry Borer (CBB) in Papua New Guinea (PNG) and Eastern Indonesia (particularly Papua)' for 5 years, starting in 2009; and

- In collaboration with DOA Malaysia, a proposal on 'Enhancing Food Security through a Regional Approach and Wide Stakeholder Participation to Plant Biosecurity' has been approved for funding by the APEC Secretariat in Singapore in 2010.

Cocoa smallholders viewing a Cocoa Pod Borer (CPB), Papua New Guinea. ©CABI

Trinidad and Tobago

There are eight staff in Trinidad and one at the Tropical Agricultural Research and Higher Education Centre in Costa Rica. As is the tradition at CABI, whenever necessary, experts from various disciplines are drawn from other CABI Centres or externally.

New activities were developed in farmer-participatory training and biological control of a new alien pest, the pink hibiscus mealybug (*Maconellicoccus hirsutus*) until, in mid-1996, Moses Kairo (recruited to the Institute's Kenya Station in 1985) was transferred from the UK Centre as the new Scientist-in-Charge, and continued to build up activities. After Kairo left in 2005, Ulrike Krauss was transferred from the Costa Rica office as co-Director alongside Keith Holmes. Holmes returned to the UK in 2009 to head up CABI Bioservices, and a new Regional Director, Lizz Johnson, an expatriate Trinidadian who had been working for USDA in North Carolina, took over.

Invasive species and the modern CABI

In the year 2010 invasive species are a major issue in the region. For example, in recent years several economically important species have become established in Trinidad and other parts of the Caribbean: pink hibiscus mealybug (*Maconellicoccus hirsutus*, 1995), black sigatoka disease of bananas (*Mycosphaerella fijiensis*, 2003), red palm mite (*Raoiella indica*, 2006) and coconut moth (*Batrachedra nuciferae*, 2006).

CABI has helped build regional capacity for management, through CBC and promoting the development and use of biological pesticides for the control of invasive pests, such as red palm mite, and has conducted research in non-traditional areas, such as their use to control ectoparasites on animals. The Centre also carries out work on regionally important commodity crops, such as cocoa and coffee.

As part of the network of the modern CABI, the Centre in Trinidad and an office in Costa Rica linked to the work of CATIE (Centro Agronómico Tropical de Investigación y Enseñanza (Costa Rica)) across a region that extends from Mexico in the north to Chile in the south, and includes the islands of the Caribbean.

The Centre seeks to be 'adaptable to project activities; possesses microbiological and general laboratories, as well as outdoor plant and insect-rearing facilities, geared towards work in pest management; and it supports an insect collection encompassing pests of agricultural importance and their natural enemies, social insects such as bees, and wasps and a collection of Lepidoptera'. The Centre also houses the Network Coordinating Institute for CARINET, the Caribbean loop of BioNET International.

Opposite: red palm mite, Eric Erbe/Chris Pooley/US Department of Agriculture. ©SPL

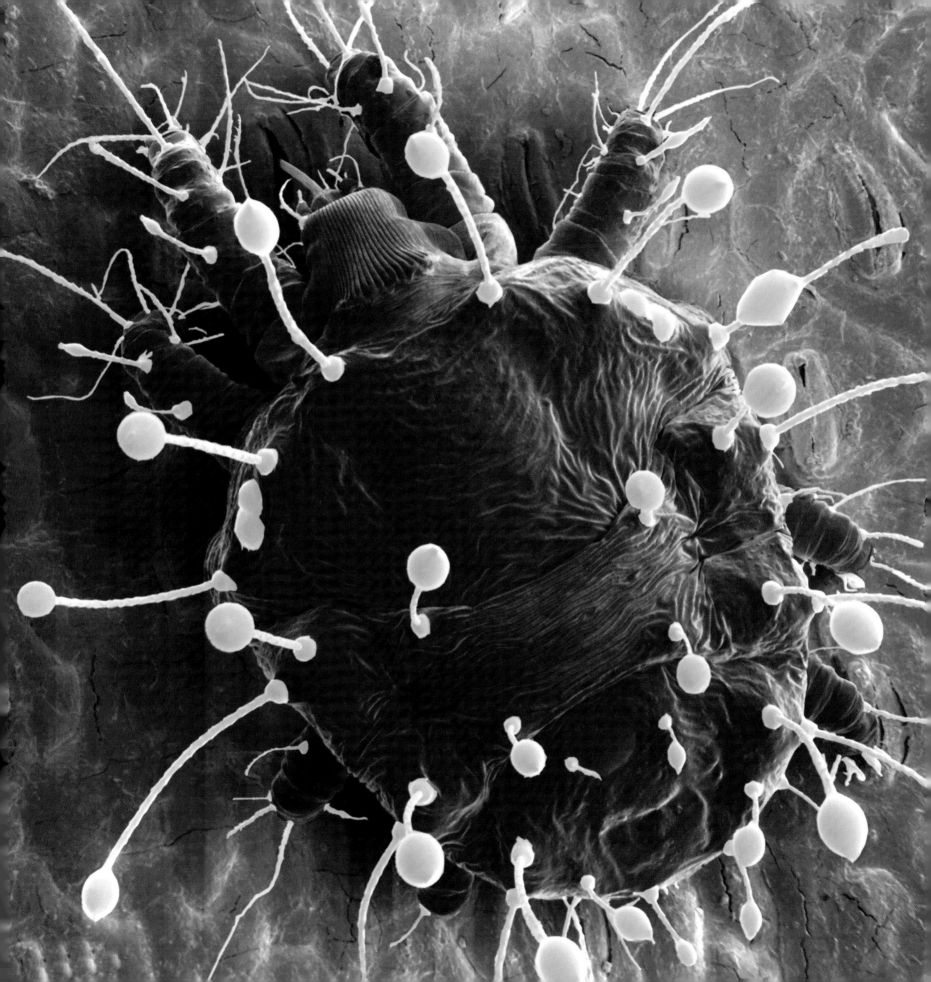

Pakistan

CABI established an office at Rawalpindi, Pakistan, in 1957. The earlier history is described in Chapter 6.

Integrated pest management: stepping off the pesticide treadmill

Following Mohyuddin's retirement, at the end of 1994, Scientist-in-Charge Ashraf Poswal built on the earlier IPM work, particularly in cotton, by developing and adapting farmer-participatory methods to work directly with rural communities. CABI became a development agency, supporting sustainable crop production as well as a biological control institute.

An extract from the Annual Report for 1997 outlines the impact of IPM training of trainers and FFS in cotton:

" A continuous decline in Pakistan's cotton production since the 1991–92 season has primarily been due to heavy insect attack in conjunction with incidence of cotton leaf curl virus transmitted by cotton whitefly, Bemisia tabaci. *However, pesticide use has continued to increase and the average number of applications has risen from 1.7 in 1987 to more than 7 in 1997 at a cost of more than 10 billion rupees to Pakistan's economy. Pesticide resistance in the key pests i.e. whitefly and bollworm (*Helicoverpa armigera*) has been documented. "*

A season-long training of the trainers and farmers was held between 5 May and 30 November, involving 23 agricultural extension officers. Ten FFS were established in ten villages scattered in three sub-districts. On average, 25 farmers were enrolled in each on a voluntary basis. Ten of the FFS obtained higher yields in their IPM plots than in the farmer practice plots, including both sites where no pesticide applications at all were made under IPM decision making (yield figures), providing resounding confirmation of the ability of natural enemies to keep cotton pests in check and of the FFS approach in convincing farmers to step off the pesticide treadmill in cotton.

The Institute changed the farmers' pest management practice in cotton, controlling what were 'uncontrollable whitefly swarms' only a year earlier through demonstrating the effectiveness of natural control by *Encarsia* and *Eretmocerus* parasitoids and a predator complex without spraying. This project on the ecology of whiteflies ran alongside the FFS in 1997. These schools increased cotton yields by more than 25% without pesticide use, and increased farmers' income by more than 43% in some cases. The project produced two simple messages: do not spray before the middle of August for sucking pests, and do not spray for bollworms if the damage is less than 10%. Within 2 years whiteflies had ceased to be a serious pest, and bollworm infestations were never threatening enough to need more than two sprays.

Following the Institute's success in cotton, the Government of Pakistan established a national IPM programme. In 2001–05 and with the support of the FAO/EU Regional Cotton Project and NATIPM (National IMP Control Programme), the Institute trained hundreds of extension staff and thousands of farmers. Its role was to: conduct training of trainers; provide technical backstopping on pests and crop issues; and to develop training curricula and quality control systems to be used in training.

Horticultural projects

In 2010 there were 16 horticultural projects under way or recently completed by the CABI Centre in Pakistan – three of them supporting agriculture in northern Afghanistan. They included the following extended contracts: fruit and vegetable development in the Punjab involving BAP (best agricultural practice) and ICM (Institute of Commercial Management) through training of farmers for sustainable vegetable production (2005–09); integrated crop management through training of farmers and FFS in northern Afghanistan (2007–10); survey of midges and their natural enemies associated with mango production and the development of non-pesticide control measures in the Punjab (2007–10); best agricultural practices and IPM in the Malakand Region of Pakistan for apple, peach, apricot, onion and cabbage (2003–07).

Farmer training, Pakistan. ©CABI

Opposite: grape farmer, Afghanistan. ©CABI

India

India is the world's second most populous country with around 1.1 billion inhabitants living across 1.2 million square miles. In the last 20 years it has become a major economy with rapid growth in trade and a large, skilled workforce. Yet huge sections of the population – particularly those in rural communities – remain in poverty.

CABI has had a presence in India since 1957, as described in chapter 6. CABI established a general agreement for collaboration with ICAR, India in 1998. This covered agricultural research information and research and training in crop protection and biosystematics and is implemented through a joint workplan. CABI also opened an Office at the National Agriculture Science Centre (NASC), Pusa, New Delhi in 2001. The CABI India office is now located at the National Agricultural Science Centre and is headed up by Country Director & Regional Science Director for Asia, Ravi Khetarpal. CABI staff work closely and in partnership with organizations like the Indian Council of Agricultural Research, the Ministry of Agriculture, Indian Coffee Board, forestry-based organizations, State Agricultural Universities, NGOs and the CGIAR (Consultative Group on International Agricultural Research).

Supporting agricultural crops

A large part of India's economy is based on agricultural products. CABI India helps farmers increase both the quality and quantity of their crops for both export and internal trade. As a part of this some work is oriented towards helping India meet World Trade Organization standards for the export of crops. CABI staff have contributed to the development of a national invasive species strategy involving ensuring that invasive plants, insects and diseases are not exported. In one major project, CABI, in collaboration with the Kerala Forest Research Institute and ICAR introduced a highly specific fungal biological control agent for the control of the invasive weed, *Mikania micrantha*, in south-west and north-east India. Staff at the centre have also helped design national quarantine facilities for BCAs that are used to control invasive species.

Enabling smallholder farmers to access markets

At the other end of the spectrum, CABI India works to give smallholder farmers a better return for their crops by helping them manage weeds, pests and diseases. Communicating best management practices to improve the quality of their produce and ensuring that they get access to markets is also key.

One recent project in collaboration with the Central Coffee Research Institute on the coffee white stem borer (a longhorn beetle killing coffee trees across India) found that the cost to the Indian coffee industry was around US$10 million a year. Ways of controlling the beetle, although effective, were not understood or being used by farmers so village level training was carried out and over 3000 smallholder farmers have been trained to date.

Arguably one of the biggest achievements of the centre has been introducing cultural control methods for coffee berry borer, leading to the cost of the pest to the industry being reduced to below the level of economic impact.

Developing capacity

An important objective of CABI's work is to develop local knowledge and capacity. CABI's UK collection of fungus cultures is world-renowned and CABI has been able to pass the skills of managing and curating culture collections on to the National Bureau of Agriculturally Important Microorganisms in India, enabling them to record and explore the microbial biodiversity that India offers. In addition to this CABI has built capacity for India to utilize exotic fungal BCAs for the management of invasive alien weeds.

Sharing information to help agriculture

Information is key to progress, and India is a large and growing market for CABI's world-renowned databases, online resources and specialist books covering agriculture and the environment.

Coffee farmers checking the pheromone traps for white stem borer. ©CABI

CAPACITY BUILDING:
FROM PATERNALISM TO MATURITY, FROM HANDBOOKS TO INTERNET DELIVERY

The history of training or capacity building in CABI is as old as the organization itself, with the first rudimentary steps having been taken in 1911. The nature of the training, however, and its rationale has changed over the years. In the first 30 years or so training focused very much on building the human resources available to the organization itself – by ensuring, for example, that the porters who accompanied the expeditions by Neave in East Africa and Myers in the Caribbean were able to undertake some technical steps to assist in their collections tasks. Later, the emphasis moved to providing training in taxonomy and documentation skills for a small number of scientists from member countries to enhance their prospects of permanent employment in CABI. In the 1970s priority was given to training scientists and technicians to improve the quality of the preparation of specimens sent to the Institutes for identification. With the reorientation of CABI to identify more clearly it as a development organization in the 1980s, capacity building became a specific objective in its own right. Training in the use of CABI's Internet and CD-ROM products and services became an integral component of CABI's publishing marketing strategies. In 2010, capacity building is also central to CABI's major effort in Plantwise.

One of the first actions of the IERC was to publish, in 1911, its *Instructions to Collectors*, a field handbook for entomologists in Africa, detailing the apparatus and techniques for identification, collection and preservation of insects. Neave was training the African porters and assistants who accompanied him on his expeditions in East Africa in the techniques of collections, finding the assistants 'invaluable'. Simpson, in West Africa, believed it was important to educate the 'natives' in the connection between insects and diseases. Similarly, Myers recorded that those he employed from local populations attained a high degree of skill in entomological work. Neave, Simpson and Myers' paternalistic efforts were laying the foundations for CABI's more mature efforts in capacity building.

Higher-level training was mainly small-scale and 'on the job'. Initially the aim, as articulated in the 1965 Review Conference, was to create training posts at CAB itself to give trainees from Commonwealth countries experience in abstracting and documentation generally, to equip them to compete for permanent posts on the staff of CAB when vacancies occurred.[201] The Conference said:

" CAB is not and, in the conference's opinion should not be, equipped to provide formal education facilities; it can and should provide opportunities for scientists from developing countries to acquire experience in documentation, with a view to qualifying for permanent

appointment to the staff of CAB. The question of training individual scientists from Commonwealth countries, for the direct benefit of those countries, was 'another matter."

Whilst CAB was happy to 'provide practical opportunities for scientists from Commonwealth countries to gain practical experience, particularly in the Institutes', the associated costs were to be 'met under arrangements made by their own countries'.

Scientists from member countries had worked at the Institute of Entomology on specific tasks, with mentoring from senior Institute scientists. In 1963–64 RH Pelley, former senior entomologist in Kenya, spent two periods working at the Institute in connection with a book on coffee pests. In this period, the Mycological Institute's activities in training included support for visiting scientists. Some of those supported in the 1950s later became pre-eminent: CV Subramanian (India) and Augusto Chaves Batista (Portugal). Mycologists from the developing world were trained on the job. There were special courses for MAFF personnel; Darwin Fellowships; UK and overseas training courses in fungal identification and characterization; support for MSc courses at Reading and Canterbury; and assistance in supervision of PhDs as an Associate Institution of the University of Reading.

During 1963–64 entomologists from India and Pakistan undertook periods of training at the Bangalore and Rawalpindi Stations of the Institute of Biological Control. An entomologist from Bolivia was trained at the West Indian Station. Later, the Institute of Parasitology also welcomed visiting students and researchers from the Commonwealth and beyond. As a snapshot, in 1979 there were four: a student from the University of the Philippines reading for a PhD; a Canadian NATO Fellow on a 1-year attachment; and two academics from Brazil and Venezuela, respectively on sabbaticals.

The Institutes were encouraged by the Review Conference of 1975 to provide training to member country scientists to enable 'full use of local expertise for the identification of organisms' in order to ensure only significant specimens were sent to the CAB Institutes for identification. But, the Review Conference warned, 'any extra costs involved are to be found from outside CAB'. This directive resulted in a series of specialist training courses run by the Institutes for scientists from member countries and elsewhere.

The first training course in CABI's history, according to a special annual report in 1993[202] of the Institute of Entomology, was held in 1979. Dr Pant, Director of the Institute, initiated a series of International Courses on Applied Taxonomy of Insects and Mites of Agricultural Importance. The basement at 56 Queen's Gate was converted into a teaching

Opposite: livestock Farmer Field School, Afghanistan. ©CABI

laboratory for this purpose and the courses, which each lasted for about 6 weeks, were devised and taught by CIE and BMNH taxonomists. After that the Institute ran annual courses with 12 to 13 trainees on each. By the end of the 1980s, more than 200 trainees from 54 different countries had participated in Institute training courses. Courses were conducted in India, Malaysia and Kenya. The Commonwealth Fund for Technical Cooperation supported participants from Commonwealth countries.

Similarly, the Mycological Institute ran 6-week courses on the Identification of Fungi and Bacteria on an annual basis from 1979, and postgraduate students gained practical experience through short attachments to the Institute. In a number of cases, senior staff at the Mycological Institute supervised Masters and PhD students. The Institute sent its first scientists to China for the second congress of Systematic Mycology and Lichenology Laboratory at Academia Sinica, the Chinese Academy of Sciences. Hawksworth gave five lectures and, with the Institute's mycologists Allsopp and Kirk, ran a 2-week training course on applied mycology at the Subtropical Forestry Research Institute of the Chinese Academy of Forestry, Zhejiang Province.

Muller, as Director of the Institute of Parasitology, sought to support and enthuse the staff to open up new horizons in international training courses. The first International Course on the Identification of Helminths of Economic Importance was held at the Institute in 1982, with 14 trainees. The first International Course on Plant Pathogenic Nematodes was held at the Institute in 1983. However, training courses in nematology stopped in the 1990s, owing to a lack of funding.

The first International Training Courses on Biological Control were held in 1981 at the Institute's Indian station, where 18 students from 13 countries participated in a 4-week course. A similar course was held at the West Indies Station in 1982.

Training emerged as an explicit priority after 1990 as CABI became increasingly involved in development assistance programmes. In the period between 1993 and 1996, for example, 61 training courses were organized by the Institutes of which 27 were conducted overseas and, of these, 21 in member countries. During the period there were about 800 participants in multiple-participant courses, and another 200 scientists were involved in individual placement programmes at the CABI Bioscience Institutes. Altogether, about 1000 people from 86 countries, including 33 CABI member countries, participated in the training and visiting-scientist programmes. In addition, more than 1000 farmers were trained in FFS in CABI-managed IPM projects in member countries.

The tangible outputs from BioNET were described to the 1999 Review Conference as: training of five postgraduate/postdoctoral fellows; training of 38 technicians from southern Africa (in the fields of entomology, nematology, mycology and virology); provision of CD-ROM Identification Keys, a global database of taxonomic expertise, a CD-ROM of Pests of Gramineae of southern Africa, and the crop protection compendium to various LOOP institutions.

New courses on modern techniques showed how advances in biochemistry and molecular biology could be applied to a range of methods in the identification of organisms and the diagnosis of plant health problems.

For biological control, emphasis was placed on the importance of natural enemies of insect pests and weeds, with courses specifically on the identification of natural enemies and the effects of pesticides on these. A major emphasis, in partnership with national programmes in the Philippines, China, Pakistan and India, was given in FFS and training-the-trainers exercises in the identification and use of indigenous natural enemies in IPM in vegetables and cotton.

A special 3-year Fellowship programme was funded by the UK Darwin Initiative, to enable established systematists to spend 1 year each at a CABI Institute, working with a CABI specialist on a group of organisms of special importance to the country of origin of the Fellow. In all, 22 Darwin Fellows were selected; 17 were from CABI member countries.

Training in information management continued, mainly for librarians and other professionals. In the 1960s, there were documentation courses for graduates at the Commonwealth Forestry Institute at Oxford University. The IFD Programme assisted China to gain and maintain access to the CAB Abstracts database.

Scientific Information Officers in CABI continued this training in the 21st century, often linked to subscriptions to CAB Abstracts. CABI's longstanding training courses in information management offered to librarians from developing countries began to include training in how to set up a PC with a CD-ROM drive, how to carry out basic computer maintenance and how to search for information with the SilverPlatter software, SPIRS. The text box below describes this form of training in Egypt in 2010.

Making knowledge available: training Egyptian scientists to access the CAB Abstracts Databases

Researchers often lack the time or funds, and sometimes the skills, to gain access to modern bibliographic databases, including those produced by CABI. Training to transfer the necessary skills, therefore, complements CABI's database marketing efforts and the capacity of users to make best use of the database. For example, in early negotiations with Ovid and the Egyptian University Libraries Consortium (EUL) for access to the CABI Databases with Ovid, it was agreed that free, on-site user training would be offered as part of an overall package. Chris Ison, International Training Manager, believes that for future collaboration with the consortium CABI should investigate the possibility of providing some tailor-made training guides, video tutorials and think about the possibility of providing Arabic translations of CABI's printed and video guides. The consortium, now with 12 subscribing members and 17 active sites, began subscribing as a single entity at the beginning of 2009, having signed a 3-year agreement, due for renewal at the end of 2011. The members currently have access to CAB Abstracts and Global Health.

Ison oversaw intensive training for 13 members of the consortium in March 2010. The training sessions conducted at a number of the consortium institutions took the CABI team the length and breadth of Egypt. Each day, a member of staff from the agent Library Information for Marketing & Services and a

member of the Supreme Council of Universities, a department of the Ministry of Higher Education, accompanying him, presenting a very professional-looking and united front.

The level of searching experience was wide and varied, with many questions about some of the basic techniques such as truncation and masking, and the use of Boolean operators and brackets. Before the second session the presentations and the distributed user guides were edited substantially, to include instruction on some of these useful techniques. Ison says that the numbers and quality of the attendees, which exceeded 800 in total, were impressive.

This was the first time that an overseas publisher had been allowed to run such a long and detailed training programme in Egypt. In the past, publishers have been limited to much shorter, joint presentations. It was very clear from the questions and the comments that such training is seen as being highly valuable. Electronic User Guides were left at each centre so that they could be loaded and distributed locally.

The CAB Full Text database, which links abstracts to the full text article where licence agreements allow, was seen as a very valuable addition to the CABI bibliographic databases. Most attendees were not aware of the existence of this database. The first part of each training session explained the Full Text database, and the concept behind it, and showed off numbers for Egyptian and Middle Eastern content. The second part of each session showed how to limit searches (to make them more specific), on OvidSP, to the CAB Full Text records and how to display the free PDF files. Both during and since the trip, Ison received several suggestions for new Egyptian content for CAB Full Text, and he returned with one print journal and a Conference Proceedings on CD, for consideration by the controller of database content. Negotiations have begun for an agreement to include some, or perhaps all, of the relevant Egyptian research journals in CAB Full Text.

Capacity building can take many forms. Training and back-up for 'plant doctors' is, for example, a feature of Plantwise, with its global plant health clinics that provide training at the grassroots level.

Under this approach 'mobile' extension services are linked to a fixed central or national facility and, where needed, an international diagnostic and advisory service. Farmers can present any crop and type of health problem at a local service that might take place at a temporary stand erected at an agricultural fair or rural bus terminal. 'Plant doctors', who may not be expert plant pathologists, can, with limited additional training (provided not by CABI but by national research and extension services) give advice on what to do. They may be equipped with rapid diagnostic tests for commonly occurring problems to aid their analysis and to demonstrate to farmers. Sometimes farmers or the 'plant doctors' need further advice or they lack equipment and materials. National research and extension centres may be able to provide this additional support. An international facility established at Egham,

known as Plantwise, with its global plant health clinics, provides further back-up, if needed. In the modern equivalent of the pest identification handbook, YouTube websites give examples of clinics, training of plant doctors, plant health problems and other aspects of plant health.

At the other end of the training spectrum, CABI's Centre in Switzerland annually hosts international student placements whereby biology and agriculture students receive hands-on training in practical aspects of applied biological control research, working in project teams with high-impact outcomes. The Centre also has a graduate student programme, with links to universities around the world. There are normally students from more than a dozen countries working together each summer.

Training can sometimes be about doing yourself out of a job. NARS, such as those in the developed member countries and, after the 1990s, those in the more advanced developing countries, have strengthened. No doubt, help from CABI's training efforts has contributed to this strengthening. This in turn may have reduced the call on CABI's identification services (although other factors such as the introduction of charges and the establishment of BioNET undoubtedly had a big effect). Similarly, the Research Stations established in India, Canada and the USA to support the work of the Institute of Biological Control were transferred to the research structures in the countries in which they were located, strengthening their national capabilities and again potentially reducing the need for CABI's services. In any case, as national capabilities strengthened, CABI's activities were to focus increasingly on identification of critical and novel material, in capability development, and in the production of manuals and other training aids.

Plant clinic, Vietnam. ©CABI

Selling papaya seeds. ©CABI

Diseased bananas are brought along to a plant clinic for diagnosis. ©CABI

THE MODERN CABI

In the modern era of CABI, which can be defined as the last 25 years, there have been three seismic developments: the unification of the Bureaux under one roof at the new headquarters at Wallingford (1987), the bringing together of the four Institutes and the formation of CABI Bioscience (1998), and the off-shoring of abstracting services (2001) which heralded wholesale changes in CABI's publishing business. The change and reorganization prompted by a testing external environment during much of the modern period, together with chronic economic difficulties, made this a turbulent time. This chapter seeks to put some perspective on events by looking at the external forces that shaped CABI in this period, how it adapted to the changing world, and where it is now heading.

The birth of the modern

In the House of Commons, at a little after 7pm on 3 March 1910, Mr Winston Churchill rose to make the following remarks about the establishment of the Entomology Research Committee that was to become CABI:

" The committee will send two very skilled investigators, one to the East Coast and the other to the West Coast, to advise and report on any special points on which it may desire information. The inquiry covers the whole region of the diseases which are conveyed by insects, not only those which affect man, but those which affect animals and plants. I am quite sure that all the Members of the House, wherever they sit, who take an interest in the scientific treatment of tropical diseases will appreciate that in developing more highly the power of research, which is now possessed by the Colonial Office, and that by calling this new Committee into being we take an important step forward far more than the comparatively small sum of money which is involved would indicate – an important step forward which may conceivably be of

priceless advantage not only to our own fellow countrymen who are serving beyond the seas, but to the great mass of the aboriginal population committed to their charge. "

It is an honour for an institute to be launched with aplomb by such an historic figure. But it is ironic that CABI should, from its very moment of birth, be expected to do so much with so little.[203] This has been CABI's fate ever since and much of its subsequent history has been shaped by funding challenges, interspersed with periodic crises; and by steady pressure from member countries that the organization should earn its way.

So CABI was born just as the Edwardian era was ending, at the apogee of the British Empire. The organization that grew into CABI, with its varied Bureaux and stations that generated and disseminated practical and punctual information, was a sort of prototype networking organization, a printed Google that was truly innovative and international. It was ahead of its time and its value became quickly understood. Ever since, the sheer amount and quality of the information that CABI distributed through this network has sustained the reputation of the organization, as it rapidly extended over the globe despite world wars, revolutions, famines and global economic crises.

This chapter concentrates less on the notable exploits of its daring and talented scientists and information pioneers, which have been covered in previous chapters, and more on the ways that it has changed and continues to change. There is an untold story here too, of the many anonymous administrators who kept the institute solvent through many difficult periods. Not all scientists appreciate the practical difficulties of funding a not-for-profit operation, and here the role of management must be acknowledged as an equally vital contribution to the life of CABI.

CABI first developed very much in the eye of its brilliant first director – Sir Guy Marshall. As neither an autocrat nor an academic, but a practical and collaborative soul, he built the organization accordingly, employing strong personalities from a wide range of countries who contributed to the organization in a deliberately original, even idiosyncratic way. That it survived for so long in the general form of its early years is a tribute to its founder and his founding vision.

1987 A new constitution, in the form of a treaty-level International Agreement, comes into effect, and the organization becomes CAB International. The formal opening of new headquarters at Wallingford by His Royal Highness the Prince of Wales marks a new phase in CABI's development.

1991 The Partnership Facility, a special fund to attract and manage funding of development projects, is established.

1993 CABI takes over the Bureaux of Hygiene and Tropical Diseases.

Doug Laing is appointed as Director General. He retires due to poor health after a year of service.

1994 Jim Gilmore appointed as Director General.

1995 CABI launches a new Public Health Database, CAB Health, later to be rebranded as Global Health.

The creation of the Publishing Division brings together all book, primary, secondary journal and electronic publishing activities with production, sales, marketing and distribution functions.

1996 CABI Review Conference is told that like other publishers CABI faces a 'Valley of Death' as subscriptions to printed journals fall and income from electronic products, which required substantial investment, grows slowly.

1998 The four Institutes are brought together to form CABI Bioscience.

1999 The Research Stations of the Institute of Biological Control become CABI Bioscience Centres.

2000 Denis Blight appointed as Director General. Increased delegation and regional responsibility to the International Centres within the framework of an integrated CABI Bioscience strategy. CABI Publishing and CABI Information Divisions are merged. CABI opens an office in New Delhi and further expands facilities at the Swiss Centre at Delémont.

2001 Elements of abstract preparation are outsourced to the Philippines and India. An external Review of CABI Bioscience is commissioned. It endorses a 'One CABI' corporate vision and strategy.

In the modern era, CABI has for compelling reasons consolidated parts of its distributed network to seek strength in a simpler and more unified structure. At the same time, delegation to the regions has reduced the concentration of decision-making in the UK and created an increasingly decentralized, international organization. Inevitably some of the changes during this period were uncomfortable for staff and there were some unavoidable casualties. But, overall, the story has been one of the successful creation of a new and coherent identity as an international development-led organization supported by both a first-class publishing division and first-class scientific research.

The aim of this chapter is very briefly to review the changes (many are covered more completely in previous chapters) and then try to explain them in terms of the global forces that CABI has had to contend with.

Unification of the Bureaux

As noted in Chapter 7, as early as 1943, the Hankey Review found that it was: 'difficult to perceive any obvious unity of general purpose or control amongst the 10 or more component parts of the Commonwealth Agricultural Bureaux, including the three Institutes'.

As Hankey noted, the Institutes and Bureaux had been started at different times and places; each was linked both physically and by identity of interest with a different and independent British research establishment (or in the cases of the Mycological and Parasitology Institutes were self-contained); and they were all characterized by individuality and strong – some might say headstrong – leadership. The Review saw the diversity, individuality, and the immersion of individual Bureaux within relevant scientific research institutions as potential strengths of the organization, provided that the various components and their users recognized that they were parts of a greater whole.[204]

This neatly sums up the problem that CABI and many other dispersed organizations have faced. Distributed systems or networks are nowadays very common: many firms have a head office in one country, a call-centre in another and a manufacturing base in a third. Many use part-time employees working from home and there are some institutes that are entirely virtual. It was nevertheless an unusual arrangement at the time, and it was certainly unique to have so many employees embedded in other organizations. The disadvantages of this clearly started to outweigh the advantages, and it is difficult to see how it could have continued to work effectively in the modern world where so much funding for science now comes from competitive bidding.

Distributed organizations tend to compensate for a dispersed structure by developing a strong centralized identity, attention to branding and skilful advertising. Such an approach is anathema to many scientists, but the advantages are clear – a network of individualist scientists can all too easily appear to be disorganized and unfocused.

The challenge therefore was to find a balance that maximized the strengths of a network and the power of a centralized system. There never is a perfect balance however, and to an extent the centre of gravity will change with circumstances and the approach of individual managers.

At any rate, the centralization of the Bureaux was accomplished with some style on to a new site at Wallingford, UK. The headquarters building was opened by His Royal Highness the Prince of Wales on 15 September 1987 and marked a new phase in CABI's development. The formalities for a change in status to a full international organization had been completed by 12 of 20 member countries signing an agreement to extend membership beyond the Commonwealth of Nations and triggering the new constitution as a treaty-level document.

Prince Charles meets CABI staff, September 1987. ©CABI

Unification of the science institutes

The four scientific institutes, IIBC, IIP, IIE and IMI, were merged into CABI Bioscience in 1998. The aim of the unification was to move to a progressively more integrated and sharper focus on plant health and the environment, and on development in developing countries, though of course an additional benefit was that it reduced costs. In considering priorities for CABI's bioscience programme, a Programme Committee of the Board, chaired by George Rothschild, identified 'three major themes for refocusing the bioscience programme: biodiversity characterization and conservation; plant health and productivity; and environmental change and quality'.

The Rothschild Committee also reported that 'biosystematics will require possible further rationalization.' This indeed very rapidly turned out to be the case, with first entomological identification services being discontinued and progressively other microbial identification services as well. The reason was simple: the cost of maintaining a taxonomic facility, with staff costs and laboratory overheads, was far in excess of income. Neither donors nor member countries, however sympathetic they appeared to be when sounded out, were willing to subsidize the costs of this service. So CABI was left with no feasible alternative than to wind them up.

CABI's properties in Kensington and St Albans were sold in the 1990s and subsequently the Ascot site in 2007.

The 'four into one' move that created CABI Bioscience was also intended to create closer collaboration amongst scientists. The hope was that a number of spin-off commercial enterprises would emerge that would generate the funds required to support its overseas roles.

One project that drew on CABI's biological control legacy and its expertise in entomology, mycology and parasitology included a major collaborative project to control the desert locust and grasshoppers in the Sahel (see box opposite – Doing the impossible in the Sahara Desert), called LUBILOSA, which led to the production of Green Muscle®, a biopesticide.

Locusts. ©iStockphoto

Doing the impossible in the Sahara Desert

LUBILOSA (derived from the French phrase for Biological Control of Locusts and Grasshoppers: LUBILOSA LUtte BIologique contre les LOcustes et les SAuteriaux) was a collaborative programme led by CABI which began in 1989. The programme cost about £15 million, lasted 12 years and succeeded in doing what most scientists had predicted was impossible – using fungi, in the heat and high light intensity of the Sahara Desert, to kill locusts, with the Desert Locust being the iconic target.

The researchers used the fungus *Metarhizium anisopliae varacridum*, originally obtained from a grasshopper in Niger.

The first breakthrough was extending the shelf life of the biological pesticide beyond the initial target of 6 months. Other advances included the development of a spore harvesting machine, based on cyclones, which resulted in the collection of a powder based on individual spores. The spores of *Metarhizium* suspend very easily in oil and a formulation made with separate particles passes easily through spinning disc application machinery. The prototype spore harvester led on to many variations, culminating in an industrial scale version, now installed in a number of commercial facilities.

Trials showed that chemical insecticides killed very rapidly, but within a few days, numbers were rising again. In contrast, only after 7–10 days did populations in the plots testing the experimental product begin to drop. However, they continued to drop and remained low well beyond the time when populations in the chemical plots were back to the control levels.[205]

Another interesting discovery was that, although locust numbers fell, very few cadavers were found. What was happening was that, as the disease progressed through the locust body, the insect became ill and un-coordinated and was less and less able to move. At that point local predators including birds, lizards and, especially, ants, moved in on this very easy prey and removed the sick individuals. This provided anecdotal support for the view that the biological insecticide was very much more environmentally benign than conventional products, but this was also confirmed by independent scientific study by non-LUBILOSA scientists.

The end result of the LUBILOSA project was an effective product, which, although slower acting, was more effective and persistent than the conventional insecticide being used, and environmentally very safe.

Green Muscle®, as it was called, has been trialled successfully in a number of African countries, on smaller scales in various Asian countries, and is being produced commercially. Most of the scientific advances were well publicized through papers written for scientific journals – a characteristic of the project was that most (although not all) of the intellectual property generated was made public.

Another commercial project that drew on CABI's scientific expertise was the test kit developed to detect the presence of a corrosive fungus in the fuel tanks of aircraft.

The fuel test kit

The filamentous fungus *Hormoconis resinae* is the most common cause of microbial corrosion in aircraft tanks. Unlike other microorganisms that feed on the alkanes found in fuel, *H. resinae* does not just float around at the interface between the water and fuel, but sticks to the bottom or sides of the tank. This means that it corrodes the tank itself, and also that it is not easily drained away with the fuel.

Whilst high levels of bacteria and yeasts tend to indicate poor quality fuel, they are not necessarily causing any problem in the tank, and are unlikely to persist after the next drain. High levels of *H. resinae*, however, indicate that there is, potentially, a serious problem.

The Fuelstat™ diagnostic kit, developed by CABI scientist Joan Kelley and her colleagues, detects *H. resinae* contamination by 'finding' material that is produced during growth on fuel. Acting and indeed looking rather like a home pregnancy test, it takes 10 minutes to detect the presence of *H. resinae*. This compares favourably with tests using traditional growth techniques, that can take up to 7 days, need sterile sampling conditions, incubation and daily monitoring – and produce a full picture of bacterial contamination when all the aircraft owners need is a simple 'yes' or 'no'.

The fuel-test kits were commercialized by Conidia Bioscience Ltd, a spin-out company formed by CABI, and in which CABI retains a share.

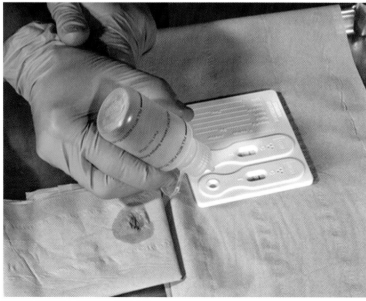

Conidia aviation fuel test kit. ©Conidia

Despite the success of projects such as LUBILOSA and the Conidia fuel-test kits, CABI has not pursued a purely commercial route. However, it does continue to seek to exploit its intellectual property (IP) as appropriate. CABI's strongest suit is precisely the know-how that accretes to a mature institution, as knowledge is handed on from senior scientists to the next generation. And it was this knowledge that CABI sought to put at the disposal of poor farmers and extension officers in developing countries as it followed a new direction as a development organization.

CABI and the development agenda

Don Mentz, Director General from 1984 to 1993, envisaged CABI as a central player in international bioscience research for development. In particular, he wanted CABI to benefit substantially from development assistance funding in partnership with National Agricultural Research Systems (NARS) in the developing member countries.

According to Dennis Greenland, this 'never worked as well as hoped' in the early days, for a range of reasons including the time-consuming and complex nature of donor tendering arrangements. It also coincided with a severe decline in donor funding for agriculture. Nevertheless, the CABI Development Service was set up to promote the organization's products in the aid sector. Whilst Mentz was always 'way ahead' of those trying to implement his plan, his work and vision laid the basis for a new direction for CABI as a development organization.

CABI used 'country assessment programmes' to identify the needs of developing countries for its services and to find ways of funding their provision. The Partnership Facility (later to be known as the CABI Development Fund), established in 1991 to provide funds from donors to help developing countries purchase CABI services, has been a major source of seed funding for CABI projects, which helped CABI show aid agencies what it could achieve. Whilst it was never large enough to underwrite more than a fraction of the costs of CABI development projects, it enabled CABI to demonstrate capacity and potential impact through exemplar activities and to build the closer relations with aid agencies that the country assessment programmes said were needed. CABI demonstrated capacity in areas of specialization including plant health, commodities, IPM, invasive species management and knowledge dissemination.

A number of projects funded by the Partnership Facility helped to build on CABI's credentials in plant health, pests and diseases. These included a pilot project in Bolivia that was the starting point for the plant health clinic concept.

An impact assessment conducted in 2009 showed that farmers who consulted a clinic benefited from improved harvests, and often with lower plant protection production costs. Some farmers spent more on plant protection though the vast majority still showed net income increases after adopting a recommendation

Others, concerning specific plant health problems, included the Good Seed Initiative which improved the quality and value of smallholder farmers' seed; enabled the poor to access and benefit from seed sourced outside their community; and taken forward learning into regional and national seed systems and policies. Since its inception it has worked with

Opposite: millet farmer selecting seed. ©CABI

local scientists in Uganda to train farmers to grow the award-winning NERICA rice. And in Tanzania the programme has been showing sorghum producers how to improve their farm-saved seed to reduce seed-transmitted diseases and increase yields.

NERICA rice. ©CABI

In addition, as CABI sought to use its information and publishing expertise, the Facility invested in an inception workshop in 2002 that led to the development of the Aquaculture Compendium; Crop Protection Compendium training in Africa that aided its take-up by donors; and the Heritage Project which digitized CABI's Abstracts archive, which was then made available free of cost to least developed member countries.

The creation of overseas CABI Bioscience Centres

Balancing the unification of institutes in the UK, more emphasis was given to the overseas stations. The history of CABI's international centres stretches back to a recommendation of Myers in the 1930s that the interests of the Commonwealth could be better served by the establishment of permanent stations in critical areas rather than by short-term investigations by staff operating from headquarters. A start was made in 1941 with an outpost in California, following the relocation of the Institute's headquarters to Canada during the Second World War. As explained in Chapter 6, further Stations and sub-stations were set up after the war and each contributed significantly to CABI's history, especially in biological control, but also in building relationships with member countries.

In 1998, the Research Stations of the Institute of Biological Control in Africa, the Caribbean, Europe, India, Malaysia and Pakistan became CABI Bioscience Centres. They operated under the science direction of CABI Bioscience headquarters in the UK but also reporting to the Director General of CABI on broader representational functions with member countries.

In early 2000, these Centres were granted a semi-independent status with allocated budgets and within a loose overall CABI Bioscience strategic framework and direction. At first, the Centres – whilst welcoming the

freedom of operation and initiative that came with devolution – baulked at the financial challenge. However, over time Centre Directors 'felt empowered by the perception that they were now driving their own agendas' and that as a consequence they strove 'to grow their project portfolios and soon even bigger projects from a more diverse funding base followed.'[206] Their combined deficits were gradually reduced to the point where several were generating surpluses. Only the UK Centre, with its higher direct cost base and carrying the costs of the various support services associated with project development and support functions for all Centres, remained in substantial deficit.

Unity of purpose and control became abiding issues as the Centres saw opportunities for growth independently of directions from headquarters. The International Centres thus started to evolve their own personalities and ambitions, bolstered perhaps by a keenness to emphasize that the UK was not always the natural centre of operations. Individuality, divided loyalties and strong leadership of the component parts were still in the mix; but CABI's leadership saw this independence as a potential strength of the organization provided it remained within a single shared vision.

This process of upgrading the International Centres and wherever possible recruiting scientists from the regions gave a strong message to donors and local governments that the colonial past of CABI was over. It also helped to quell the misconception in many quarters that CABI was predominantly a UK government-backed organization. Accordingly, these International Centres started to attract more funding and far more south–south collaboration started between different Centres too, which further helped to develop expertise and build a common vision.

A drawback was that much of the project funding was for relatively short-term work, usually no longer than 3 years, sometimes much shorter, often on very complex pest and disease problems that had for one reason or another flared up in a particular region. Increasingly too, to the irritation of some of the 'pure' scientists, these projects became complex, multi-country exercises where CABI's role became more concentrated on project management, disbursement of funds, workshop organization and so on, rather than first-hand research.

Funding was never abundant enough for consistent growth, because many donors had lost interest in agriculture as they concentrated on more intangible concepts such as good governance and industrialization. Until recently the growing power of transnational agribusiness companies and confidence in globally free trade gave rise to a belief that the power of the free market could solve all global problems. Ironically however, at the same time, the free-market doctrine was imposed on many of the poorest countries through structural adjustment programmes, which insisted on the downsizing of national agricultural research institutes, commodity boards and much else.

Hence just at a time when these countries should have been increasing investment in order to feed growing populations in a sustainable fashion, the opposite happened. This meant that the term 'sustainable development' so widely current after the 1987 Bruntland report[207], in practice meant little more than market-led growth. Hence much of CABI's expertise, that could so readily have been used to support capacity building of agricultural extension systems, was never called upon to the extent that CABI felt was necessary. CABI could see the problems developing in the 1990s that have since become clear to all, but was powerless to intervene.

Examples of this can be seen in Africa, where 'new' plant diseases such as coffee wilt disease, banana bacterial wilt, cassava brown streak and other diseases and pests have spread largely unchecked over recent years. Coffee wilt disease alone has caused losses of more than US$1 billion to farmers. With proper vigilance, early identification and rapid response, this disease could have been contained and even eradicated for at most a few million dollars. But the funds and response structures were not there. It has now been tackled in Africa and India through a multi-country CFC-funded project led by CABI.

With the emergence onto the global stage in 2008 of the world food crisis, some national governments and donors pledged higher priority to agricultural research. This, together with increased recognition of biodiversity as global priorities, provides some hope of increased resources being available for CABI's work.

Refocusing CABI Publishing

CABI's publishing activities have been the solid generator of funds that has kept CABI afloat during its turbulent recent history. At its heart are the 9 million abstracts of agricultural, environmental and health science that reach back a century; a mine of information that can help people become remarkably well informed.

The 1990s was a period of great change in academic publishing worldwide, as subscriptions to printed journals fell and new, electronic-based publishing models began to emerge. The economic climate was difficult (1991 saw a global recession), and this also coincided with the start of a general reduction in membership fees.

Jim Gilmore – Director General 1993 to 1999

This note on Jim Gilmore is adapted from remarks by Rob Williams made on his retirement and at a memorial tree planting at CABI shortly after his death in the year 2004.

Jim began at CABI in 1987 in the post of Systems Manager and then Director of Information Technology. It was in these posts that Jim first had a significant impact on CABI and its future development. He made sure that CABI was at the forefront of exploiting the power of modern IT, for its processes and management as well as its information products.

In the summer of 1993 Jim stepped into the breach after the retirement, due to ill health, of Doug Laing. He was formally appointed Director General in July 1994. During his time as Director General he drove further 're-engineering' of CABI. He demonstrated a stubborn steadfastness of purpose, not being deflected by the many alarms and crises. He was 'always calm

and focused on the key elements, looking for solutions, guided by his commitment to the best interests of CABI. When it came to hard decisions, and there were several, once he was sure he had all the relevant facts, there was no question of taking soft options or an easy route.'

During his time as Director General five new countries became CABI members. Gilmore took a leading role in relations with China, and through his careful and patient guidance, China joined CABI and established important partnerships with CABI, e.g. the White Agriculture Programme. He was steadfast, honourable, fair and diligent.

Tony Llewellyn, then CABI's head of Publishing, described the issues affecting the publishing business in the 1990s in a presentation to the 1996 Thirteenth Review Conference[208] in the following way:

- The gap between increased research funding and the increasing demand for the output of published data, and the ability of libraries to purchase, continues to widen;

- Coincidental with this is the accelerated development of an electronic publishing environment. This is causing fundamental change in how information is used, produced and made available, including:

  – the trend away from ownership of information to access to information, and from subscription to transactional purchasing by customers gaining momentum with the development of electronic formats and delivery systems;

  – new 'entrants' to the world of information publishing, notably telecommunication and software companies;

  – primary publishers exerting greater influence on the current awareness and abstracting processes; and

  – issues concerning copyright and ownership of information in the digital environment are growing in significance.

These trends were just part of a worldwide revolution in the way that not only information but all aspects of commercial life were changing, away from a just-in-case approach where printed copies are archived in libraries for perusal, to a just-in-time mode where information is downloaded when required.

For CABI this meant that sales of its printed abstract journals, which in 1993 had represented 60% of its publishing income, were falling by about 12% a year. CABI's response to this was to provide progressively more of its output online; CABI's publishing team successfully migrated customers from print to digital products and developed a delivery platform, CAB Direct, which was launched in 2000. The primary journals list, which had been available both in print and online, was sold in 2006 to Cambridge University Press, allowing CABI a greater focus on its core assets: abstract databases and books.

In 1998 the keyboarding of CAB Abstracts data was outsourced to a company in the Philippines and India. This was a bold and inevitably controversial decision that moved most non-editorial functions offshore.

Quite soon afterwards, in 2001, CABI implemented a change programme that moved the whole process (data capture, abstracting and indexing) from the UK to the Philippines and India, creating over 100 high-quality jobs in these two member countries. The change also entailed the loss of some jobs in the UK, which caused significant upheaval. However, CABI was able to refocus UK-based staff into new roles, expand content coverage, and develop new web-based resources such as Global Health. This helped to sustain the profitability of the publishing services and released funds for investment in sales and marketing as well as providing financial support for the rest of the organization.

Peter Scott. ©CABI

Under the direction of Peter Scott, Director of Programme Development, CABI also began to develop specific products that used the abstracts but which also added considerable value in terms of more easily accessible information and knowledge through hundreds of expert contributors. The first of the Compendia, as they became known, was the Crop Protection Compendium launched in 1996.

Using information, creating knowledge

A major product and way of working emerged from a 1989 International Crop Protection Information Workshop, co-organized by CABI, Technical Centre for Agricultural and Rural Cooperation ACP-EU (CTA) and FAO and attended by delegates from 32 countries in the developed and developing world. Delegates expressed profound concern over inadequate delivery of information to support effective crop protection in developing countries, and suggested that information technology could tackle this. CABI demonstrated a prototype CD-ROM containing abstracts on crop pest and pathogen species, text and images from published data sheets about them, and images of distribution maps. A list of names and synonyms of the species allowed 'hot-linking' between related information. This enthused the delegates and they recommended concerted action to compile information on pests and diseases in a standardized way, and to exploit the emerging capabilities of information technology to deliver it, especially to developing countries.

The Australian Centre for International Agricultural Research (ACIAR) funded a feasibility study, which began in 1992 with a small international workshop to consider user needs and develop an outline structural and navigational scheme. A consultant (Charles Schotman) prepared a more detailed specification, assessed resource needs, and developed a further prototype to show potential users. This was a powerful tool in engaging attention, and was extensively used in a survey of user needs, focusing on South-east Asia and the Pacific, generating an enthusiastic response.

The Feasibility Study also led to a Project Proposal to develop a working Compendium, with global coverage provided in a stepwise fashion. The first module focused on pests of particular importance in South-east Asia, southern China and the Pacific.

A Development Consortium of 20 organizations each committed funding. The principle of shared ownership of the project and

commitment to its completion proved invaluable. It successfully embraced both public- and private-sector organizations, and allowed in-kind commitment of resources as well as financial support. Consortium Members benefited through public identification with this innovative project, influence on the project and its output, the gearing effect of

cooperative funding, mutual confidence that the project would deliver on schedule, and privileged access to the finished product. CABI published the Compendium on CD-ROM, using a dual-pricing formula that allowed customers in developing countries a 75% discount on the price charged in the developed world. Sales revenue assured maintenance through annual updates as a mechanism for sustainability of the Compendium – an important consideration for its stakeholders.

Further Compendia were developed in Forestry, Animal Health and Production, Aquaculture and Invasive Species.

The Compendium programme was hugely innovative when it first appeared, winning a Pirelli Prize in 1999. Since then it has been constantly updated, embracing developing Internet technology and ensuring that the Compendia are consistently the most comprehensive and up-to-date encyclopaedic resource for practitioners in agriculture.

Books publishing

In 1988, the publishing business appointed its first books commissioning editor, Tim Hardwick, who began to build what would become a major book list in niche areas of the life sciences.

Production-oriented agriculture was then unfashionable, at least in developed countries. Other publishers were withdrawing from the subject. Butterworths phased out its agriculture book programme and Longmans swapped its list for the Blackwell science list in hairdressing and beauty care! But this provided an opportunity for CABI to build. While the larger life science publishers were active in plant sciences, and medical publishers were active in veterinary science, this still left room in subjects such as animal science, horticulture and relevant social sciences.

The book list grew rapidly during the 1990s and subsequently. After a few years CABI was publishing more than 50 new titles per annum and became widely regarded as a leading international publisher in animal, plant and related social sciences. Flagship publications include the *Dictionary of Fungi*, now in its 65th year, and the *UK Pesticide Guide*, which by 2008 had reached its 21st edition. Nigel Farrar took over the lead commissioning role in 2006.

With the Google-led renewed market interest in e-books, in the mid-noughties CABI made its books available via third party e-book vendors. This was followed in 2008 by the launch of 'CAB eBooks', a subscription-based product allowing access to the entire e-book collection directly from CABI, and in 2009 the CAB eBooks product was the recipient of an Outstanding Academic Title award from Choice.

With most of CABI's books now available in electronic format, book content is increasingly being used to support and enhance CABI's online

resources, such as Environmental Impact and VetMed Resource. The coming years will see this trend growing further, and the emphasis will be more on the content, which can then be delivered via different platforms to suit different users.

Towards structural unity

So by the end of the 20th century, the organization had consolidated into two distinct parts: CABI Bioscience, including the international Centres, and CABI Publishing.

This apparent simplicity of course masked a number of continuing complexities. With even the best-managed structural changes, human emotions take some time to catch up, and old allegiances die hard. In addition, thanks to a turbulent external environment, the change process in publishing was particularly protracted. Having coalesced on the Wallingford site in 1987, it was not until 2003 that all the publishing activities were formally brought together under the single CABI Publishing brand.

The simplified structure, too, presented its own problems. Denis Blight, Director General from 2000 to 2005, had wanted two equally strong but complementary brands to reinforce each other. But while CABI Publishing was rapidly established as a leading brand in its markets, CABI Bioscience – possibly because it lacked tangible 'products' – could never match it. The directors of both divisions were highly focused with strong personalities. And for whatever reasons the two divisions found it hard to work together with only a few notable exceptions.

Denis Blight[209]

Denis Blight became Director General in 2000, just as CABI was about to implement the decision to outsource all of its abstracting to the Philippines and India. He successfully steered the organization through this contentious change – including a move of the whole process (data capture, abstracting and indexing) in 2001, which gave CABI a more flexible cost base and strengthened relationships with two key member countries.

He ensured the organization's survival throughout severe financial difficulties and instigated a number of key reviews, including the KPMG review in 2004. Following the KPMG review he started the process of bringing together all the corporate functions, which laid the foundations for today's more professional and streamlined approach.

Blight had the unenviable task of uniting a group of highly individualistic senior managers and asking them to support him in making some tough decisions. While the demands of the job must have been hugely stressful, and did not always result in popularity, many staff remember him as always laughing, approachable and warm. In 2004 he was awarded an Order of Australia for his contribution to international education, bioscience and development.

The CABI Review Plan of 2005/2006, prepared by Blight in discussion with then Chair of the Governing Board John Regazzi, was implemented and further developed by Blight's successor as chief executive, Trevor Nicholls, who also took over the completion of the CABI review plan.

Trevor Nicholls

The CABI that Trevor Nicholls joined in 2005 was also in the throes of a major dispute over the unsustainably expensive final salary pension scheme. Nicholls needed to find a way forward that would be acceptable to both staff and the Board. This he successfully achieved by considering all the options and in the end finding a solution that he felt worked for the organization.

It integrated and streamlined CABI's sales, marketing, finance and administration services, ensured that all its component parts were represented on its leadership team, and abolished the CABI Publishing and CABI Bioscience brands. The whole organization was brought together in 2006 under a single CABI brand.

Since then, he has worked steadily to move CABI on to a financially sound footing and to sharpen and professionalize its processes while strengthening and continuing to pursue its mission. The sale of the primary journals list in 2006 cleared CABI's overdraft as well as enabling a greater focus on the abstracts databases and books. Selling the leasehold of the Ascot building in 2007 had the double benefit of uniting all the scientific and development staff, based in the UK, on one site and reducing a major financial commitment.

CABI's activities are now restructured around two business units: publishing and international development. The development activities were in turn concentrated in four thematic areas where CABI has world-class expertise and a recognized track record: commodity crop health, invasive species management, knowledge for development, and bioservices.

Between 2005 and 2010, the organization delivered an operating surplus every year with the exception of 2009, when it was affected by the global crisis.

Nicholls has pulled together a new management team and worked with them to give CABI a clarity of identity and purpose that it had previously lacked. The single CABI brand was launched within 6 months of his joining and he has been a tireless advocate for the need for integration and collaboration across the organization.

This new structure allowed CABI the flexibility to focus on addressing issues of food security by helping farmers lose less of their crops to pests and diseases. It was able to continue to provide practical support and guidance on both commodity and food crops to extension workers and farmers. And its work on controlling invasive species and preserving its fungal reference collection contributed to protecting biodiversity and developing sustainable agricultural techniques as illustrated by its work on Japanese knotweed in the UK (see box) and the rubber vine weed in Australia. This agenda is a global one serving its developed and developing member countries.

Common to all activities was a belief in the creation, transference, and application of knowledge as the key to development. And this really shows the extent of CABI's development over the past century.

A hundred years ago, most of the work that CABI undertook was purely science-based and descriptive: the process of ordering and classifying knowledge in ways that can be retrieved and understood by others. But, partly as a result of its networked structure and partly because of the way its information provision activities metamorphosed into publishing, by the time this new structure was in place CABI had moved far beyond being purely or even principally a science organization.

With its databases, network of contacts, its science tradition and institutional knowledge of many aspects of environmental and agricultural science, CABI was well positioned to become a true example of that 21st-century phenomenon – the knowledge organization. Its challenge now is how it can bring all of its knowledge into play to solve some of the grave and pressing problems faced by its member countries, as population growth, environmental degradation and climate change bear down upon us all.

Joining up CABI

CABI's mission, defined during the development of the single CABI brand launched in 2006, is to 'improve people's lives worldwide by providing information and applying scientific expertise to solve problems in agriculture and the environment'. What CABI strives to do is to find a comprehensive way to help people with a wide range of complex real-life problems: how do I adapt to climate change? What should I plant instead of a crop that has just failed? How quickly is this new banana disease spreading? Who might know about it in my district? How can I get a better price in the market for my crop?

Most of CABI's international development projects already go some way towards answering these sorts of questions. CABI enables smallholder commodity growers to compete in global markets and otherwise improve livelihoods through the use of integrated pest management and improved agricultural practices. CABI works to reduce the spread and impact of invasive alien species, and supports communities in identifying and addressing plant health problems.

But as information technology has developed and CABI has focused its expertise in international development, the potential for joining up what CABI does has become clearer. Building on its existing work in all three units it can develop a new approach that integrates a much wider source of information in new dynamic ways: something that is so useful that everyone will want to be a part of it. It can find new ways to involve

Cocoa harvesting, Tokiala, Papua New Guinea. ©CABI

scientists so that they can be of more direct assistance to those who need their assistance and connect them as part of an integrated system.

In 2009, CABI undertook an extensive strategic and scientific review, with input from external strategy consultants, LEK, and a science review panel. This resulted in a number of recommendations that were approved by member countries at the Review Conference that year. Principal amongst these was the decision to develop a comprehensive global information resource on plant health, building on CABI's publishing and knowledge management expertise as well as on the existing plant clinic development project.

Other priorities over the 2 years have been to create a service focused on making scientific knowledge accessible, which is being developed as part of the Knowledge Management theme; to build on the strong work being done on biological control in the centres in Europe; and to begin screening the fungal genetic resource collection, held at Egham for novel biological compounds having potential commercial value.

Lack of access to research information has been identified as a key constraint to economic development for the world's poorest countries. It can often be a challenge for the right people to be able to access the right information at the right time. Farmers in particular face problems, based as they are in rural locations and often in countries with little extension support and advice. Researchers lack funds or time to find the information they need, and often find developing country research hard to find because large sections of it are not digitized. Policy makers face the challenge of finding organizations with the experience to advise and that they can trust to give impartial advice.

CABI's ability to combine leading-edge digital information management techniques with a long history of working directly with the rural poor puts it in a strong position to be able to contribute to development in this area. Specific projects have included creating and running DFID's R4D (Research for Development) website and communications portal.

CABI also has a long history of researching invasive species that affect agriculture and the environment. It was among the leading organizations in developing methods of biological control. In recent years that role has expanded: CABI's scientists now advise on policy for invasive species management and implement countrywide management plans.

One of the highest profile projects in this area has been the investigation of biological control techniques for the 'concrete-cracking superweed' Japanese knotweed.

Psyllids given green light to control Japanese knotweed

Japanese knotweed is one of the most damaging and invasive weeds in Europe. It was brought to Britain from Japan as a popular and expensive garden ornamental plant in the mid-19th century. It now grows and multiplies at an extraordinary rate, can cause serious structural damage to buildings, and is extremely difficult and expensive to control. But CABI may hold the key to its long term management – in the form of a tiny insect.

Natural (or biological) control is the use of living organisms to control invasive species. After extensive research, CABI scientists have determined that a psyllid from Japan, known as *Aphalara itadori*, can effectively control the weed in the UK without damaging native flora. The team has paid numerous visits to Japan since the turn of the millennium to find a natural enemy of Japanese knotweed which feeds on or damages the plant in its native range, but does not affect flora or fauna. After intensive research, they narrowed down the options from 186 species to just one. The psyllid is a true Japanese knotweed specialist, having co-evolved with its host plant. Thorough testing on UK plants has found that it cannot feed or reproduce on anything else, even when given no choice. Now the UK's Minister for Wildlife has granted a licence for its release – the first time an insect will be officially released to control an invasive weed in Europe.

Vigorous growth of Japanese knotweed, UK. ©CABI

Aphalara itadori adult. ©CABI

As mentioned briefly in a previous chapter, CABI's Plant Clinic concept, developed by Eric Boa and others, has been successful in taking science knowledge into the field and adding to it by collecting data about pests and diseases, many poorly understood by the farmers themselves, that are currently causing them problems.

Plant clinic team, Nepal. ©CABI

Consultation from a plant clinic doctor, Nepal. ©CABI

Consultation from a plant clinic doctor, Rwanda. ©CABI

Plant Clinics

CABI introduced a new approach to extension based on a trial in Bolivia in 2000 that links mobile services, a fixed central or national facility and, where needed, an international diagnostic and advisory service.

Under this scheme, farmers attend plant clinics which operate like a doctor's surgery. The clinics run weekly in a prominent local meeting place, such as a market. When the farmer has a problem with a crop, he or she can bring a sample along to the plant clinic. At the clinic trained 'plant doctors' listen to the farmer, examine the sample, diagnose the problem and offer a treatment recommendation.

CABI helps link each clinic to a network of national diagnostic laboratories which can support them. When the national diagnostic laboratories can't help samples are sent to CABI in the UK, which has an expert diagnostic service with an international reputation and accepts diseased plant samples from all countries.

Since 1997, CABI has helped to establish more than 80 plant health clinics in nine countries throughout Latin America, Africa and Asia.

The next crucial step is to take the plant clinic concept and turn it into a fully functioning complex adaptive system. This is what CABI has taken on by integrating it with a web-based 'knowledge bank'. Together the two systems have been called Plantwise.

The idea of Plantwise is to take the very practical field data collected by the Plant Clinics, which gives very up-to-date information on what problems farmers are currently facing, and link it to data from a variety of national and internationally sources as well as CABI's databases and expertise. Taken together, this will create a deep and immediate picture (including detailed maps) of pest and disease incidence is produced and made available online. When widely rolled out, it will for instance give much earlier warning of emerging problems, accurately pinpointed with GPS technology. Information will include new invasive pests and give both national and international institutes a much greater chance of stopping problems before they get out of hand, and direct help to where it is most needed. As we have already noted, such problems have in the past caused billions of dollars of losses, which could have been avoided if such a system had been in place.

In the process it would further fulfil the long-held wish to unite the two strands of CABI, the active field-based science and the information/knowledge-building activities to create something considerably greater than the sum of its parts.

Ultimately most of CABI's activities will adopt the characteristics of an adaptive system, with strong web-based support that keeps information up-to-the-minute and gives CABI a competitive advantage over products which simply abstract published journals. There are many more possibilities, including the option of a broader service, through Plantwise, to cover all aspects of plant and soil health, which are increasingly threatened and poorly appreciated by many.

In conclusion

Having now followed the twists and turns of CABI's story over the past 100 years, it is interesting to consider the qualities that have enabled it to survive, and indeed thrive, for so long. Of the thousands of organizations established in the same year, very few are still in existence in any form. What were the factors that meant that a small scientific research committee, barely more than a one-man band, would grow and develop from its colonial beginnings to the international, intergovernmental development organization that CABI is today?

Humility and dedication to the task in hand may be two. Unlike the founders of many commercial enterprises, Sir Guy Marshall was not interested in status or personal enrichment. His passion for his subject, energy, and willingness to collaborate with others have echoed down the generations of CABI people, and can be seen today in every one of the teams involved in our publishing, research and development projects.

Flexibility has been a crucial component for CABI as an organization and for the individuals who work within it. No organization reaches the age of 100 without having had to reinvent itself on at least one occasion – and CABI has probably seen more than the usual number of changes. Staff have relocated, developed new skills, adapted to new structures, names, brands and systems of governance. Any one of these might have triggered a terminal crisis in any other organization. But in CABI, while change is perhaps not universally welcomed, it is recognized as necessary and borne accordingly.

Change's close companion, of course, is innovation. The history of CABI is crammed with examples of visionary thinking, new ideas and exploitation of cutting-edge technology, continuing today with products such as CAB Abstracts, the encyclopedic, mixed-media Compendia, and the unique mix of advanced database and on-the-ground farmer advisory service that is Plantwise.

Perhaps above all, the secret of CABI's endurance lies in its strong international network of relationships that keep its finger on the pulse of what is important in the world and to its members. Its unique system of governance by 45 member countries keeps it in touch with governmental priorities, while staff and partners working on projects around the world are experiencing daily the concerns and challenges of farmers working on the ground. CABI's scientific research, therefore, which is where the organization started, is never the product of an ivory tower mentality but always led by human need and designed for practical application.

CABI's virtues have never really been hidden, but it is only in the last few decades, as we discovered for ourselves a renewed commitment and purpose as a development organization, that they have truly become apparent. As we now embark upon the next century of CABI's journey, we do so with a clear mission to improve people's lives and sense of what we have to offer the world through our scientific knowledge, information and expertise in agriculture and the environment.

> " *We shall not cease from exploration*
> *And the end of all our exploring*
> *Will be to arrive where we started*
> *And know the place for the first time.* "
>
> TS Eliot[210]

ABBREVIATIONS

ADB	Asian Development Bank
AHBU	Animal Helminthology Biosystematics Unit
ASARECA	Association for Strengthening Agricultural Research in Eastern and Central Africa
BCA	Biological control agent
BMNH	British Museum (Natural History)
BMS	British Mycological Society
CAB	Commonwealth Agricultural Bureaux
CABI	CAB International
CABI-PF	CABI Partnership Fund
CBC	Classical biological control
CDC	Centers for Disease Control
CEC	(Commission of the European Communities)
CGIAR	Consultative Group on International Agricultural Research
CIBC	Commonwealth Institute of Biological Control
CIDA	Canadian International Development Agency
CIE	Commonwealth Institute of Entomology
CIMMYT	International Maize and Wheat Improvement Centre
CIP	Commonwealth Institute of Parasitology
CMI	Commonwealth Mycological Institute
DFID	Department for International Development
EPPO	European and Mediterranean Plant Protection Organization
EU	European Union
FAO	Food and Agriculture Organization
FFS	Farmer field schools
GEF	Global Environmental Facility
GM	Genetic modification
ICIPE	International Centre of Insect Physiology and Ecology
ICRISAT	International Crops Research Institute for the Semi-Arid Tropics
IERC	Imperial Entomological Research Committee
IFIS	International Food Information Service
IIBC	International Institute for Biological Control
IIE	International Institute of Entomology
IIP	International Institute of Parasitology
IMI	International Mycological Institute
IOBC	International Organization for Biological Control
IPM	Integrated pest management
IPPC	International Plant Protection Convention
IRRI	International Rice Research Institute
ISPM	International Standard for Phytosanitary Measures
IUBS	International Union of Biological Sciences
IUMS	International Union of Microbiological Studies
LOOPs	Locally organized operational partnerships
LSHTM	London School of Hygiene and Tropical Medicine
MARDI	Malaysian Agricultural Research and Development Institute
MAFF	Ministry of Agriculture, Fisheries and Food
NARS	National agricultural research systems
NERC	Natural Environment Research Council
NHM	Natural History Museum
NIBSC	National Institute for Biological Standards and Control
ODA	UK Overseas Development Administration
OECD	Organisation for Economic Co-operation and Development
PCR	Polymerase chain reaction
PNBU	Plant Nematology Biosystematics Unit
SARS	Severe acute respiratory syndrome
SEM	Scanning electron microscope
SERC	Science and Engineering Research Council
SIO	Scientific Information Officer
SPL	Science Photo Library
TEM	Tunnelling electron microscope
TPDU	Tropical Parasitic Diseases Unit
TPN	Tropical Plant Nematology Unit
TPNRAU	Tropical Plant Nematology Research and Advisory Unit
UN	United Nations
UNEP	United Nations Environment Programme
UNESCO	United Nations Educational, Scientific and Cultural Organization
USAID	United States Agency for International Development
USDA	United States Department of Agriculture
VLA	Veterinary Laboratories Agency
WHO	World Health Organization

ENDNOTES

1. Speech by GM Carman, Director-General, Information Services, Agriculture Canada, in Report of Proceedings, CAB Review Conference, 1980.

2. See, for example: *CAB International – A Corporate Strategy for the 1990s*. CAB International, February 1990.

3. National Bureau of Agriculturally Important Insect Pests, Bangalore, http://www.pdbc.res.in/ 14 November 2009.

4. Andrew Bennett *et al*. *CABI Science Review 2009*. CABI, Wallingford, UK.

5. House of Commons (1910) 14, 1047–1052.

6. Baker, RA and Bayliss, RA (2009) *The Linnaean* 25(1), 21.

7. Plant Diseases: research in the Empire: Work of Mycological Institute (1934) *The Times*, 18 September, p. 17.

8. An Imperial Model: Clearing-house for science (1937) *The Times*, 13 January, p. 11.

9. House of Commons debates, 6 December 1948.

10. An extract from an obituary: Sir Guy Marshall, KCMG, FRS by Hall, WJ (1959) *Nature* 183(4672), 1364.

11. First-hand accounts from Keith Harris and others on the Bureau/Institute of Entomology have informed this history of the Institute.

12. This note on Neave and Simpson is drawn from an article in the *Linnean Journal* (2009) 25(1), 21.

13. Gilbert, P (2010) Sheffield Airey Neave: administrator, editor, systematist. *Archives of Natural History* 37(1), 171–172.

14. The late Airey Neave MP was the son of SA Neave. He was the first British POW to make a home run from Colditz, and it is claimed that he saved Chartres Cathedral from bombardment by the Americans by putting his own life on the line. His role in the D-Day invasion of France is noted briefly in Antony Beevor's *D-Day, the Battle for Normandy*, Penguin, Viking, London (2010). As Major Airey Neave of MI9, he was said to be 'in pursuit of a British Sergeant who had betrayed a French Resistance network to the Germans'. Later he became a Conservative Member of Parliament, representing an electorate including the town of Wallingford, the location of CAB International's head office. He was tragically assassinated at Westminster in 1978.

15. Uvarov, BP (1921) A preliminary revision of the genus *Dociostawus, Fieb. Bulletin of Entomological Research* 11(4), 397–407.

16. Uvarov, BP (1928) Locusts and Grasshoppers. *A Handbook for their Study and Control*. Imperial Bureau of Entomology, London, UK, 352 pp.

17. Huxley, E (1957) *No Easy Way: a History of the Kenya Farmers' Association and UNGA Limited*. Kenya.

18. *The Globe*, 7 February 1930.

19. Innes, M (1939) *The Spider Strikes*. Dodd Mead, New York.

20. Evans was, in fact, British. He had emigrated from the UK to Tasmania but returned to the UK to take up employment with the Institute during World War II. After leaving the Institute he returned to Australia.

21. Jolivet, PHA and Cox, ML (1996) *Chrysomelidae Biology*. The Chrysomelidae Book Series. SPB Academic Publishing Amsterdam/New York, 1273 pp. in 3 vols.

22. Cox, ML (ed.) (1999) *Advances in Chrysomelidae Biology* 1. Backhuys Publishers, Leiden, the Netherlands, 691 pp.

23. Duffy, EAJ (1953) *A monograph of the immature stages of British and imported timber beetles (Cerambycidae)*. British Museum (Natural History), London, UK, 350 pp.

24. Duffy, EAJ (1960) *A monograph of the immature stages of neotropical timber beetles (Cerambycidae)*. British Museum (Natural History), London, UK, 327 pp.

25. Duffy, EAJ (1968) *A monograph of the immature stages of oriental timber beetles (Cerambycidae)*. British Museum (Natural History), London, UK, 434 pp.

26. Williams, DJ and Watson, GW (1988) *The Scale Insects of the Tropical South Pacific Region. Part 1*. The armoured scales (Diaspididae). CAB International, Wallingford, UK, 290 pp.

27. Williams, DJ and Watson, GW (1988) *The Scale Insects of the Tropical South Pacific Region. Part 2*. The mealybugs (Pseudococcidae). CAB International, Wallingford, UK, 260 pp.

28. Williams, DJ and Watson, GW (1990) *The Scale Insects of the Tropical South Pacific Region. Part 3*. The Soft Scales (Coccidae) and Other Families. CAB International, Wallingford, UK, 267 pp.

29. Williams, DJ and Granara de Willink, MC (1992) *Mealybugs of Central and South America*. CAB International, Wallingford, UK, 635 pp.

30. Wilson, MR and Claridge, MF (1991) *Handbook for the identification of leafhoppers and planthoppers of rice*. CAB International, Wallingford, UK, 150 pp.

31. Crosskey, RW (1973) A conspectus of the Tachinidae (Diptera) of Australia, including keys to the supraspecific taxa and taxonomic and host catalogues. *Bulletin of the British Museum (Natural History), Series Entomology*, Suppl. 21, 222 pp.

32. Crosskey, RW (1976) A taxonomic conspectus of the Tachinidae (Diptera) of the Oriental Region. *Bulletin of the British Museum (Natural History), Entomology*, Suppl. 26, 357 pp.

33. White, IM and Hodkinson, ID (1982) *Psylloidea (nymphal stages) Hemiptera, Homoptera*. Royal Entomological Society of London, London, UK, 50 pp.

34. Harris, KM (1961) Sorghum midge, *Contarinia sorghicola* (Coq.), in West Africa. *Nature* 192(4798), 187–188.

35. Harris, KM (1964) The sorghum midge complex (Diptera, Cecidomyiidae). *Bulletin of Entomological Research* 55(2), 233–247.

36. CIE: A Personal Account 1950–2000 by Keith Harris.

37. Holloway, JD (1988) Family Arctiidae, subfamilies Syntominae, Euchromiinae, Arctiinae; Noctuidae misplaced in Arctiidae (*Camptoloma, Aganainae*). *Moths of Borneo* 6, 101 pp.

38. Harris, KM and Nwanze, KF (1992) *Busseola fusca* (Fuller), the African maize stalk borer: A handbook of information. *Information Bulletin* 33. ICRISAT.

39. Youm, O, Harris, KM and Nwanze, KF (1996) *Coniesta ignefusalis* (Hampson). The millet stem borer: a handbook of information. *Information Bulletin* 46. ICRISAT.

40. *1998 in Review*. CAB International 1998.

41. Hawksworth, DL and Rossman, AY (1997) Where are all the undescribed fungi? *Phytopathology*, 87(9), 888–891.

42. First-hand accounts from Hawksworth and others of the workings of the Mycological Bureau/Institute have informed this history of CABI's Mycological Institute. There is also a full account of the history of the Institute – from 1920 to 1992 by Aitchison and Hawksworth – published by CAB International in 1993, some 17 years ago: *IMI: Retrospect and Prospect, a celebration of the achievements of the International Mycological Institute 1920–92*. CAB International, 1993.

43. Australia, Canada, Egypt, the Sudan and self-supporting colonies, India, New Zealand, South Africa, and the Imperial Government on behalf of the 'State-aided' colonies.

44. The first report of a scanning electron microscope (SEM) appeared in CAB Abstracts: Martin, LC (1938) The electron microscope. *Nature* 142 1062–1065.

45. Hawksworth, DL (1985) The Commonwealth Mycological Institute (CMI). In: 'Famous Laboratories' *Biologist* 32(1), 7–12.

46. Scrivenor, T (1980) *CAB – the first 50 years*. Commonwealth Agricultural Bureaux, Farnham, UK, 73 pp.

47. Australia, Canada, Egypt, the Sudan and self-supporting colonies, India, New Zealand, South Africa, and the Imperial Government on behalf of the 'State-aided' colonies.

48. War against insects (1921) *The Times*, 23 August, p. 9.

49. Butler, EJ (1921) The Imperial Bureau of Mycology. *Transactions of the Imperial Bureau of Mycological Society* 7, 168–172.

50. The Review covered the broad field of applied mycology but became more restricted later and hence its name was changed to *Review of Plant Pathology* from 1970.

51. Mason, EW (1943) Edwin John Butler: 1874–1943. *Obituary Notices of Fellows of the Royal Society* 4(12), 455–474.

52. Plant plagues: a campaign on Kew Green; Microscopic Foes of the Empire (1931) *The Times*, 7 February, p 13.

53. This biography was drawn from *The Bulletin of the British Mycological Society* (1975) 9, 114, 1975, *Transactions of the British Mycological Society* (1976) 66, 371–372.

54. Bisby, GR (1945) *An introduction to the taxonomy and nomenclature of fungi*. Imperial Mycological Institute, Kew, UK, 117 pp.

55. Hawksworth, DL (1974) *Mycologist's handbook*. Commonwealth Mycological Institute, Kew, UK, 231 pp.

56. Aitchison, EM and Hawksworth, DL (1993) *IMI: Retrospect and Prospect. A Celebration of the Achievements of the International Mycological Institute 1920–1992*. CAB International, Wallingford, UK.

57. CAB, 35th Annual Report of the Executive Council, p 18.

58. Goodall, J (1999) *In the Shadows of Man*. Mariner Books, Houghton Mifflin Harcourt, Boston, USA.

59. Hawksworth, DL (1985) The Commonwealth Mycological Institute (CMI). In: 'Famous Laboratories'. *Biologist* 32(1), 7–12.

60. The Institute of Entomology never had its own collection of insects – insect specimens sent to the Institute for identification were housed within and owned by the Natural History Museum. In contrast, the Mycological Institute held its own collection of dried (the herbarium, now transferred to Kew with ownership retained by CABI) and living fungi (the microbial genetic resource collection, which stays with CABI).

61. A Christopher Hayward, Bacteriologist at the Institute 1959 to 1965, private communication, January 2010.

62. Bradbury, JF (1986) *Guide to Plant Pathogenic Bacteria*. CAB International Mycological Institute, Kew, UK.

63. JF Bradbury, private communication, April 2010.

64. A second sequencer was purchased in 2006.

65. Gerry Saddler, private communication 2010.

66. Gardan, L, Dauga, C, Prior, P, Gillis, M and Saddler, GS (2000) *Acidovorax anthurii* sp nov., a new phytopathogenic bacterium which causes bacterial leaf-spot of anthurium. *International Journal of Systematic and Evolutionary Microbiology* 50(1), 235–246.

67. Hughes, SJ (1953) Some foliicolous Hyphomycetes. *Canadian Journal of Botany* 31(5), 560–576.

68. Ellis, MB (1971) *Dematiaceous hyphomycetes*. Commonwealth Mycological Institute, Kew, UK, 608 pp.

69. Sutton, BC (1980) *The Coelomycetes*. CAB, IMI, Kew, UK, 696 pp.

70. Minter, DW, Kirk, PM and Sutton, BC (1982) Holoblastic phialides. *Transactions of the British Mycological Society* 79, 75–93.

71. Sutton, BC and Hennebert, GL (1994) Interconnections amongst anamorphs and their possible contribution to Ascomycetes systematics. In: Hawksworth, DL (ed.) *Ascomycete systematics. Problems and Perspectives in the Nineties*. Plenum Press, New York, USA, pp. 77–100.

72. Waterhouse, GM (1963) Key to the species of Phytophthora de Bary. *Mycological Papers* 92, 1–22.

73. Booth, C (1959) Studies of Pyrenomycetes. IV. Nectria (Part I). *Mycological Papers* 73, 115 pp.

74. Booth, C (1970) *Fusarium oxysporum*. (Descriptions of Fungi and Bacteria). CAB International, Wallingford, UK, *IMI Descriptions of Fungi and Bacteria* 22 pp., Sheet 211.

75. Sivanesan, A (1977) The taxonomy and pathology of *Venturia* species. *Bibliotheca Mycologica* 59, 139 pp.

76. Sivanesan, AJ (1984) *The bitunicate ascomycetes and their anamorphs*. Lubrecht & Cramer, Vaduz, Liechtenstein, 701 pp.

77. Kozakiewicz, Z (1989) *Aspergillus* species on stored products. *Mycological Papers* 161, 188 pp.

78. Hawksworth, DL (1991) The fungal dimension of biodiversity: magnitude, significance, and conservation. *Mycological Research* 95, 641-655.

79. May, RM (1991) A fondness for fungi. *Nature* 352, 475–476 (8 August).

80. Hawksworth, DL and Rose, F (1970) Qualitative scale for estimating sulphur dioxide air pollution in England and Wales using epiphytic lichens. *Nature* 227(5254), 145–148.

81. Jones, TH, Thompson, LJ, Lawton, JH, Bezemer, TM, Bardgett, RD, Blackburn, TM, Bruce, KD, Cannon, PF, Hall, GS, Hartley, SE, Howson, G, Jones, CG, Kampichler, C, Kandeler, E and Richie, DA (1998) Impacts of rising atmospheric carbon dioxide on model terrestrial ecosystems. *Science* 280, 441–443.

82. This material is based on a contribution from Jim Waller, the founding Liaison Officer for Plant Pathology and a long-time staff member of CAB International who still serves as a CABI Bioscience Fellow.

83. Colwell, RK and Coddington, JA (1994) *Philosophical Transactions of the Royal Society of London, Series B* 345, 101–118.

84. Imperial Bureaux (1928) *British Medical Journal* 2, 1148–1149.

85. Gibson gives two references: Sambon, LW (1926) *The Journal of Tropical Medicine and Hygiene* 29(18), 314–322; and Cerquiera Falcao, E de (1959) Piraja da Silva o incotestavel descobridor '*Schistosoma mansoni*'. Sao Paulo, Brazil, pp. 56–70.

86. Farley, J. *Oxford Dictionary of National Biography*.

87. Commonwealth Agricultural Bureaux Review Conference, London 1955. Report of Proceedings December 1955.

88. Thirty-Fifth Annual Report of the Executive Council, CAB 1963–64.

89. Williams, HW and Jones, A (1994) *Parasitic worms of fish*. Taylor & Francis, UK, 593 pp.

90. Khalil, LF, Jones, A and Bray, RA (eds) (1994) *Keys to the cestode parasites of vertebrates*. CABI Publishing, Wallingford, UK, 768 pp.

91. Edited version of Profile appearing in *Systematic Parasitology* 23, 157–158, 1992 by MB Burton.

92. Beryl Cunningham, private communication.

93. Peter Gooch, private communication.

94. Siddiqi, MR (1985) *Tylenchida parasites of plants and insects*. CAB, Farnham Royal, UK, 645 pp.

95. Siddiqi, MR (2000) *Tylenchida parasites of plants and insects*, 2nd edn. CABI Publishing, Wallingford, UK, 833 pp.

96. David Hunt, CABI Bioscience, private communication, 2009.

97. Hunt, DJ (1993) *Aphelenchida, Longidoridae and Trichodoridae: their systematics and bionomics*. CABI Publishing, Wallingford, UK, 352 pp.

98. David Hunt, CABI Bioscience, private communication, 2009.

99. Scrivenor, T (1980) *CAB the First 50 Years*. Commonwealth Agricultural Bureaux, Farnham, UK, 73 pp.

100. Luc, M, Sikora, RA and Bridge, J (eds) (1990) *Plant parasitic nematodes in subtropical and tropical agriculture*. CABI Publishing, Wallingford, UK.

101. Orton Williams, KJ (1990) Plant parasitic nematodes of the Pacific. *Technical Report 8*, UNDP/FAO, 192 pp.

102. International Institute of Parasitology Biennial Report 1989–1990.

103. See IIP Tropical Parasitic Diseases Unit Brochure.

104. Wallace Peters, 'Emeritus Professor, King Faisal International Prize Laureate', Malariologist, CABI Bioscience and, Department of Infectious and Tropical Diseases, London School of Hygiene and Tropical Medicine, UK.

105. Tailliez, P, Pages, S, Ginibre, N and Boemare, N (2006) *International Journal of Systematic and Evolutionary Microbiology* 56, 2805–2818.

106. Simon Townson, personal communication, 2010.

107. This chapter has been prepared with the assistance of Matthew Cock and Jeff Waage. The chapter has drawn heavily on annual reports of work carried out each year that were produced from 1958 (when FJ Simmonds became Director) until 1998 (when IIBC became part of CABI Bioscience).

108. Elliot, W (1927) The Parasite 'Zoo'. *The Times* 21 June, p. 17.

109. Thompson, WR (1930) The Biological Control of Insect and Plant Pests – A Report on the Organization and Progress of the Farnham House Laboratory. *Empire Marketing Board Publication 29*, 128 pp. Cited in a Commonwealth Institute of Biological Control Report, c. 1965.

110. Greathead, DJ (1994) the *Bulletin of the Royal Entomological Society* 18(4), 181–199.

111. Carson, R (1963) *Silent Spring*. Hamish Hamilton, London, UK, 304 pp.

112. Scrivenor, T (1980) *CAB – the First Fifty Years*. Commonwealth Agricultural Bureaux. Farnham, UK, 73 pp.

113. The Colorado Beetle: Science and the Farm (1927). *Evening Post* (New Zealand), 3 September, p. 9.

114. The Institute of Biological Control, whether as Commonwealth, CAB International or International, is referred to throughout this chapter simply as the Institute, unless the context requires otherwise.

115. Commonwealth Institute of Biological Control, Report for January–December, 1982: Investigations on the natural enemies of cassava mealybugs.

116. A world search for insect allies: recruits for Cawthron (1930) *Evening Post* (New Zealand), 5 November, p. 9.

117. Myers, JG. A Preliminary Report on Investigations into Biological Control of West Indian Insect Pests. Empire Marketing Board, *Publication 42*, 178 pp. Cited in a Commonwealth Institute of Biological Control Report, c.1965.

118. Matthew Cock, CAB International, private communication, 2010.

119. For a review of biological control of pests of sugarcane see Chapter 6 in Cock, MJW (ed.) (contribs: Bennett, FD, Cock, MJW, Hughes, IW, Simmonds, FJ and Yaseen, M) (1985) *A Review of Biological Control of Pests in the Commonwealth Caribbean and Bermuda up to l982*. Technical Communication No. 9, Commonwealth Institute of Biological Control, Farnham Royal, UK, 218 pp.

120. McCook, J (1941) Pest Base in Canada – Laboratory Turns Out Fighter for Empire against Insects. *Windsor Daily Star* 25 February, p. 15.

121. Britain Turns Thumbs Down on Insect Plan (1944).

122. History of the Development and a Resume of the Activities of the CIBC (1965).

123. Jeff Waage, private communication, September 2010.

124. This collaborative work is well documented in *Biological Control Programmes in Canada*, which CABI has published in 1962, 1971, 1984 and 2002.

125. Proceedings Sixth Imperial Entomological Reference Conference, CAB 1954.

126. HSMO London (1951) *Report of Proceedings, Commonwealth Agricultural Bureaux Review Conference, London, 1950*.

127. A list of projects undertaken between 1959 and 1964 is tabulated in The History of the Development and a Resume of the Activities of the Commonwealth Institute of Biological Control.

128. Annual Report 1997 International Institute of Biological Control.

129. See, for example, Commonwealth Agricultural Bureaux, Commonwealth Institute for Biological Control, Report of Work Carried Out During 1958.

130. This note on Simmonds is drawn from the Annual Report of Commonwealth Institute of Biological Control, 1985/86.

131. Popov was, like Uvarov, an emigre from the Soviet Union.

132. Greathead married Annette in 1958. A graduate of the University of St Andrews in Scotland, Annette was recruited by ALRC in London and then temporarily seconded as a librarian to the International Red Locust Control Service in Northern Rhodesia (now Mbale, Zambia). After their marriage, she was to become Greathead's professional colleague.

133. Greathead, DJ (1976) A review of biological control in Western and Southern Europe. Technical Communication, Commonwealth Institute of Biological Control, 182 pp.

134. James Ogwang went on to be a driving force in the biocontrol effort against water hyacinth in East Africa, and the instigator of the community-based mass releases of *Neochetina* weevils that famously led to the weed's biological control on Lake Victoria in the late 1990s.

135. Neuenschwander, P, Borgemeister, C and Langewald, J (eds) (2003) *Biological Control in IPM Systems in Africa*. CABI Publishing, Wallingford, UK, 414 pp.

136. Neuenschwander, P, Murphy, ST and Coly, EV (1987) Introduction of exotic parasitic wasps for the control of *Liriomyza trifolii* (Dipt., Agromyzidae) in Senegal. *Tropical Pest Management* 33, 290–297.

137. Simmonds, FJ and Greathead, DJ (1977) Introductions and pest and weed problems. In: Cherrett, JM and Sagar, GR (eds) *Origins of Pest, Parasite, Disease and Weed Problems*. Blackwell Scientific Publications, Oxford, UK, pp. 109–124.

138. Greathead, DJ (1994) History of biological control. *Antenna* 18, 187–199.

139. Julien, MH and Griffiths, MW (1998) *Biological Control of Weeds: a World Catalogue of Agents and their Target Weeds*, 4th edn. CAB International, Wallingford, UK, 223 pp.

140. Simmonds, FJ (1980) Biological control of *Cordia curassavica* (Boraginaceae) in Malaysia. *Entomophaga* 25(4), 363–364.

141. Yaninek, JS and Hanna, R (2003) Cassava green mite in Africa – a unique example of successful classical biological control of a mite pest on a continental scale. In: Neuenschwander, P, Borgemeister, C and Langewald, J (eds) *Biological Control in IPM Systems in Africa*. CABI Publishing, Wallingford, UK, pp. 61–75.

142. Beshir, MO and Bennett, FD (1985) Biological control of water hyacinth on the White Nile, Sudan. *Proceedings of the VI International Symposium on Biological Control of Weeds*. Agriculture Canada, Ottawa, Canada, pp. 491–496.

143. Cilliers, CJ, Hill, MP, Ogwang, JA and Ajuonu, O (2003) Aquatic weeds in Africa and their control.

144. Greathead, DJ and Monty, J (1982) Biological control of stableflies (*Stomoxys* spp.): results from Mauritius in relation to fly control in dispersed breeding sites. *Biocontrol News and Information* 3, 105–109.

145. See also: Thompson, WR (ed.) (1943–1965) *A Catalogue of the Parasites and Predators of Insect Pests*. Commonwealth Agricultural Bureaux, Farnham Royal, UK; Herting, B (1971–1982) *A Catalogue of Parasites and Predators of Terrestrial Arthropods*. Commonwealth Agricultural Bureaux, Farnham Royal, UK; and Fry, JM (1989) Natural Enemy Databank, 1987, *A catalogue of natural enemies of arthropods derived from records in the CIBC Natural Enemy Databank*. CAB International, Wallingford, Oxon, UK.

146. This biography is drawn from Wikipedia.

147. Abdullah, M (2003) *Planter's Tales*. IPC Services Sdn. Bhd, Malaysia.

148. Caudwell, RW, Hunt, D, *et al.* (2003) Insect pollination of oil palm – a comparison of the long term viability and sustainability of *Elaeidobious kamerunicus* in Papua New Guinea, Indonesia, Costa Rica, and Ghana. *ASD Oil Palm Papers* 25, 1–16.

149. Private communication, Jeff Waage, September 2010.

150. Howarth, FG (1983) Classical biological control: panacea or Pandora's box? *Proceedings of the Hawaiian Entomological Society* 24(2), 239–244.

151. Commonwealth Institute of Biological Control Annual Report, 1988.

152. Kairo, MTK, Cock, MJW and Quinlan, MM (2003) An assessment of the use of the Code of Conduct for the Import and Release of Exotic Biological Control Agents (ISPM No. 3) since its endorsement as an international standard. *Biocontrol News and Information* 24 15N–27N.

153. Rubbervine in terminal decline (2002) *Biocontrol News*.

154. International Institute of Biological Control, Annual Report 1997.

155. Cock, MJW (2003) Risks of non-target impact versus stakeholder benefits in classical biological control of arthropods: selected case studies from developing countries. In Van Driesche, RG (ed.) *Proceedings of the International Symposium on Biological Control of Arthropods, Honolulu, Hawaii, 14–18 January 2002*. United States Department of Agriculture, Forest Service, Morgantown, West Virginia, USA, pp. 25–33.

156. Kairo, MTK, Pollard, GV, Peterkin, DD and Lopez, VF (2000) Biological control of the hibiscus mealybug, Maconellicoccus hirsutus Green (Hemiptera: Pseudococcidae) in the Caribbean. *Integrated Pest Management Reviews* 5, 241–254. Cock, MJW (2003) Risks of nontarget impact versus stakeholder benefits in classical biological control of arthropods: selected case studies from developing countries. In: Van Driesche, RG (ed.) *Proceedings of the International Symposium on Biological Control of Arthropods, Honolulu, Hawaii, 14–18 January 2002*. United States Department of Agriculture, Forest Service, Morgantown, West Virginia, USA, pp. 25–33.

157. Harvey, S (1979) CAB/CAIN Evaluation Project – A comparative Study of the performance of two agricultural databases in a computerized current awareness service. Centre for Agricultural Publication and Documentation, *British Library Research and Development Report No 5483*.

158. Norman Jones, private communication, 2009.

159. Activities of the Imperial Agricultural Bureaux (1936) *Nature* 138, 1048–1049 (19 December).

160. *New Scientist* (1965) 27, 451, 8 July, p. 69.

161. *British Medical Journal* (1934) 20 January 20, p. 108.

162. Proceedings of the Third Meeting of the Animal Husbandry Wing of the India Board of Agriculture and Animal Husbandry, 1939.

163. Peck, EF (1939) The Life of a Veterinarian and Agriculturalist in British Somaliland. *Canadian Journal of Comparative Medicine* 3(1), 5–8.

164. First Imperial Veterinary Congress (1936) *Canadian Journal of Comparative Medicine* 3(1), 26.

165. Roy Mack, private communication, 2010.

166. Much of the information in this section on the International Bee Research Association is drawn from the Association's website http://www.ibra.org.uk.

167. Private communication, Elizabeth Dodsworth, 2010.

168. The Eleventh Annual Report of the Imperial Agricultural Bureaux, Appendix IV, 1939–40.

169. *Daily Telegraph*, 30 September 1937.

170. World-wide soil erosion – a disquieting picture (1938) *The Times*, 11 April, p. 18.

171. Jacks, GV and Whyte, RO (1938) Erosion and soil conservation. *Imperial Bureau of Pastures and Forage Crops Bulletin 25*, Aberystwyth, UK, 206 pp.

172. McDonald, P (1994) Characteristics of Soil Science Literature. In: McDonald, P (ed.) *The Literature of Soil Science*. Cornell University Press, Ithaca, USA, pp. 43–72.

173. Tempany, HA (1949) The practice of soil conservation in the British Colonial Empire.

174. Greenland, DJ (1965) Interactions between Clays and Organic Compounds in Soils. Part I Mechanisms of interactions and Part II Adsorption of soil organic compounds and its effect on soil properties. *Soils and Fertilizers* (1965) 28, 415–425, 521–532.

175. Peter Wightman, private communication, 2010.

176. The Commonwealth Bureau of Horticulture and Plantation Crops, *Ministry of Food Bulletin No. 706*, HMSO, June 1953.

177. Akenhead, D, 29 May 1949.

178. Bourke, DO'D (1980) The work of the Commonwealth Bureau of Horticulture and Plantation Crops in providing horticultural information. *Acta Horticulturae* 100, 437–440.

179. Leitch, I (1937) The Determination of the Calcium Requirements of Man. *Nutrition Abstracts and Reviews* 6, 553–578.

180. Hytten, FE (2010) Isabella Leitch's contributions to the development of systematic reviews of research evidence. *Journal of the Royal Society of Medicine* 103(3), 114–117.

181. Leitch, I (1940) The Feeding of Camels. *Technical Communication No. 13*. Imperial Bureau of Nutrition, Aberdeen, UK.

182. Grant for Nutrition Research (1964) *The Times*, 26 May, p. 8.

183. Bellamy, MA (1991) The role of CAB International's *World Agricultural Economics and Rural Sociology Abstracts* in meeting the information needs of agricultural economists. In: Olsen, WC (ed.) *Agricultural Economics and Rural Sociology: the Contemporary Core Literature*. Cornell University Press, Ithaca, USA.

184. Imperial Forestry Bureau – Deputy Director's Report for 1939–40.

185. Annual Report of the Executive Council 1946–47.

186. The Commonwealth Forestry Bureau, 1976–86, William Finlayson (adapted from an unpublished autobiography).

187. Whyte, RO (1948) History of Research in Vernalization. In: Murneek, AE (ed) *Vernalization and Photoperiodism*. Chronica Botanica Co., Waltham, Massachusetts, USA, pp. 1–37.

188. Hawkes, JG (2004) *Hunting the wild potato in the South American Andes. Memories of the British Empire potato collecting expedition to South America 1938–1939*. Botanical and Experimental Garden University of Nijmegen, 224 pp.

189. Genial Soviet Hospitality: Farm scientists in Moscow (1954) *The Times*, 28 August, p. 6.

190. Richens, RH (1977) 'Reapers' by Stubbs. *The Times*, 10 August, p. 15.

191. Sparck Jones, K (2000) R.H. Richens: translation in the NUDE. In: Hutchins, WJ (ed) *Early Years in Machine Translation*. John Benjamins, Amsterdam, the Netherlands, pp. 263–278.

192. East, H, Wainwright, JM and Vickery, BC (1969) The Commonwealth Agricultural Bureaux and computers: a feasibility study. ASLIB, 108 pp.

193. The CAB Abstracts Computer System. CAB, October 1977.

194. Harvey, S (1979) CAB/CAIN Evaluation Project – A comparative Study of the performance of two agricultural databases in a computerized current awareness service. Centre for Agricultural Publication and Documentation, British Library *Research and Development Report No 5483*.

195. CAB Review of Abstracting and Editorial Services.

196. CAB Review Conference 1980.

197. This text box was prepared by Andrea Powell, Executive Director Publishing.

198. See, for example: CAB International – A Corporate Strategy for the 1990s, CAB International, February 1990.

199. Based on an article in *Biocontrol News and Information*.

200. Rasmann, S, Kölner, TG, Degenhardt, J, Hiltpold, I, Toepfer, S, Kuhlmann, U, Gershenzon, J and Turlings, TCJ (2005) Recruitment of entomopathogenic nematodes by insect-damaged maize roots. *Nature* 434, 732–737.

201. HMSO (1996) *Commonwealth Agricultural Bureaux Review Conference London 1965, Report of Proceedings*.

202. International Institute of Entomology 80th Year 1913 to 1993, CAB International.

203. The sum granted by parliament was £1,000, equivalent to £76,000 today in terms of inflation; though in terms of mean earnings, the figure is more like £400,000.

204. Even then, Hankey fretted that the Bureaux and the problems of science they addressed were not broadly appreciated.

205. Langewald, J, Ouambama, Z, Mamadou, A, Peveling, R, Stolz, I, Bateman, R, Attignon, S, Blanford, S, Arthurs, S and Lomer, C (1999) Comparison of an organophosphorus insecticide with a mycoinsecticide for the control of *Oedaleus senegalensis* and other Sahelian Grasshoppers at an operational scale. *Biocontrol Science and Technology* 9, 199–214.

206. Dennis Rangi, private communication, 2010.

207. Bruntland, G (ed) (1987) *Our Common Future, Report of the World Commission on Environment and Development*. Oxford University Press, Oxford, UK.

208. Thirteenth Review Conference, 1996, Report of Proceedings.

209. This box on Dr Blight was prepared by the editors.

210. Eliot, TS (1943) Little Gidding. From *Four Quartets*. Harcourt Brace, New York, USA.

INDEX

Page numbers in **bold** refer to photos.

Waterston, James 15, 17, 19
Watkins, Ray 105
Watson, JM 43, 47
Way, Michael J 16, 22, 78, 81
Weed Abstracts 94, 105
weed biocontrol agents 66, 82, 123
    Aphthona spp. (flea beetle) 66, **66**
    Maravalia cryptostegiae (rubber vine rust) 82
West Indian Station (CIBC, Curepe, Trinidad) 59, 60, 61, 63, 68
    Barbados substation 63–64
    library 63
Western corn rootworm (WCR) beetle **120**, 121
Weybridge, Central Veterinary Laboratory 47, 92
White (Microbial) Agriculture Programme, China 123, 145
White House, The (St Albans) 43, **46**, 47–48, 50
White, IM 21
Whitten, Lloyd 44
Whyte, RO 104
Wightman, Peter 94, 95, 105, 107, 110
Wilkinson, Ellen 98
Wilkinson, Lieut DS 19, 31
Williams, Charles 78
Williams, DJ 21
Williams, Rob 35, 57, 145
Willmott, Sheila **48**, **51**
    biography and career 48
    Director, Helminthology Institute 43, 47
    journals and information services 50, 51
    White House premises 48, 50, 56, 57

Wilson, MR 21
Wilson, Paul 96
Wiltshire, SP 27, 28, 30–31
Winches Farm, St Albans 43, 44, 50, 53
    Commonwealth Institute of Parasitology building **50**, 54–55, 57
Windward Islands 41
Woodham, AA 100
World Agricultural Economics and Rural Society (Sociology) Abstracts (WAERSA) 101
World Health Organization (WHO) Onchocerciasis Research Unit 44, 53
Wucheria bancrofti (parasitic nematode) **45**
Wyatt, Leonard B 17

Xanthomonas manihotis (cassava bacterial blight) 35
Xenorhabdus hominickii (bacterium) 55

yams, parasitic nematodes of 56
    Scutellonema bradys **56**
Yaseen, Maajid 64
Yemen 41, 67–68, 70
Youm, O 22

Zaire (Congo) 16, 35, 73
Zam Karim 75, 76
Zambia 115, 117
Zamzam Mohamed, A 125
Zanzibar 41
Zimbabwe (formerly Rhodesia) 12, 16, 41, 47, 117
Zwolfer, Helmut 84